M.Gunasekaran

DISCARDED

D1172770

DR. M. GUNASEKARAN
DEPARTMENT OF BIOLOGY
FISK UNIVERSITY
NASHVILLE, TN   37203 U.S.A.

Botanical Histochemistry

PRINCIPLES AND PRACTICE

By William A. Jensen

UNIVERSITY OF CALIFORNIA, BERKELEY

Drawings by EVANELL M. TOWNE

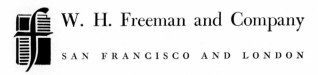

W. H. Freeman and Company

SAN FRANCISCO AND LONDON

A Series of Books in Biology

EDITORS: Douglas M. Whitaker, Ralph Emerson, Donald Kennedy, George W. Beadle (1946–1961)

Principles of Human Genetics
(Second Edition)
 Curt Stern

Experiments in General Biology
 Graham DuShane and David Regnery

Principles of Plant Physiology
 James Bonner and Arthur W. Galston

General Genetics
 Adrian M. Srb and Ray D. Owen

An Introduction to Bacterial Physiology
(Second Edition)
 Evelyn L. Oginsky and Wayne W. Umbreit

Laboratory Studies in Biology: Observations and their Implications
 Chester A. Lawson, Ralph W. Lewis, Mary Alice Burmester, and Garrett Hardin.

Plants in Action: A Laboratory Manual of Plant Physiology
 Leonard Machlis and John G. Torrey

Comparative Morphology of Vascular Plants
 Adriance S. Foster and Ernest M. Gifford, Jr.

Taxonomy of Flowering Plants
 C. L. Porter

Growth, Development, and Pattern
 N. J. Berrill

Biology: Its Principles and Implications
 Garrett Hardin

Animal Tissue Techniques
 Gretchen L. Humason

Microbes in Action: A Laboratory Manual of Microbiology
 Harry W. Seeley, Jr., and Paul J. VanDemark

Botanical Histochemistry: Principles and Practice
 William A. Jensen

Modern Microbiology
 Wayne W. Umbreit

Laboratory Outlines in Biology
 Peter Abramoff and Robert G. Thomson

Molecular Biology of Bacterial Viruses
 Gunther S. Stent

Principles of Numerical Taxonomy
 Robert R. Sokal and Peter H. A. Sneath

Structure and Function in the Nervous Systems of Invertebrates
 Theodore Holmes Bullock and G. Adrian Horridge

Population, Evolution, and Birth Control: A Collage of Controversial Readings
 Garrett Hardin, Editor

Plants in Perspective: A Laboratory Manual of Modern Biology
 Eldon H. Newcomb, Gerald C. Gerloff, and William F. Whittingham

Thermophilic Fungi: An Account of Their Biology, Activities, and Classification
 Donald G. Cooney and Ralph Emerson

Dissection of the Fetal Pig
 Warren F. Walker, Jr.

© Copyright 1962 by W. H. Freeman and Company
 The publisher reserves all rights to reproduce this book, in whole or in part, with the exception of the right to use short quotations for review of the book.
Printed in the United States of America
Library of Congress Catalog Card Number: 62-12268   (C3)

M. Gunasetaran

TO JOAN

PREFACE

GREAT ADVANCES have been made in the field of histochemistry in the past twenty years. The number of procedures alone has increased many-fold and now numbers many hundreds. Yet few of these procedures have been used by botanists. There appear to be two primary reasons for this neglect of so vast a body of techniques by investigators in the plant sciences.

One reason lies in the nature and origin of the procedures. Most of the newer methods have been developed primarily for use with animal tissue and, secondarily, if at all, for use with plant tissue. Many have appeared in journals little read by botanists and thus remain unknown to them. Moreover, to the investigator unfamiliar with them, the procedures frequently seem difficult and the results hard to interpret. Often the techniques of histochemistry appear to require expensive equipment or reagents, which prohibit or restrict their use. In addition the procedures frequently necessitate a knowledge of both standard morphological microtechnique and biochemical procedures.

The second reason lies in the lack of appreciation for the application of histochemical techniques to the solution of botanical problems. Plants and their parts are extremely complex, both morphologically and physiologically. Histochemical procedures permit the recognition of this complexity and provide data which can be interpreted in terms of cells, tissues, and tissue systems. As botanists are becoming increasingly concerned with problems which require answers in these terms, histochemical methods—if they are appreciated—must become increasingly important in research with plants.

The aim of this book is, therefore, twofold: to present a basic core of histochemical procedures, and to give examples of the employment of these procedures in botanical problems. Through this combination it is hoped that botanists will be able to understand the procedures of histochemistry and be able to adapt them to their own problems.

A basic core of approximately 200 procedures is given. The bases for the reactions are presented as well as the details of the techniques. As a knowledge of classical histological technique is required for many of the methods, these procedures have also been included. To resolve some of the initial difficulties and doubts generally encountered in using histochemical procedures for the first time, a set of basic axioms has been presented. This covers general problems and is intended as a guide in the use of all the procedures.

Not all known histochemical procedures are presented. To try to do so would be a hopeless and useless task. The procedures which are given have been selected because they illustrate basic principles and are of general applicability. Most, but not all, have been used on plant material, many in my own laboratory. The exclusion of a procedure from this book does not imply that it is faulty or inapplicable to plant tissues. Some techniques have been omitted either because they require large capital outlays or because they demand extensive discussion of instrumentation which are covered in detail elsewhere. Electron microscope techniques are considered to be outside the scope of the present work.

In presenting the procedures it has been assumed that the reader has some knowledge of plant biochemistry, plant anatomy, and analytical chemistry. However, an attempt has been made to present the procedures in such a manner that both morphologists and physiologists will be able to use them with ease and understanding.

I would like to acknowledge the assistance and encouragement given me by many people during the preparation of this book. The stimulation I received at two great laboratories, those of Professors H. Holter and J. Brachet, was a major factor in my beginning this book. Reflected throughout the book are the results of discussions with and instruction by Cecily Chapman-Andresen, Karen Holter, Søren Løvtrup, and Max Møller of the Carlsberg Laboratory, Copenhagen, and Mme. Ficq of the University of Brussels. I would like to acknowledge the help and patience of the people from my own laboratory, who perfected many of the methods given here, namely, Mary Ashton, Pat Healey, Ed Pollock, and Bill Wilson. The assistance of Barbara Long and Barbara Griffin in typing and reading the manuscript is also gratefully acknowledged. Special thanks are due to Dan Branton, whose many inventive ideas and welcome constructive criticism were embodied in the manuscript. Finally, but most important, I wish to acknowledge the help and devotion of my wife, Joan, who at times was the only one who believed this manuscript would ever be finished.

June 1962   William A. Jensen

CONTENTS

PART I

General Considerations

CHAPTER 1

Introduction

Why a book on botanical histochemistry? The answer is evident in every microscope slide of plant material. The anatomical and cytological diversity present in all plant tissues must reflect an equal physiological and biochemical diversity. Conventional chemical and biochemical techniques cannot be meaningfully applied to such heterogeneous material. Methods are needed that will permit the botanist to locate and measure substances and activities in terms of tissues, cells, and cell parts. These are the procedures of histochemistry.

A large number of histochemical techniques already exist; new techniques appear in the literature every day. Excellent books on animal histochemistry exist. Why, then, a book dealing specifically with plant histochemistry? The differences between plants and animals are sufficiently great as to present special problems when many of the methods developed for animal cells are applied to plant cells. The walls, vacuoles, and plastids of plant cells present special problems as do the unique anatomical, physiological, and biochemical characteristics of plants.

I believe that a distinct collection of procedures, most of which are known to work with plant tissue, will increase the accessibility of the methods to botanists. It is not sufficient, however, to merely present a collection of techniques. In addition, it is necessary to present an appreciation of the types of problems which will yield to histochemical techniques. These are problems which require a combination of morphological and biochemical-physiological data for their solution. Such problems abound in botany. They are problems in which morphological techniques can only suggest the physiological-biochemical basis of a particular phenomenon and in which physiological-biochemical techniques cannot deal with the anatomical diversity of the material.

3

A problem of this type can be illustrated with the work of Van Fleet (1954). Employing a variety of localization procedures, he acquired data on the differentiation of a specific tissue—the endodermis. He was then able to extend his studies and to investigate some of the factors influencing the differentiation of this tissue. The data he gathered could not have been obtained by either conventional morphological or conventional physiological techniques. A similar example is the recent work of Avers (1958), who is investigating cell differentiation in the epidermis of roots. She has been able to demonstrate striking enzymatic differences between cells which will form root hairs and those which will not. This was accomplished by the use of localization procedures which permitted the identification of individual cells. Any method which treated the root as a collection of uniform cells would have given meaningless data.

Another example is the work of Pollock and Olney (Pollock and Olney, 1959; Olney and Pollock, 1960) on the problem of seed dormancy. Realizing that the analysis of whole seeds would not yield meaningful data, they turned to histochemical methods. Dissecting out various parts of the embryo, they determined the oxygen uptake, nitrogen content, and phosphorus content after various periods and under various conditions of storage. The results demonstrated changes in the metabolism of the parts of the embryo which would not have been discernible if the seed had been analyzed whole.

A similar approach was used by Sunderland, Heyes, and Brown (1957). They were interested in the physiology of the shoot apex and leaf primordia. Using the apex of *Lupinus albus*, they measured the protein content and respiration of the dome and of the first seven primordia and internodes by histochemical methods. The differences they observed among the various regions would not have been detected by conventional biochemical procedures.

In each of the examples given here—and this applies to those that will be given in other chapters—conventional biochemical or morphological methods would not have provided meaningful data. The number of unsolved botanical problems which require histochemical data for their solution is legion. The development of the megaspore, the megagametophyte, and the embryo in both gymnosperms and angiosperms can be investigated by these procedures. Cambial development is another major problem that is open to attack. Numerous cytological problems are histochemical in nature, including the important ones of gene function and nucleus-cytoplasm interaction. However, the procedures of histochemistry are not restricted to problems of vascular plants. Many problems concerning the cryptogams are amenable to the methods of histochemistry.

But before any histochemical procedure can be applied, two conditions must be fulfilled. One is knowledge of the technique; the second is willingness to think in the combined terms of morphology, physiology, and biochemistry. When the investigator understands histochemical techniques and appreciates the data they yield, histochemical methods become the natural adjunct to a thousand lines of botanical research.

The methods of histochemistry form a broad continuum, but, to facilitate discussion, they can be roughly divided into two groups. The first group, here termed microscopic histochemistry, consists primarily of localization procedures. Such procedures usually give data directly in terms of cells or cell parts. These methods encompass staining procedures, techniques of enzyme localization, and autoradiography. The second group includes the scaled-down chemical or biochemical methods. The aim of these methods is to reduce the amount of material necessary for a determination in order that differences between samples can be detected—differences which would not be detectable if larger amounts of material were required. This group of techniques is here termed quantitative histochemistry.

Microscopic and quantitative histochemical techniques can often be used together in a given problem. Since the data are complementary, there is frequently great advantage to be gained from such a combination of methods. To stress the potential of this approach, this book is organized by cell constituents (except for the first chapters), with both the microscopic and quantitative histochemical procedures being given in the same chapter.

The early chapters of the book deal with general matters of technique, equipment, and tissue preparation. The second and third chapters contain not only the description of items of equipment but also general remarks about histochemical procedures. These statements are directed to those readers who are unfamiliar with histochemical methodology rather than to the experienced histochemist. The fourth chapter deals with classical microtechnique, which is basic to a great part of histochemistry. Classical microtechnique is directly involved in many microscopic histochemical procedures and is necessary for the morphological controls needed in all histochemical procedures. The methods presented are designed to form a core sufficient for most histochemical problems, and do not pretend to be an exhaustive treatment of the classical methods. Chapters 5 and 6 give methods of tissue preparation other than by chemical fixation, which is presented in Chapter 4. These are the methods of freeze-substitution, freeze-drying, fresh sectioning and frozen sectioning. Chapters 7 and 8 deal with the methods and problems of cell analysis on both the microscopic and quantitative histochemical level. The remaining chapters are concerned with the various cell components, and both the microscopic and quantitative histochemical methods are presented in each chapter. The only exceptions to this are the two chapters on enzymes, one of which is devoted to microscopic histochemistry and the other to quantitative histochemistry. The last chapter deals with autoradiography.

The aims of this book are to provide an understanding of the bases of the techniques and to develop an appreciation of them. I therefore urge that the reader avoid using the book as a mere collection of recipes to be thumbed through until an appropriate technique is found.

LITERATURE CITED

Avers, C. J., 1958. Histochemical localization of enzyme activity in root epidermis of *Phleum pratense*. *Am. J. Botany*, **45**:609–613.

Olney, H. O. and B. M. Pollock, 1960. Studies of the rest period. II. Nitrogen and phosphorous changes in embryonic organs of after-ripening cherry seed. *Plant Physiol.*, **35**:970–975.

Pollock, B. M. and H. O. Olney, 1959. Studies of the rest period. I. Growth, translocation, and respiratory changes in the embryonic organs of the after-ripening cherry seed. *Plant Physiol.*, **34**:131–142.

Sunderland, N., J. K. Heyes, and R. Brown, 1957. Protein and respiration in the apical region of the shoot of *Lupinus albus. J. Exptl. Botany*, **8**:55–70.

Van Fleet, D. S., 1954. Cell and tissue differentiation in relation to growth (plants). In *Dynamics of Growth Processes*. E. S. Boell (Editor) Princeton Univ. Press, Princeton.

CHAPTER 2

Quantitative Histochemistry

Introduction

In 1931, the first of a long series of papers entitled "Studies in Enzymatic Histochemistry" by Linderstrøm-Lang and Holter appeared. In their first paper they set as their goal the reduction in scale of biochemical procedures in order that the data obtained from their determinations would reflect the morphological complexity of the tissue used. Their basic assumption was that a good biochemical method could be reduced a thousand times and still yield valid data. This assumption proved to be a completely sound one, and their work laid the foundation for modern quantitative histochemistry.

However, the reduction in scale of biochemical procedures produces certain problems. When the size of the test tube is reduced, it becomes difficult to introduce samples and to mix and stir small volumes of liquids. Titrations require the use of microburettes with capacities of 100 μl. Specially designed micropipettes must be used, and techniques for their use must be developed. Spectrophotometers must be adapted for work with small volumes and weak absorption. Tissue sampling and handling become increasingly difficult as the scale is reduced.

The work of Linderstrøm-Lang, Holter, Kirk, Glick, Lowry, and many other histochemists has resulted in the design and development of special pieces of apparatus to overcome these problems. In general, the titration procedures were the first to be reduced to the histochemical level. The first procedures developed in the early 1930's by Linderstrøm-Lang and Holter at the Carlsberg Laboratories, Copenhagen, and by Kirk at the University of California, Berkeley, were titration methods.

Many of the earliest papers of the Carlsberg group dealt with the application of these methods to barley roots and seeds.

The development of the Cartesian diver microrespirometer by the Carlsberg group and the development of differential capillary microrespirometer by Kirk and his associates (late 1930's, early 1940's) added gasiometric methods to the list of histochemical techniques. The Cartesian diver, in particular, combines sensitivity with versatility and has become the histochemists' Warburg apparatus.

Colorimetric procedures, first attempted in the early 1930's, were not generally adapted to histochemistry until the mid 1940's. Lowry, Kirk, Glick, and Holter led in the general development of colorimetric methods that could be applied to histochemistry. Colorimetric, spectrophotometric, and, more recently, fluorimetric methods are becoming increasingly important and are replacing many of the earlier methods based on titration.

Thus, many of the major groups of biochemical techniques are now available to the histochemist. Most of the special pieces of glassware and apparatus necessary for these procedures are available commercially. Moreover, much of the apparatus can be made without great difficulty. The equipment necessary for the vast majority of histochemical procedures is neither difficult nor expensive to obtain if a reasonably well-equipped biochemical or physiological laboratory is already available.

A more serious problem than that of obtaining the necessary equipment faces the person who has not previously worked on the reduced scale of histochemistry—namely, the psychological adjustment that must be made from thinking in terms of milliliters to thinking in terms of microliters. Until this transition is complete, the techniques will appear difficult, the equipment will seem too small, the tissue will be too difficult to handle, and the data collected will be too precarious. With experience, however, the equipment will become manageable, the tissue easier to handle, and the data collected convincing. Consequently, even though the first, second, and third attempts at a new histochemical procedure may end in failure, success may be imminent. After a time, ordinary equipment will appear clumsy, amounts of material necessary for macro determinations wasteful, and the data resulting from such determinations crude.

Although most histochemical procedures are based on biochemical methods, it must not be forgotten that the ultimate aim of histochemistry is to express the chemical data in morphological terms—either directly, as amount per cell, or indirectly, by correlating chemical change with morphological change. The histochemist, therefore, must treat the morphological aspect of his problem as carefully as the biochemical.

Several generalizations concerning histochemical techniques are so important that they may be considered as basic axioms. These are listed below, with a brief discussion of each.

Know your material. Before any chemical work is done, a detailed morphological analysis of the tissue should be made. Even if the cell number of a sample can be estimated without looking at sections of the tissue, sections should be made and studied with care. The character of the tissue, together with the particular requirements of the specific histochemical procedure to be used, will determine the method to be used in collecting the tissue and the amount of the tissue to be used. The importance of keeping in mind the relationship between the form of the tissue and the problem to be solved cannot be overemphasized.

The simplest procedure is the best procedure. All histochemical procedures should be kept as simple as possible. All unnecessary steps should be eliminated, and transfers of tissue or of solutions should be kept to a minimum. If an entire procedure can be carried to completion in the vessel into which the tissue was initially placed, the possibility of error will be greatly reduced. Probably the greatest danger is the loss of tissue.

Adequate controls must be run at all times. Controls in histochemistry are of great importance, and must include morphological controls. It is always necessary to prove that the tissue analyzed chemically is the same as the tissue analyzed morphologically. Every step of the chemical procedure must be carefully examined and checked, particularly in adapting a biochemical procedure to histochemistry for the first time. Special care must be taken when a procedure developed for animal tissue is applied to plant material.

The first several attempts at almost any histochemical procedure with which the investigator is unfamiliar, even though he is an experienced histochemist, are apt to be unsatisfactory. But as the investigator becomes familiar with the procedure, the determinations should become reproducible. If they do not, the technique should be carefully reexamined. When possible, more than one procedure should be used to measure the same cell component or enzyme. Only by adequate replication is it possible to judge the validity of the data obtained.

Cleanliness is essential. This could well be the motto of every histochemical laboratory. All glassware must be absolutely clean. Chemicals of the highest purity must be used. Dust must be kept to a minimum. A bad determination can often be traced back to dirt.

These, then, are the basic axioms common to all histochemical procedures. Of equal importance are the considerations which underlie the mode of approach to the histochemical analyses and the method of obtaining samples of the tissue. Here, again, knowledge of the plant material to be used is of importance.

The work of Pollock and Olney (1959), mentioned briefly in the first chapter, illustrates the way histochemical methods can be applied to a botanical problem. The basic problem they were interested in was seed dormancy. They noted that, "While the seed may be considered to be a closed system, it cannot be treated as a homogenous system since it is structurally complex with physiological specialization closely associated with this structural complexity." They concluded that only through dissection and analysis of the various parts of the seed could meaningful data be collected. The embryonic axis (root primordium, hypocotyl, and shoot apex), the leaf primordia, and the whole seed were used in the analyses.

To establish a basis for expressing the chemical data, Pollock and Olney made linear measurements of the leaf primordia and the embryonic axis with an ocular micrometer, dry weights of the same organs were obtained using a quartz fiber balance (p. 25), and cell counts were made using maceration techniques (Chapter 7). The measurement of oxygen consumption was complicated by the differences in the size of the various parts and by the fact that only a limited number of seeds could be dissected within a practical time period. Therefore, for the whole seeds, which were large and which did not require dissection, oxygen uptake was measured with a conventional Warburg manometer and 10–20 seeds. A differential volumeter (a semimicrorespirometer; see p. 303) was used to measure the oxygen uptake of the embryonic axis. Five axes were required. Finally, one or two leaf primordia were placed in a Cartesian diver (a microrespirometer; see p. 306) to measure the oxygen uptake. The technique used in each part of the investigation depended on the nature of the material and on the difficulty in obtaining it.

The method they used for dealing with the leaf primordia data can be used to illustrate one general approach to the problem of finding a basis on which to express the data obtained. After the oxygen uptake of a pair of primordia was obtained, one primordium was used for cell counting while the other was dried, weighed, and its nitrogen content measured. The leaf primordia from any one seed proved to be so similar that there was no essential difference between them. On the basis of these measurements, the oxygen uptake data could be expressed per cell, per unit dry weight, or per unit nitrogen. This example, which represents only a small part of the work of Pollock and Olney, illustrates one possible type of histochemical analysis.

An example of another approach is the work of Jensen and Ashton (1960). Here the problem was to study the relation of wall composition to cell development in the tip of the onion root. Large numbers of roots were obtained from onion bulbs under standard conditions. The root tips were frozen rapidly and were dehydrated by substitution of the ice with cold alcohol (see p. 154). Some roots were used for a detailed cellular analysis (p. 105), using standard morphological techniques (Chapter 7). On the basis of this analysis it was decided to use 100 μ-segments of the root. This length segment provided enough material for the chemical analysis while being small enough to permit interpretation of the data in terms of cell development. From the cellular analysis the average number of cells per segment was determined for the first twenty 100 μ-segments.

A survey of the various methods which could be used for an analysis of the cell wall revealed that colorimetric sugar tests could be best adapted to the histochemical scale. These tests, mainly from the laboratory of Dische (1955), were made histochemical primarily by reducing the volume of the reagents and by measuring the absorption in a microcuvette attachment for a Beckman spectrophotometer. Difficulty was encountered in some of the procedures, which were originally developed for animal tissue, because of the large amount of hexuronic acids present in plant tissue. Another difficulty was the resistance to hydrolysis of the polysaccharide formations of the wall—again, a problem not encountered in the original techniques.

The roots were sectioned at 10 μ, and 9 sections were placed in a small vessel. A tenth section was placed on a slide. The sections in the vessel were used in the histochemical analysis, and the section on the slide was stained for use as a morphological control. This morphological control was used to observe the uniformity of the tissue. The histochemical analysis provided data on the amount of various carbohydrates present in the segment analyzed. These data, in turn, were expressed on a per cell basis by dividing the amount of material measured per section by the average number of cells normally found in the section. By such analyses it was possible to follow changes in wall composition that would not have been possible if larger segments had been used.

These two examples illustrate several important points regarding the application of histochemical methods to botanical problems. In both cases the fact that small amounts of material could be handled made the analyses meaningful. Because small amounts of material could be used, the morphological and physiological complexity of the material could be recognized at least to some degree. In both cases an understanding of the morphology of the tissue played a significant role in the application of the histochemical technique.

The examples given here will be further expanded in the following chapter, and new examples will be introduced to illustrate a variety of possible histochemical approaches to botanical problems.

Histochemical and microchemical techniques are now common enough such that a whole array of special glassware and apparatus has been designed for them. Although much of the necessary apparatus is commercially available it should be emphasized that much of it can be made by the investigator, provided he is reasonably dexterous and has the time. For example, the reaction vessels (p. 13), pipettes (p. 15), burette (p. 19), and microbalance (p. 25) can be made for a few dollars. The notion that all histochemical investigations require large capital outlays is not correct. This should be kept in mind when considering a histochemical procedure as part of a larger investigation.

Finally, a word must be said about the units of measure used in histochemistry. Most of the volumes and weights are measured in microliters (μl) or in micrograms (μg). The relation of these measures to grams and liters is shown in Table 2-1.

TABLE 2-1. *Units of Measure Used in Histochemistry*

WEIGHTS

$$1 \ \mu g \ (\text{gamma or } \gamma)^* = 10^{-3}mg = 10^{-6}g$$
$$1 \ m\mu g \qquad\qquad = 10^{-6}mg = 10^{-9}g$$
$$1 \ \mu\mu g \qquad\qquad = 10^{-9}mg = 10^{-12}g$$

VOLUMES

$$1 \ \mu l \ (mm^3)(\text{lambda or } \lambda) = 10^{-3}ml = 10^{-6} \text{ liters}$$

*The terms in parentheses are other names used in the literature in place of μl and μg.

Histochemical Equipment

The special equipment required for specific histochemical procedures will be described when those procedures are discussed. There are, however, certain basic pieces of apparatus which are used in a wide range of histochemical techniques, and these are described in this chapter. A list of manufacturers will be found at the end of the chapter.

Vessels

The size and type of reaction or digestion vessel will vary with the procedure and with the amount of material to be used. The most convenient are small pyrex test tubes: 6 mm (O.D.) ×25 mm, 6 mm (O.D.) ×50 mm, and 10 mm (O.D.) ×75 mm (Fig. 2-1A). These may be purchased commercially or may be made by hand. The smaller ones can be made easily by hand and are frequently more durable than their manufactured counterparts. When making the vessels by hand, care must be taken to form the inside of the bottom round and smooth.

These vessels may be sealed by slipping a short piece of rubber tubing over the end of the vessel and by closing the other end of the tube with a piece of solid glass rod (Fig. 2-1B). For some work, marbles or solid glass beads may be placed on top of the vessels to allow steam to escape and while keeping water loss to a minimum.

A vessel which has proved remarkably convenient for general use is the 1 ml centrifuge tube made by the Microchemical Specialties Co., Berkeley, California. The conical tube combines the advantage of the small volume of narrow reaction vessels with the convenience of the wide neck of the larger vessels. It is made of clear, relatively thin glass and thus permits the sample to be easily observed during the manipulations.

For holding small vessels, useful bases can be made by setting three prongs into an aluminum block (Fig. 2-1B). For the larger tubes, wooden blocks having holes slightly larger than the tubes work effectively.

The use of small vessels involves both advantages and disadvantages. Among the latter are difficulties in stirring or mixing solutions they contain. Various devices for stirring will be discussed in another section of this chapter. The small vessels are also difficult to fill by hand, but if they are held in a clamp in a moveable platform, and if the pipette or burette is held stationary, they can be filled easily. Occasionally, liquid will creep up the sides of a narrow vessel. This can be prevented by siliconing its inner walls.

The application of silicone to vessels, pipettes, and divers (page 306) is accomplished by filling them with a 5% solution of GE Dri-film SC-87 in chlo-

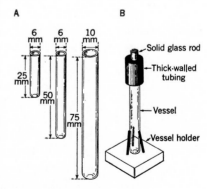

Figure 2-1
A. Reaction vessels. B. Stopper and holder for reaction vessel.

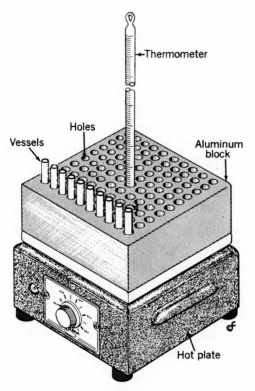

Figure 2-2
Heating block for reaction vessels.

roform (Doyle and Omoto, 1950). They are then emptied, drained, and placed in an oven at 110°C for from 2 hours to overnight. The silicone makes the surface of the vessel extremely hydrophobic. A drop of water in the bottom of a siliconed vessel can be completely removed with a pipette. Moreover, after siliconing, a drop of water can be suspended on the wall of the vessel to form a seal across the neck. This technique is of great importance in several histochemical procedures.

Vessels are best cleaned by boiling them in a cleaning solution or in a strong detergent. They are then rinsed in running water and are again thoroughly rinsed by running distilled water down to the bottom of the vessel through a drawn out piece of glass tubing. Most of the water can be shaken out; the remaining water can be removed by suction. The vessels are finally dried by placing them in an oven at 110°C. They may be rinsed with alcohol before they are dried. Sonic cleaners also work well in cleaning all sizes of reaction vessels.

Heating Blocks

Small reaction tubes can be heated easily in 4 x 4 x 2-in. aluminum blocks into which holes the size of the tubes have been bored (Doyle and Omoto, 1950) (Fig. 2-2). The depth of the holes is determined by the procedure to be followed: for use in digestion for nitrogen determinations, the holes should be shallow in order that the upper part of the tube will remain relatively cool; for various extraction procedures in which the entire mixture should be uniformly heated, deeper holes should be used. Aluminum blocks may be used equally well to keep the tubes cold. The blocks can be thoroughly chilled in a refrigerator or deep freeze before use.

Micropipettes

Many useful pipettes are available to the histochemist. One very simple pipette consists of a piece of glass tubing drawn into a long stem with a narrow construction at the tip (Fig. 2-3A). A rubber bulb or mouth-operated rubber tube is used to provide the suction. This type of pipette is particularly useful in removing liquids from the tissue, as, for example, during deparaffinization.

Another pipette that is useful either for handling tissue or moving fluids is the Holter braking pipette (Holter, 1943). (See Fig. 2-3B.) Here a capillary constriction determines the rate of movement in the stem, regardless of the suction applied at the top. These pipettes are made by drawing a constriction in a piece of capillary tubing of suitable diameter

Figure 2-3. *Various types of micropipettes.*

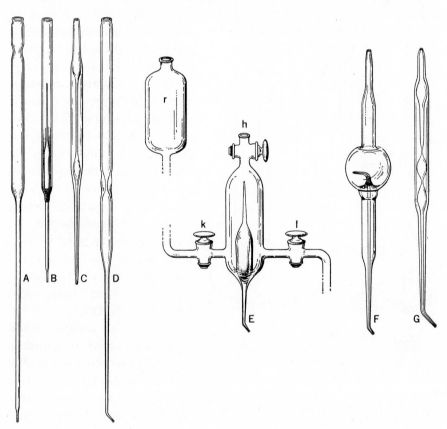

and cementing this in a piece of tubing of standard diameter with glass cement. Care must be taken to prevent liquid from reaching the constriction and blocking it. Should this happen, the liquid can be removed by strong suction or by gently heating the constricted area to vaporize the liquid.

Several types of pipettes are available for the measurement of small volumes. One is a thick-walled capillary with a mark on the side indicating a given volume (Kirk, 1950) (Fig. 2-3C). Liquids are drawn up into the pipette by the action of a screw or syringe arrangement attached to the end. These pipettes are accurate and are easy to use, although they are relatively slow in operation. They can either be made in the laboratory or can be purchased from Microchemical Specialties Co., Berkeley, California.

Another type of pipette is the constriction pipette (Levy, 1936; Linderstrøm-Lang and Holter, 1940). The volume of this pipette is determined by a constriction located at a given distance from the tip (Fig. 2-3D). The diameter and shape of both the constriction and the tip are important. The constriction should be sharp and narrow. The constriction diameter used is determined by the surface tension of the solution being pipetted; consequently, a constriction of smaller diameter must be used with alcohol than with water. The tip should also be narrow and should have sharp, clean edges (Fig. 2-3D).

For greatest accuracy these pipettes are used as shown in Fig. 2-4. The pipette is held in a clamp and is connected to a source of constant air pressure by means of a double T tube

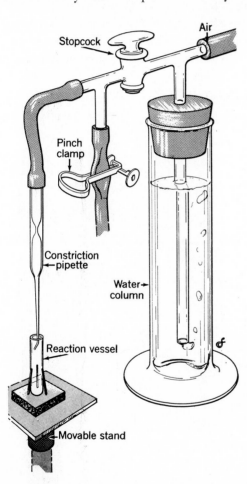

Figure 2-4
Use of a constant pressure source with a constriction pipette.

equipped with a stopcock. One arm of the T tube is long, and extends to the bottom of a water-filled cylinder. The pressure in the system is measured by the length of the tube in the cylinder. The other arm of the T tube is attached to a piece of rubber tubing fitted with a pinch clamp. By closing the stopcock, opening the pinch clamp, and sucking on the tubing, liquid is drawn up past the constriction in the pipette. By closing the pinch clamp and opening the stopcock, the liquid is caused to flow from the pipette under the constant air pressure. As the meniscus reaches the constriction, the surface tension increases, the air pressure is balanced, and movement stops. The air pressure must be adjusted such that the surface tension of the liquid in the constriction and in the tip are equal to the pressure when the tip is not immersed. Then, when the tip of the pipette is immersed or brought against the side of a vessel, the equilibrium will be disrupted and the pipette will discharge.

Constriction pipettes can also be operated by a mouth tube. The accuracy is not as great, but it is adequate for most determinations. In constriction pipettes made to be used directly by mouth control, the constriction is usually smaller. Extra pressure is then used to force the meniscus past the constriction when the pipette is discharged. With a little practice these pipettes are convenient to use.

Constriction pipettes can be made in three steps (Bessey, Lowry, and Brock, 1946).

(1) Draw a fairly long uniform neck from suitable size tubing. The size of the tubing will depend on the desired capacity of the pipette. When using heavy-walled capillary tubing, it is necessary to blow a small bubble in the glass first, to decrease the wall thickness before pulling.

(2) Using a small flame, draw a sharp, even constriction at the site of the tip. Using a diamond point, cut the tube at this constriction to produce a tip.

(3) Draw into the pipette a known volume of water or mercury determined by weight, and mark the level of the fluid. Using a sharp flame, melt the glass at the scratch mark to form constriction.

An alternate method of making constriction pipettes (Pollock, personal communication) is to first make a temporary tip longer than necessary. The pipette is then calibrated approximately, the constriction is made, the exact volume of water is introduced, the position of the final tip is marked, and the permanent tip is made. In either case, calibrate the finished pipette by weighing the liquid it holds.

With some practice, constriction pipettes can be made without difficulty to an accuracy of 0.1 μl. Excellent constriction pipettes are available from H. E. Pedersen, 37 Peter Bangsvej, Copenhagen, F., Denmark.

A third type of pipette is shown in Fig. 2-3E (Linderstrøm-Lang and Holter, 1931). A reservoir is attached at r above the level of the pipette. When the stopcocks, h and k, are opened the liquid rises above the tip of the pipette and fills the pipette when h is closed. When h and l are opened the liquid drains to a level below the tip. Closing h and l and opening k forces the liquid out of the pipette. When the pipette is empty, opening h refills it; the pipette is then ready for another cycle. This type of pipette is particularly useful in delivering relatively large volumes rapidly, accurately, and repetitively. These pipettes can be made in the laboratory or can be obtained from R. H. Thomas, Philadelphia, from Microchemical Specialties Co., Berkeley, or from H. E. Pedersen, Copenhagen.

What amounts to a modification of this pipette is the Grunbaum-Kirk pipette shown in Fig. 2-3F. This pipette is used by filling it with the reagent, and holding it such that the reagent will enter and fill the capillary. In pipettes with small volumes this is automatic, whereas in the larger sizes, pressure must be applied by blowing into the pipette. When the capillary is filled, the pipette is rotated, and the reagent is delivered by blowing into the pipette. This pipette can also be used by filling the bulb with a rinse solution. The capillary is filled from a reagent bottle and discharged as usual. The pipette is then rotated; the capillary is filled from the bulb; and the pipette is again rotated and discharged. The cycle can then be repeated. These pipettes are available from Microchemical Specialties Co., Berkeley, California.

There are several other types of pipettes which can be especially useful in particular procedures. One of these is the double-constriction pipette used in making the neck seals discussed on p. 14. A neck seal is made by depositing a drop of liquid on the side of a siliconed vessel with a pipette. The tip of the pipette is then used to draw the edge of the drop out such that contact is made with all surfaces of the vessel, thus forming a seal. With narrow-necked vessels this is no problem, but for many vessels a larger amount of liquid is needed to form the seal than is wanted in the final seal. Therefore, a pipette with two constrictions is used (Fig. 2-3G). The volume occupied between the two constrictions is the volume desired in the final seal. To obtain the desired seal, the total volume of the pipette is used to make the initial seal. Liquid is then drawn from the seal into the pipette, up to the first constriction. The volume of liquid remaining in the seal is thus equal to the volume between the two constrictions. Many other special pipettes exist, but these will be described in later chapters.

Microburettes

Titration procedures were among the first histochemical methods to be developed. It is hardly surprising, therefore, that there are a relatively large number of microburettes available.

One of the earliest microburettes, and one still in general use, is the Carlsberg type I (Fig. 2-5A) (Linderstrøm-Lang and Holter, 1931). This burette consists of a carefully calibrated length of capillary tubing (a) fitted with a narrow tip and screw plunger arrangement which forces mercury into the capillary (b). The mercury, which is in contact with the solution in the capillary, forces the solution out as the plunger is turned in. Reversing the plunger draws the solution into the burette. This type of burette is used with the tip inserted below the surface of the liquid to be titrated. The action is direct, the change in the meniscus being read at the top of the mercury column. The burettes have a total capacity of 100 μl. A commercial model of this burette is available from A. H. Thomas and Co., Philadelphia. They can also be made by hand.

The major difficulty with this type of burette is that the mercury is in direct contact with the standard solution. Without changing the action of the burette, Kirk redesigned the burette by adding a small air space between the mercury and the standard solution (Kirk, 1933; Sisco, Cunningham, and Kirk, 1941). These burettes have the same range in capacity and accuracy as the Carlsberg burettes. They are available from Microchemical Specialties Co., Berkeley.

Another approach to the problem of mercury-solution contact is the Carlsberg type II burette illustrated in Fig. 2-5B (Linderstrøm-Lang and Holter, 1933). When the plunger (similar in design to that used in the type I burette) is moved out, the mercury drops in arm a. This causes a decrease in pressure in arm b. If the tip of the burette is submerged, this decrease in pressure causes the solution to rise into the burette. To discharge the burette the plunger is moved in, causing the pressure in arm b to increase. Liquid will not flow from the burette, however, while the tip is surrounded by air, since the surface tension in the tip effectively counterbalances the hydrostatic pressure of the solution. When the tip is submerged and the surface tension of the tip is reduced, the solution is forced out by the pressure exerted by the air in b. Thus, the amount of solution discharged by the burette is regulated by moving the solution to be titrated in and out of contact with the tip of the burette, which is

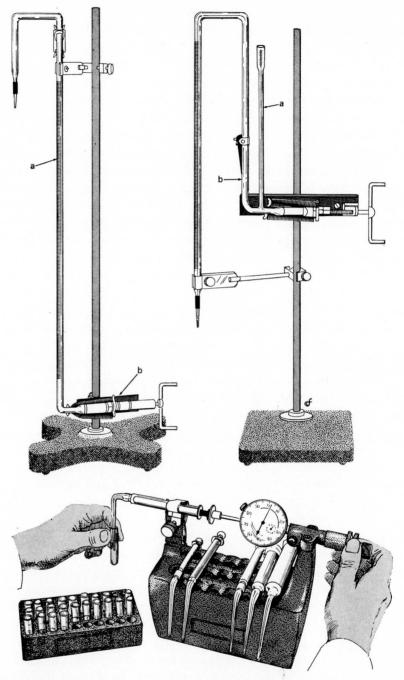

Figure 2-5. *Various types of microburettes. Left. Linderstrøm-Lang Type I. Right. Linderstrøm-Lang Type II. Center. Direct-reading microburette based on mechanical control of the discharge of a calibrated syringe.*

held stationary. A movable platform (p. 22) is used for this purpose. This burette is available from A. H. Thomas and Co., Philadelphia.

Boell (1945) designed a less elaborate burette, which works on the same principle (Fig. 2-6). This effective burette can be made easily by mounting a fine capillary horizontally and connecting it with small-bore pressure-tubing to a rubber reservoir containing mercury. A screw clamp on the mercury reservoir is used to regulate the pressure. An air gap is left between the mercury and the solution. A fine tip is attached to the other end of the burette by means of resistant tubing.

Another way to measure burette discharge is to note the distance moved by the plunger in burettes of the direct mercury contact type, rather than to measure the distance the meniscus moves. In these burettes, a micrometer is used to measure the movement of the plunger (Scholander, Edwards, and Irving, 1943). Such burettes are available from Emil Greiner Co., New York. A very precise adaptation of the Scholander burette was made by Gilmont (1948, 1953), and is available from the same source.

A versatile burette that operates on still a different principle is shown in Fig. 2-5C (Lazarow, 1950). This burette is actually a syringe that is discharged by the forward movement of a mechanically driven piston. The capacity of the burette is determined by the size of the syringe used. The syringes are easily changed, and the solutions are in contact only with glass. However, viscous solutions, such as concentrated sulfuric acid, are troublesome in that they force the tips off. This burette is made by Micro-Metric Instruments, Cleveland.

Figure 2-6. *Handmade microburette, a microtitration stand made from an old microscope body, and a stirring apparatus made from an electric shaver.* [*Redrawn from Boell,* Conn. Acad. Arts Sci., Trans. **36**, *1945.*]

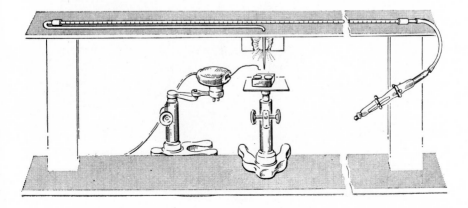

Adjustable Platforms

In working with small vessels, micropipettes, and microburettes, it is frequently desirable to hold the pipette or burette stationary and to bring the tube to it by some controlled mechanical means (Linderstrøm-Lang and Holter, 1931). This is usually accomplished by holding the pipette in a clamp and placing the vessel in a holder on a platform which can be raised and lowered by a rack and pinion gear. An early model of an adjustable platform is available from A. H. Thomas, Philadelphia.

Figure 2-7. *Apparatus for removing solutions from reaction vessels incorporating a movable platform and micropipette.*

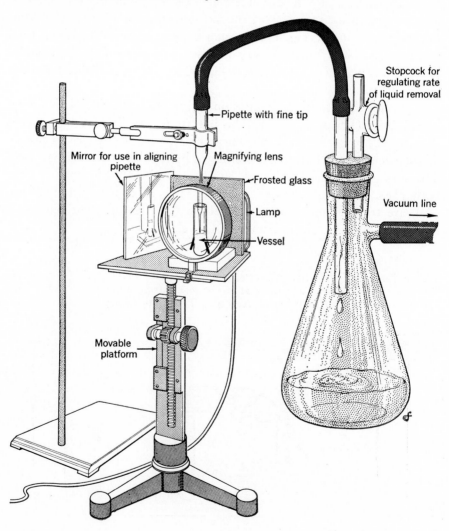

An advanced model is produced by O. Dich, Copenhagen. Adjustable platforms of various types are available from Microchemical Specialties Co., Berkeley. Almost any type of rack and pinion gear arrangement, however, can be adapted to serve as the basis for an adjustable platform. Old microscope bodies and adjustable magnifier mounts can be easily adapted to this purpose.

One example of an arrangement using a fixed pipette and an adjustable platform is shown in Fig. 2-7. This apparatus is used to remove paraffin from tissue sections. The sections are placed in the bottom of a small vessel, and toluene is added. The vessel is then placed in the holder and, with the aid of the mirror, is aligned under the pipette. The platform is then raised such that the tip of the pipette is just beneath the surface of the toluene. As the vacuum gently draws off the toluene, the platform is raised in order that the tip of the pipette will remain just beneath the surface of the liquid but not in contact with the tissue.

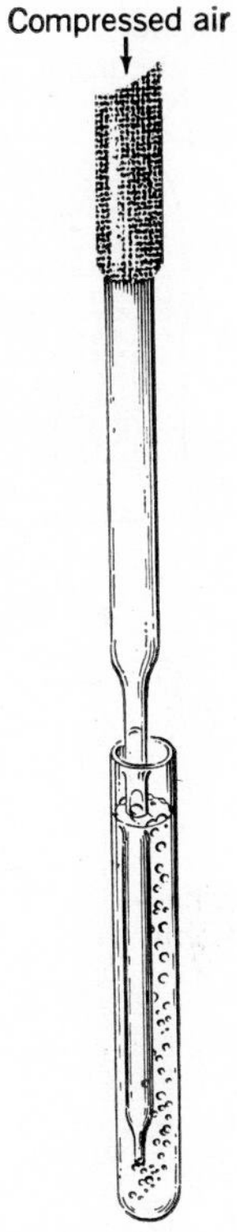

Compressed air

Figure 2-8
Stirring a solution by means of a stream of air.

Stirring Devices

The problem of stirring small amounts of liquid can be met in a variety of ways. One of the simplest is to bubble a stream of clean air or nitrogen through the solution (Fig. 2-8). This is effective for volumes of 1 ml or more.

Drill chuck
Flattened nail

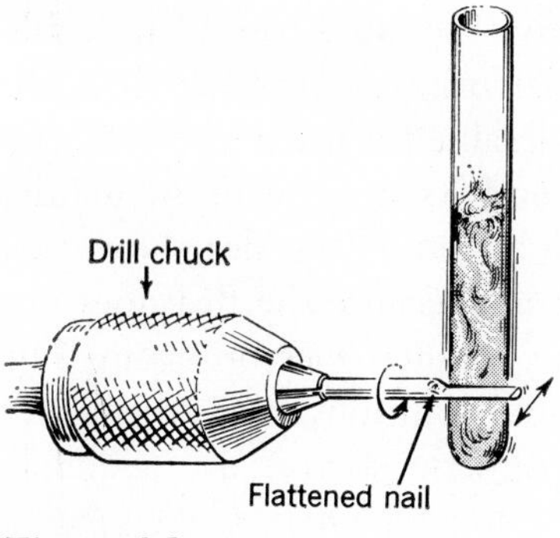

Figure 2-9
Stirring a solution by means of a flattened nail.

Another approach is to hold the vessel against a partially flattened nail moving in a drill (Fig. 2-9) or against a rubber stopper with an off center hole mounted either on a motor shaft or on a commercial vibrator used for reducing and relaxing. If a vibrator is utilized, a Variac is used to control the speed, and a short length of rubber tubing is used to hold the tube.

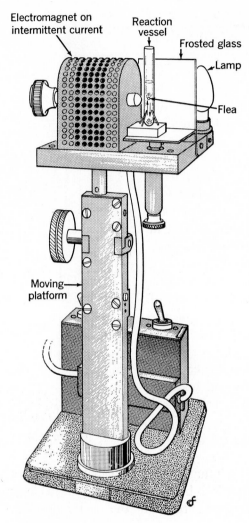

Electromagnet on intermittent current

Reaction vessel

Frosted glass

Lamp

Flea

Moving platform

Figure 2-10
Magnetic stirring apparatus.

Mixing may also be accomplished by rotating the tubes very rapidly (Lazarow, 1951). This type of mixer is available from Micro-Metric Instruments, Cleveland.

Small volumes can be stirred with thin glass rods attached to an electric vibrator (Kirk, 1950). The vibrators are available from Microchemical Specialties, Berkeley. They may also be made by removing the top of a discarded electric shaver and attaching a rod to the vibrating unit (Boell, 1945).

For very small volumes a small glass sphere filled with iron powder (called a "flea") is introduced into the liquid, and the tube is placed near an electromagnet energized by pulses of current (Fig. 2-10) (Linderstrøm-Lang and Holter, 1931). The intermittent action of the magnet causes the flea to jump up and down, mixing the solution. This type of device is usually mounted on a movable platform and is particularly valuable for use with the Carlsberg microburettes. The flea is so light, and its movement so gentle, that it may be used in a neck seal. The lightness of the flea, however, means that mixing viscous solutions is difficult because the flea does not have time to fall to the bottom before the magnet goes on again. For viscous solutions, such as strong sulfuric acid solutions, a hand magnet may be used to move the flea. Electromagnetic stirrers are available from A. H. Thomas and Co., Philadelphia and O. Dich, Copenhagen. They may also be constructed without much difficulty, for they consist essentially of a circuit breaker, a wire coil, and a soft iron bar.

Homogenizer

Small pieces of tissue or tissue sections can be homogenized in the small homogenizer shown in Fig. 2-11. The body is made from hard plastic; the plunger, from stainless steel. This homogenizer is easily cleaned and very effective in use.

Microcentrifuge

Special, small, relatively high-speed centrifuges have been designed for histochemical procedures. Two well-made centrifuges are available; one from Microchemical Specialties Co., Berkeley, and the other from O. Dich, Copenhagen. They hold tubes with 0.1, 0.2, and 1 ml capacities. An International centrifuge (Model MB), which holds 1 ml tubes, is available from Aloe Scientific, St. Louis. The commercial tubes have a tendency to break at high speeds, such as 15–200 g, but tubes made by hand from ordinary tubing will withstand these speeds. Polyethylene and polystyrene centrifuge tubes with a 1 ml capacity can be obtained from Aloe Scientific, St. Louis. These centrifuges are small enough such that they can be refrigerated easily by placing them in a cold room, refrigerator, or deepfreeze.

Microbalances

The dry weight of tissue can be determined by the use of micro-balances. Various such balances have been designed, each employing a different principle. One of the cheapest, easiest to use, and most sensitive is the quartz "fish pole" balance designed by Lowry (1941, 1953). The major component of this balance is a quartz fiber (Fig. 2-12). One end of the fiber is fixed to a solid glass rod; the object to be weighed is attached to the other end. The bending of the fiber is pro-portional to the weight of the material.

Quartz fibers for such balances are made by drawing out slender quartz tubes until a fiber of uniform diameter is obtained. The diameter of the fiber will determine its flexibility and, hence, the sensitivity of the balance. The fiber is mounted in a glass case (Fig. 2-12). The fiber and the case are coated with platinum by painting the outside of the fiber and the inside of the case with a 5% solution of chloroplatinic acid in alcohol and by heating them gently until conversion to platinum occurs. The platinum coating reduces

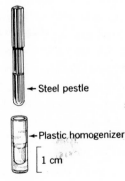

Steel pestle

Plastic homogenizer

1 cm

Figure 2-11
Microhomogenizer.

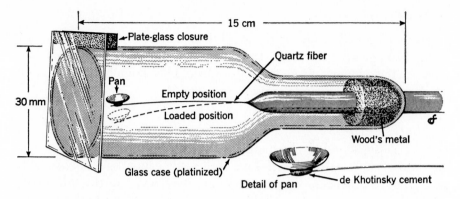

Figure 2-12. *Fishpole quartz balance* [*Redrawn from Lowry*, J. Histochem. and Cytochem. **1**, *1953*].

static electricity by increasing the conductivity of the parts. A balance pan is made of thin glass obtained by rapidly blowing out a glass bubble. The glass should be thin enough to show interference colors. A speck of hard de Khotinsky cement is sealed to the bottom of the pan by using the heat from a soldering iron. The pan is next held in a small paper jig and is cemented to the fiber by remelting the cement with a soldering iron. After the balance is assembled as shown in Fig. 2-12, a small piece of metal which has been painted with 10 or 20 μg of a radium salt is introduced into the bottom of the chamber. This is done to further reduce static electricity. A piece of plate glass is used to close the chamber.

A horizontally mounted dissecting microscope equipped with a micrometer disk is used to measure the displacement of the fiber. A hair point is used to place the tissue on the pan, and a slide is used to support the pan while it is filled. Lowry (1953) states that weighings can be made at the rate of 1 or 2 per minute. To calibrate the balance, single crystals of any highly colored compound are weighed, dissolved, and measured against a standard. Lowry has made such balances with a sensitivity and reproducibility of 0.01 μg. The major difficulty with this type of balance is its limited range, for the range becomes smaller as the sensitivity increases. Such balances are relatively easy to make, however, and several can be made, each with a different range.

A quartz fiber balance of even greater sensitivity (0.0001 μg) and with a capacity of 0.05 μg has been described by Lowry, Roberts, and Chang (1956). The design is essentially the same, but the fiber is only 1 cm long and is mounted in a glass tube 8 mm in diameter and 20 mm long. Quinine bromide crystals are used to calibrate the balance and are dissolved in 1 ml of 0.1 N H_2SO_4 and are measured fluorometrically.

Quartz torsion balances can also be made by hand (Kirk, 1950; Lowry, 1944) or can be purchased commercially (Microtech Services Co., Berkeley, California or Microchemical Specialties Co., Berkeley, California).

A quartz fiber, wound in the form of a helix, may also serve as the basis for a microbalance. A uniform fiber about 0.1 mm in diameter, wound to a length of about 40 cm, was used by Stern and Kirk (1948) to weigh fresh Trillium anthers. The helix was suspended inside a glass tube 30 mm in outside diameter; an overlapping tube at the bottom, 34 mm in diameter, was used for closing the balance. A small quartz cradle supported the tissue. The elongation of the helix, which was proportional to the weight, was read with a cathetometer. Weights as small as 0.01 mg could be measured quickly and accurately. Quartz fibers may be purchased from Microchemical Specialties Co., Berkeley.

A good commercial microbalance is the Roller-Smith torsion balance fitted with a total scale of 3 mg. The sensitivity of this balance is 2 μg. The Cahn Electrobalance, another good microbalance, offers the advantage of a greater range.

A completely different approach to weighing small pieces of tissue is provided by the Cartesian diver balance (Zeuthen, 1948). With this balance the tissue is weighed under water to obtain the reduced weight (R.W.). The R.W. of an object is the weight of the object minus the weight of an equal volume of water. For most tissues the R.W. closely approximates the dry weight. The Cartesian diver balance will be discussed in detail in Chapter 14. Briefly, the diver balance is a small, hollow glass bulb partially filled with the medium in which it is submerged. A small air bubble trapped in the glass bulb determines the buoyancy of the balance. Attached to the top of the bulb is a plastic cup for holding the tissue. To make a weighing, the pressure necessary to bring the diver balance to a given mark is measured. The diver is then loaded with the tissue, and the pressure now necessary to bring the diver to the mark is found. By following the same procedure for a standard weight, the weight of the tissue can be determined.

The advantages of the diver balance are that the tissue is alive at the end of the weighing and the reduced weight is obtained. The fresh weight of the same tissue can be obtained by weighing the tissue in a medium of different density (see Chapter 14). However, when weighing plant tissue by this method, no air must be present in the sample. Consequently, the weighing of such objects as sections of mature stems, roots, and leaves becomes difficult unless all the air can be removed. Root tips, stem tips, embryos, and meristematic tissues usually can be successfully weighed by this method. Most algae and fungi should be easy to handle in the Cartesian diver balance. The possibility exists that such processes as starch accumulation could be studied by placing the diver and tissue in a solution containing a suitable precursor and following the changes in R.W. with time.

Colorimeters, Spectrophotometers, and Fluorimeters

The small samples used in histochemical methods present special problems when working with color reactions. The amount of color produced will frequently be small if the volumes regularly used in biochemical procedures are employed. By reducing the volume of the reactants the color intensity can be increased, but then modifications must be made in the colorimeter or spectrophotometer in order that small volumes can be used. The increase in number of quantitative histochemical methods based on color reactions has led to the design of a number of micro and semimicro colorimeters, spectrophotometers, and fluorimeters. Some of these are simple adaptations of standard instruments, whereas others are based on combinations of microscopes, monochrometers, and photometers.

The simplest adapters are modifications in the cells of the colorimeter or spectrophotometer, which allow the use of a smaller volume of liquid. In most such adapters the beam of light passing through the cell is not narrowed, nor is the width of the cell altered. The Klett colorimeter, for example, can be fitted with a flat-bottom cell which reduces the necessary volume to 1 ml, without other changes in the instrument being necessary. One source of these cells is A. H. Thomas Co., Philadelphia. One type of microadapter available for the Bausch and Lomb Spectronic 20 Spectrophotometer-Colorimeter makes use of a solid plastic insert into the standard cell, which reduces the volume necessary for a determination to 1 ml. This insert displaces the solution such that the light beam passes through the liquid, whereas in the standard cell, 1 ml is not sufficient. This adapter is available from Aloe Scientific, St. Louis. A second adapter for the same instrument consists of a special small cell held in a carrier designed to position it in the light beam. This cell requires only 0.4 ml, and is available from A. H. Thomas, Philadelphia. The flat-bottomed Klett cell can also be used in the Bausch and Lomb instrument. If it is raised such that the bottom of the cell is just below the lower edge of the light beam, less than 1 ml of solution is necessary for a determination. The useful and versatile Coleman spectrophotometers and colorimeters can be used with volumes as low as 0.5 ml.

The spectrophotometer which has been most widely used in histochemical work is the Beckman spectrophotometer model DU. Its popularity is the result of its ubiquitous distribution, its large range, which extends into the ultraviolet, and the number of excellent microcells which have been designed for it.

The microadapters for the Beckman spectrophotometer illustrate nicely the problems involved in converting spectrophotometers for use with very small volumes (10–50 μl). Three microadapters will be discussed: the microcuvettes of Lowry and Bessey (1946), the capillary microcuvettes of Kirk, Rosenfels, and Hanahan (1947), and the microliter cells of Glick and Grunbaum (1957).

The microcuvettes of Lowry and Bessey are essentially the standard cells used in the Beckman instrument, but with thick side walls (Fig. 2-13). By making the side walls thicker the volume of the cell is reduced without altering the length of the absorption path. Increasing the thickness of the walls, however, means that the light beam coming from the monochromater is wider than the microcuvettes. The light beam must be reduced in diameter or some of the light would pass through the walls of the cells and affect the absorption measurements. A simple sliding panel with holes of various sizes is used to mask the opening in the monochromater and to produce a narrow beam of light. The diameter of the beam is slightly narrower than the inner dimension of the cell. The cells must, consequently, be positioned with care such that the beam is neither partially blocked by the wall nor reflected from the walls. To obtain a minimum volume the beam should also pass near the bottom of the cell. The cells are thus made slightly shorter than a standard cell and are held in a modified carrier which permits vertical adjustment of the cells. The complete adapter and microcuvettes can be obtained from Pyrocell Manufacturing Co., New York.

The Lowry and Bessey microcuvettes allow readings of volumes down to 50 μl without difficulty. The microcuvettes are made of fused silica and can be used in ultraviolet light. They are easy to fill, empty, and clean. The adapter is easily removed from the instrument, thus allowing the spectrophotometer to be used for other purposes. The chief difficulty with this method is that the length (1 cm) of the light path

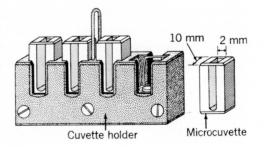

Cuvette holder   Microcuvette

Figure 2-13
Lowry and Bessey microcuvette for the Beckman spectrophotometer.

through the solution is the same as in the standard Beckman spectrophotometer. Therefore, solutions with weak absorption cannot be accurately
measured.

To overcome this difficulty, Kirk, Rosenfels, and Hanahan (1947)
designed a microcuvette in the form of a capillary with a length of
5 cm. This increase in length results in a five-fold increase in sensitivity.
The cuvettes are made from Teflon plastic rods $\frac{5}{8}$ in. in diameter. A hole
either 2 mm or 4 mm in diameter is drilled through the length of the rod.
Two holes are drilled through the wall to the central capillary for filling.
Windows of glass or quartz are fitted over the ends of the capillary by
means of hollow plugs.

Teflon plastic is used to make these cuvettes because it is resistant to
both organic and inorganic solvents, it can be machined, and it is not
easily distorted. However, Teflon is exceedingly hydrophobic; for this
reason, care must be taken in filling the cuvettes to see that no air
bubbles are trapped in the capillary. The capillary is filled by introducing the solution through one of the side holes by means of a micropipette; the second side hole acts as an air vent.

A special holder is used to align the microcuvettes. The capillary must
be parallel to the light beam, or the readings will be affected. No slide
or mask is used to narrow the light beam before it reaches the cuvettes,
since the plastic of the cuvettes is opaque and acts as a built-in mask.
The microcuvettes and adapters are available from Microchemical Specialties Co., Berkeley.

The commercial capillary microcuvettes have either 2 mm or 4 mm
diameters and require 160 μl or 320 μl of solution for a determination.
The 4 mm cuvettes are considerably easier to use and have been used
more than the smaller cuvettes. However, even these are not as easy to
use as are the Lowry and Bessey cuvettes. Although the increase in
length in the capillary cuvettes increases the sensitivity, it also increases
the necessary volume and, to a considerable extent, offsets the advantage
of increased sensitivity over the Lowry and Bessey cuvette. Owing to
this advantage and to its general ease in use, the Lowry and Bessey
adaptation has found much wider acceptance than the capillary microcuvette.

The microliter cell designed by Glick and Grunbaum (1957) is essentially a further modification of the Lowry and Bessey microcuvette.
Glick and Grunbaum have designed a Teflon microcell which is inserted
in the microcuvette (Fig. 2-14). In this microcell, an 0.8 mm hole (k),
parallel to the beam of light, holds the test solution. Grooves on the
side of the microcell (l) permit the escape of air when the microcell

is slid into the microcuvette. Two 1.5 mm holes (i) are drilled in the face of the micro-cuvette a short distance above the hole (k) in the microcell. These holes are used to fill the microcell. The microcell is raised until the holes are in line, and the microcell is filled carefully with a micropipette. Care must be taken to prevent air bubbles from becoming trapped in the cell. This is done by filling the cell slowly in order that a continuous column of liquid fills the hole. The liquid should slightly protrude from both ends. The cell is now slid to the bottom of the microcuvette. Again, care should be taken to see that no air bubbles are trapped at the mouth of the hole in the microcell.

A pair of pinhole diaphragms is used to restrict and collimate the light beam. One diaphragm is a brass disk that fits into one of the holes in the standard filter holder on the Beckman spectrophotometer. The second diaphragm is of the standard Lowry and Bessey design. Both holes are 0.3 mm in diameter.

The light beam is 0.3 mm

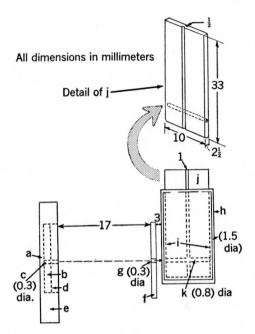

Figure 2-14

Microliter absorption cell for the Beckman spectrophotometer. a. Light beam; b. Brass disk which fits into one of the holes in the standard filter holder of the Beckman spectrophotometer. c. Hole in brass disk (b). d. Retaining-spring ring for (b). e. Standard filter holder of Beckman spectrophotometer. f. Sliding brass strip used in Standard Lowry-Bessey cell with new hole (g) present. g. Hole (0.3 mm in dia.) in brass strip (f). h. Lowry-Bessey cell. i. Holes in faces of Lowry-Bessey cell. j. Teflon insert fitted into Lowry-Bessey cell. k. Hole into which a micropipette is inserted when filling (j) is raised to a position when (k) and (i) coincide. l. Surface grooves on each face of (j) which permit escape of air during insertion into (h). [Redrawn from Glick and Grunbaum, Anal. Chem. 29, 1957.]

in diameter, and the hole in the microcell containing the solution is 0.8 mm in diameter. The beam must pass through the center of the hole in the microcell. Therefore, positioning the microcell is of great importance and requires very careful adjustment. Glick and Grunbaum (1957) designed a precision cell-positioning device for use with the Beckman spectrophotometer when equipped with microcells. Since Glick and Grunbaum provide detailed directions for the production of this device, they will not be repeated here. The cell-positioning device is also excellent for use with the standard Lowry and Bessey microcuvette.

The Glick and Grunbaum microliter cell has the same absorption-path length as do the standard Beckman cell and the Lowry and Bessey micro-cuvette; therefore it has the same sensitivity. The volume necessary for a measurement in the microcell is about 10 μl. The microliter cell is relatively easy to use, and, again, as can the Lowry-Bessey microcuvette, the Beckman spectrophotometer can be used for macro work without difficulty.

The Beckman spectrophotometer model DU has been employed in the greatest number of histochemical investigations, but it is by no means the only spectrophotometer which can be used. The Zeiss spectro-photometer can also be adapted to histochemical procedures. Indeed, a commercial spectrophotometer is not necessary as the basis of a micro-spectrophotometer. The essential elements are a monochromatic light source, a means of restricting and collimating the light, a microcell and a means of positioning it, and a photometer. By combining these with a microscope body, Holter and Lovtrup (1949) built a microcolorimeter that required only 10 μl of solution. This design was slightly altered by Krugelis (1950) and by Malstrom and Glick (1951) whose apparatus is illustrated in Fig. 2-15.

Figure 2-15. *A. Microcolorimeter. B. Lens system for illumination of the micro-colorimeter. a. Microscope illuminator. b. Lens system. c. Right-angle prism. d. Microscope condenser with top half removed. e. Objective (5×). f. Micro-photographic adapter. g. Photocell. h. Adjustable support. i. Vertical adjust-ment. j. Horizontal adjustment. k. Collimator. l. Double convex lens (15.2-mm focal length). m, n, o. Mounted projection lens unit (15-mm focal length). p. Setscrews. q. Post. r. Mounting tube.* [From Malstrom and Glick, Anal. Chem. **23,** 1957.]

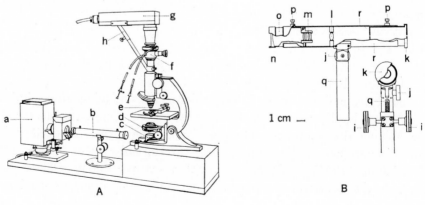

The cuvettes are pieces of capillary tubing (7 mm in length and 0.9 mm in diameter) attached to a microscope slide with silicone stopcock grease. These are filled with a long-necked micropipette, care being taken to see that no air is trapped in the bottom or on the sides of the cuvette. The cuvette is filled to just overflowing, and a cover slip is placed on the top. The centering of the cuvette is accomplished by means of a mechanical stage under a $5\times$ objective. The cuvettes can be obtained from O. Dich, Copenhagen; Canal Industrial Corp., Bethesda, Md.; or Fischer and Porter Co., Hatboro, Pa.

The light source is a microscope lamp of high intensity, and must be very steady. Malstrom and Glick (1951) used a Bausch and Lomb microscope lamp type 31-33-85 equipped with a ribbon filament bulb, a voltage regulator, and a transformer. A lens system consisting of a projection lens unit, a double convex lens, and two pinhole diaphragms fitted in a tube were used to produce a narrow, parallel beam of light.

A right-angle prism is used in place of the microscope mirror, and the condenser is used with the top half removed. A $5\times$ objective is employed, and the photocell is attached to the microscope by means of a microphotographic adapter equipped with a shutter, an observation eyepiece, and a $10\times$ microscope ocular. The photometer most frequently used is the Model 512 made by the Photovolt Corp., New York. Filters are placed in the light path to provide light of the proper wave length.

To make a measurement, the cuvette is centered and the condenser adjusted such that the focal point comes in the middle of the cuvette. The microscope is focused on the top surface of the cuvette using the observation eyepiece. The instrument is set to a galvanometer reading of zero with the shutter of the microphotographic adapter closed. A cuvette containing a blank is set in position, and the instrument is adjusted with the shutter open to a galvanometer reading of 100. The sample is treated in the same way, and the percent transmittance is read.

A microspectrophotometer for use with 10 μl of solution was designed by Wallach and Surgenor (1958). The design is similar to the microcolorimeter described above, but a glass prism monochromator is used as the light source. The same general type of cuvette is used. The absorption of the light by the solution is measured by a balanced photomultiplier bridge circuit. This is a good design, and should prove of general interest. A commercial microspectrophotometer based on this general design is available from Canal Industrial Corp., Bethesda, Md.

In the last few years there has been an increase in the number of fluorimetric methods adapted to the histochemical level. A leader in this development has been O. H. Lowry of the Washington University School of Medicine, St. Louis. In 1948, Lowry described a highly sensitive fluorimeter that is now available from the Farrand Optical Co., Inc., New York. The standard Farrand fluorometer can be used with as little as 0.5 ml of solution. In view of the nature of fluorimetric procedures as discussed in Chapter 10, this constitutes a reasonable volume for histochemical work.

For those procedures which require a further reduction in volume, Lowry has designed a microadapter for the Farrand fluorometer (Lowry, Roberts, Leiner, Wu, and Farr, 1954). Using tubes with an 8 mm bore, the volume necessary for a determination can be reduced to 10 μl. The adapter consists of a modified cell carrier which replaces the one used with the larger tubes. This modified carrier is a wooden block which is drilled to accommodate a brass rod which in turn holds the tubes. The details for the construction of this adapter are given by Lowry, Roberts, Leiner, Wu, and Farr, 1954.

Microburners

Microburners are useful primarily for the fabrication of various pieces of histochemical equipment, such as micropipettes and Cartesian divers. The simplest of all microburners is a piece of pyrex tubing drawn to a narrow opening and attached by a piece of rubber tubing to a gas outlet. An equally simple microburner can be made by filing the point from a hypodermic needle. The needle can be soldered to a piece of metal tubing which is then attached to a length of rubber tubing.

A well-made, inexpensive microburner in which the gas-air mixture can be controlled is produced by Microchemical Specialties Co., Berkeley, California. The same manufacturer also makes a very fine microtorch which can be used with oxygen.

Sources of Histochemical Equipment

Aloe Scientific, Division of A. S. Aloe Co., 5655 Kingsbury, St. Louis 12, Mo.

Arthur H. Thomas Co., West Washington Sq., Philadelphia 5, Penn.

California Laboratory Equipment Co., 98 Rincon Rd., Berkeley 7, Calif.

Canal Industrial Corp., 4940–51 St. Elmo Ave., Bethesda 14, Md.

Farrand Optical Co., Inc., Bronx Blvd. and E. 238th St., New York, N.Y.

Micro-Metric Instrument Co., P.O. Box 884, Cleveland 22, Ohio.

Microchemical Specialties Co., 1834 University Ave., Berkeley 3, Calif.

National Instrument Laboratories, 828 Evarts St. N.E., Washington 18, D.C.

Ole Dich, 37, Peter Bangsvej, Copenhagen, F. Denmark.

Pyrocell Manufacturing Co. 207 East Eighty-fourth St., New York.

Research Specialties Co., 2005 Hopkins St., Berkeley 7, Calif.

Literature

A large body of histochemical literature exists. About 95% of this literature is concerned with animal material, and much of it is of a highly clinical nature. It does serve, however, as a very rich source of techniques and ideas for the botanist. Many times the procedures can be applied directly to plant tissues, but frequently they cannot. Listed at the end of this chapter and the next are a number of books on histochemical techniques which are of general interest and importance. Books that deal mainly with quantitative histochemistry are listed below; those that deal with microscopic histochemistry are given at the end of the next chapter. Also listed below are the names of journals that contain papers on histochemical procedures.

Books on Histochemistry of General Interest

Brachet, J. and A. E. Mirsky (Editors), 1959. *The Cell.* Vol. 1. Academic, New York. The first half of the volume is a collection of excellent review articles on a variety of quantitative and microscopic histochemical procedures.

Glick, D., 1949. *Techniques of Histo and Cytochemistry.* Interscience, New York. One of the classics in the field; it covers both quantitative and microscopic histochemical procedures up to 1948.

Kirk, P. L., 1950. *Quantitative Ultramicroanalysis.* Wiley, New York. Includes many microchemical procedures that are of importance in histochemistry, written by the man who originated many of them.

Linderstrøm-Lang, K. U., 1952. *Lane Medical Lectures: Proteins and Enzymes.* Stanford Univ. Press, Stanford. A concise presentation of the Carlsberg school of histochemical technique by one of the principal founders of histochemistry.

Oster, G., and A. W. Pollister (Editors), 1956. *Physical Techniques in Biological Research* (3 volumes). Academic, New York. Another fine collection of review papers on many special techniques in histochemistry.

Journals which Regularly Publish Papers on Quantitative Histochemistry

Analytical Biochemistry
Analytical Chemistry
Annales d'Histochimie
Archives of Biochemistry and Biophysics
Biochimica et Biophysica Acta
Comptes rendus des travaux du Laboratoire Carlsberg, série chimique et série physiologique
Experimental Cell Research
Journal of Histochemistry and Cytochemistry

LITERATURE CITED

Bessey, O. A., O. H. Lowry, and M. J. Brock, 1946. A method for the rapid determination of alkaline phosphatase with 5 cubic millimeters of serum. *J. Biol. Chem.*, **164**:321–329.

Boell, E. J., 1945. Technique for the estimation of total nitrogen in tissues and tissue extracts. *Conn. Acad. Arts and Sci.*, **36**:429–441.

Dische, Z., 1955. New color reactions for the determination of sugars in polysaccharides, pp. 313–358. In *Methods of Biochemical Analysis*. II. D. Glick (Editor). Interscience, New York.

Doyle, W. L. and J. H. Omoto, 1950. Ultramicrodetermination of nitrogen. *Anal. Chem.*, **22**: 603–604.

Gilmont, R., 1948. High-precision ultramicroburet. *Anal. Chem.*, **20**:1109.

——, 1953. Ultrafine high-precision microburet. *Anal. Chem.*, **25**:1135.

Glick, D. and B. W. Grunbaum, 1957. Microliter absorption cell and its adaptation to the Beckman Model DU Spectrophotometer. *Anal. Chem.*, **29**:1243–1244.

Holter, H. and S. Løvtrup, 1949. Proteolytic enzymes in *Chaos Chaos*. *Compt. rend. trav. lab. Carlsberg, Sér. chim.*, **27**:27–62.

Jensen, W. A. and M. Ashton, 1960. Composition of developing primary wall in onion root tip cells. I. Quantitative Analyses. *Plant Physiol.*, **35**: 313–323.

Kirk, P. L., 1933. Quantitative drop analyses I. General apparatus and technique. *Mikrochemie*, **14**:1–4.

——, 1950. *Quantitative Ultramicroanalysis*. Wiley, New York.

Kirk, P. L., R. S. Rosenfels, and D. J.

Hanahan, 1947. Capillary absorption cells in spectrophotometry. *Ind. Eng. Chem., Anal. Ed.*, **19**:355–357.

Krugelis, E. J., 1950. Properties and changes of alkaline phosphatase activity during amphibian development. *Compt. rend. trav. lab. Carlsberg, Sér. chim.*, **27**:273–290.

Lazarow, A., 1950. A universal syringe burette and its use in microcolorimetric analysis. *J. Lab. Clin. Med.*, **35**:810–814.

——, 1951. Ultra-micro rotating stirrer. *J. Lab. Clin. Med.*, **38**:660–662.

Linderstrøm-Lang, K. and H. Holter, 1931. Contributions to the histological chemistry of enzymes. I. The estimation of small cleavages by enzymes. *Compt. rend trav. lab. Carlsberg, Sér. chim.*, **19**, No. 4:1–19.

——, 1933. Studies in Enzymatic Histochemistry. V. A micro-method for the estimation of sugars. *Compt. rend. trav. lab. Carlsberg, Sér. chim.*, **19**, No. 14:1–12.

——, 1940. Die enzymatische Histochemie, pp. 1132–1162. In Bannan, E. and K. Myrbäck, *Die Methoden der Fermentforschung*, Thieme, Leipzig.

Lowry, O. H., 1941. A quartz fiber balance. *J. Biol. Chem.*, **140**:183–189.

——, 1944. A simple quartz torsion balance. *J. Biol. Chem.*, **152**:293–294.

——, 1953. The quantitative histochemistry of brain—Histological sampling. *J. Histochem. and Cytochem.*, **1**:420–428.

Lowry, O. H. and O. A. Bessey, 1946. The adaptation of the Beckman spectrophotometer to measurements on minute quantities of biological materials. *J. Biol. Chem.*, **163**:633–639.

Lowry, O. H., N. R. Roberts, and M.-L. Chang, 1956. The analysis of single cells. *J. Biol. Chem.*, **222**:97–107.

Lowry, O. H., N. R. Roberts, K. Y. Leiner, M.-L. Wu, and A. L. Farr, 1954. The quantitative histochemistry of brain. I. Chemical methods. *J. Biol. Chem.*, **207**:1–17.

Malstrom, B. G. and D. Glick, 1951. Determination of zinc in millimicrogram quantities. *Anal. Chem.*, **23**: 1699–1703.

Pollock, B. M. and H. O. Olney, 1959. Rest Period. I. Growth, translocation, and respiratory changes in the embryonic organs of the after-ripening cherry seed. *Plant Physiol.*, **34**:131–142.

Scholander, P. J., G. A. Edwards, and L. Irving, 1943. Improved microme-ter burette. *J. Biol. Chem.*, **148**:495–500.

Sisco, R. C., B. Cunningham, and P. L. Kirk, 1941. Quantitative drop analyses. XIII. The formol titration of amino nitrogen. *J. Biol. Chem.*, **139**:1.

Stern, H. and P. L. Kirk, 1948. The oxygen consumption of the microspores of *Trillium* in relation to the mitotic cycle. *J. Gen. Physiol.*, **31**: 243–248.

Wallach, D. F. H. and D. M. Surgenor, 1958. Simple microspectrophotometer. *Anal. Chem.*, **30**:1879–1882.

Zeuthen, E., 1948. A cartesian diver balance weighing reduced weights (R.W.) with an accuracy of ±0.01γ. *Compt. rend. trav. lab. Carlsberg, Sér. chim.*, **26**:243–266.

CHAPTER 3

Microscopic Histochemistry

Introduction

The aim of microscopic histochemistry is the localization and identification of substances and enzyme activity within cells and tissues.
Inasmuch as it was founded by the French botanist Raspail in 1825
(Baker, 1943), microscopic histochemistry is hardly a new field. Raspail's
difficulties in having his research published are indicative of the general
position of microscopic histochemistry in his day. In 1830, Raspail published his major work at his own expense after it had been rejected by a
committee consisting of a physiologist, a chemist, and a botanist. The
reason for the rejection, according to Raspail, was that the physiologist
was ignorant of chemistry, the chemist of microscopy, and the botanist
of both (Baker, 1943).

During the latter half of the nineteenth century botanical histochemistry flourished, and botanists routinely used histochemical procedures
in research on the composition and development of vascular and nonvascular plants. At the beginning of the twentieth century, however, the
emphasis in botanical research shifted. In general, there was a separation
of the fields of morphology, physiology, and biochemistry. The result
was a loss of interest in histochemical procedures—procedures that require a synthesis of these three fields.

Roughly the same course of events was occurring in research on
animal tissues, although animal histochemistry in the nineteenth century
was not as well developed as its botanical counterpart. During the 1920's
and 1930's, however, interest in animal histochemistry gradually increased. The Feulgen stain for deoxyribonucleic acid (DNA) came into

general use, the ultraviolet microscope was developed, freeze-drying of tissues, conceived in 1890, was revived, and many new procedures were originated. The publication in 1936 of Lison's *Histochimie Animale* marks the beginning of the modern period of histochemistry. In this work Lison summarized existing procedures and pointed to future problems.

Interest in animal histochemistry was given further stimulus in 1939, when Gomori and Takamatsu independently published a method for the localization of alkaline phosphatase activity. This was the first of the modern enzyme localization procedures. These procedures have had a great impact on microscopic histochemistry, and for some years appeared to be almost the sole occupation of histochemists.

Recent years have seen the continued development of enzyme localization procedures, and similar qualitative methods based on color development, for a variety of cell constituents. The adaptation of microcolorimetric and microspectrophotometric methods to the study of single cells and cell parts has shifted the interest of many histochemists to the possibility of quantitative studies. To date, such studies have been highly successful with the nucleic acids, DNA in particular. The use of fluorescent dyes and fluorescence-labeled antibodies as specific indicators is another recent development of considerable interest and importance.

Autoradiography is a post-war technique that has stimulated great interest not only among histochemists but among biologists in general. This method, in which silver grains exposed by radiation from radioactive chemicals are used to indicate the site of the radioactive isotope in the cell, is one of the most widely used of the modern histochemical procedures.

During the 1940's and 1950's a technique was developed for the separation of cell parts by maceration and differential centrifugation. The separated parts can then be analyzed by biochemical methods for composition and enzyme activity. This approach yields intracellular data directly, the data being expressed in terms of the various cell organelles. The major difficulty with this method, with regard to histochemistry, is that information is obtained for an average organelle of an average cell. All differences in the various cells of the organism are eliminated in the procedure. Nevertheless, this approach yields information of great importance to the histochemist because it provides a basis on which to build histochemical research which can recognize differences in tissues and cell types. This technique is discussed further in Chapter 8.

Another allied technique that is having an impact on microscopic histochemistry is electron microscopy. The electron microscope has increased our knowledge of the morphological organization of the cell. As a result, the cell has been demonstrated to be a more complicated structure than most cytologists believed and hence a more difficult one for the histochemist to treat. One way to approach this problem, of course, is to adapt histochemical methods to the scale of the electron microscope. Research in this direction has already begun and is developing rapidly (Barrnett and Palade, 1958). There can be little doubt that this will be one of the major future developments in microscopic histochemistry.

During the last three decades the majority of new developments in histochemistry have been made by animal workers, primarily anatomists, cytologists, and pathologists. Botanical histochemistry has continued, although interest by botanists as a group has been slight. Van Fleet and his students deserve credit for focusing the attention of botanists on the enzyme and protein histochemistry of plant tissues. Microspectrophotometric research with plant tissues, particularly with regard to DNA, has been undertaken by a number of botanists and zoologists. Autoradiographic procedures on a truly microscopic scale were developed primarily by Pelc and Howard, using plant cells. Probably more botanists have used autoradiographic procedures than any other modern histochemical method. These procedures have been used in studies on chromosome formation, nucleic acid and protein metabolism, cell-wall synthesis, cell division, translocation, and radiation effects. Recently the use of fluorescent methods in the study of plant cells has increased, and their use will undoubtedly continue to increase.

From this brief survey of the development of microscopic histochemistry, it is clear that the range of histochemical procedures is great. Methods based on the development of color are the oldest and numerically the most important. However, the fluorescent methods are a modern development. Other histochemical procedures exist that do not rely on the development of color, such as microincineration, ultraviolet microspectrophotometry, and autoradiography. These will be discussed in later chapters. The importance of the color methods is so great, however, that it is necessary to examine them as a group before discussing them individually in later chapters.

When the procedures based on color development are examined in this way, certain basic similarities become apparent. Thus, although the actual method of obtaining color may differ widely, the relationship between the final colored product and the original substance or activity will follow one of three major patterns.

In the first major pattern the substance is visualized by direct combination, either chemical or physical, with the coloring agent. The majority of such dye-based reactions as the methyl green reaction for DNA, the fast green test for histones, and the azure B method for RNA and DNA are found in this group. The old and famous iodine test for starch also falls into this category, as do some enzyme localization procedures, for example, the tetrazolium reaction for dehydrogenases. The use of a single solution to obtain the color does not necessarily mean that the procedure is a member of this group. Thus, the chloro-zinc-iodide reaction does not fall into this category, although only one solution is used. In this test the solution has two actions which occur almost simultaneously.

The second major pattern always involves two-step reactions. In the first step an agent reacts with the substance to be visualized but does not produce color. Through the action of this agent the substance can be colored in the next step. The nature and action of the first agent is highly variable from one procedure to the next. One entire series of histochemical procedures is based on the use of an oxidant as the agent in the first step. The oxidant produces aldehydes in the substance to be localized. The second agent is leucofuchsin, which forms a highly colored complex with the aldehydes in the next step. By varying the nature of the oxidant a wide variety of substances (carbohydrates, proteins, and lipids) can be selectively visualized. The Feulgen reaction for DNA is a modification of this type of procedure. Another large group of procedures which comes under this second pattern of histochemical reactions is based on the combination of the first agent with the substance to be localized. The second agent then combines with the first, and the original substance becomes colored in this indirect way. Many of the new and highly successful protein localization procedures have this pattern. A large number of the enzyme localization procedures also work on this principle. The enzyme is presented a substrate in a solution of the first agent. As the enzyme acts on the substrate, the first agent combines with and precipitates the end product or the by product of the enzymatic reaction. This new combination is then colored by the second agent. The localization of acid phosphatase is a procedure of this type. In this procedure the enzyme is given glycerophosphate (at an acid pH) in the presence of lead ions, which act as the first agent. The enzyme splits off the phosphate, which is precipitated by the lead as an insoluble lead phosphate. Since lead phosphate is not colored, it is converted by the second agent, ammonium sulfide, to black lead sulfide.

The third main pattern involves an additional step in the procedure.

This pattern is less common than the first two and is found primarily in enzyme procedures. The localization of alkaline phosphatase, probably the best known and most influential enzyme method ever devised, is in this category. As in the acid phosphatase procedure, the enzyme is presented glycerophosphate (at an alkaline pH) in the presence of calcium ions (not lead, as in the acid phosphatase method). The calcium phosphate formed is converted not to calcium sulfide but to cobalt phosphate, by placing the tissue in a solution of cobalt ions. Finally, as the third step, the cobalt phosphate is converted by ammonium sulfide to black cobalt sulfide.

The vast majority of the color methods are qualitative although it is hoped that more of them can be made quantitative. To date, only a few of the hundreds of color methods have proved suitable for quantitative measurements (Pollister and Ornstein, 1959). Of these the most important is the Feulgen reaction for DNA. In this reaction the color produced is proportional to the amount of DNA present. By the use of a microspectrophotometer (page 47) the amount of absorption can be measured and the amount of DNA per nucleus calculated.

. In general, microscopic histochemical methods are not technically difficult to perform. Moreover, they do not generally require elaborate or expensive equipment. Microscopic histochemistry thus becomes the natural adjunct to many morphological and developmental lines of research. There are pitfalls, however, for the novice in microscopic histochemistry. One of the greatest dangers is the inclination to accept a localization as correct merely because a vivid and colorful picture is obtained. The very beauty of some of the preparations tends to deaden the critical senses and to permit the acceptance of artifact as fact. The object of the localization must be kept in mind and the entire histochemical procedure examined critically before the data can be accepted.

When working with any histochemical procedure it is essential that the following axioms be kept in mind.

A technique is valid only if the specificity of the reaction is known. The best techniques are those for which the chemical basis is completely understood. Although such complete understanding may not always be necessary, reactions having completely unknown chemical bases and unknown chemical specificities cannot be considered as histochemical techniques. The validity of a reaction that is used even though incompletely understood can be established only by corroborative evidence and adequate controls. The pyronin test for RNA is an example of such a reaction. The test may be used as a histochemical procedure only when a ribonuclease control substantiates the results.

Morphological stains and histochemical techniques must not be confused!

All possible sites of the localized cellular substance in the living cell must still exist within the cell at the end of the histochemical procedure. The fallacy in concluding that DNA is found only in the cytoplasm if the procedure used destroys the nucleus is easily recognized. That the same thinking applies to other cell parts is not always as clearly recognized. It is necessary not only to demonstrate that the substance visible at the end of a histochemical procedure is localized on a particular site within the cell, but it is equally important to demonstrate that all possible sites still exist. From this it is clear that the method of fixation is an integral part of any histochemical procedure. The method of fixation used will depend on the solubility of the substance to be localized, the suspected site, and the type of data desired. A histochemical procedure begins with the initial treatment of the tissue and is complete only when the cover slip is mounted, with every intervening step assuming importance in turn.

A histochemical reaction must yield in the first step an insoluble product that must not be made soluble in any subsequent steps. In microscopic histochemistry the question of solubility is very important to the validity of the final result. One form of the solubility problem is to make insoluble the product of a reaction designed to demonstrate a soluble component, such as ascorbic acid. Another is to make insoluble the product of an enzymatic reaction at the actual site of the enzyme. Still another is to make visible an insoluble cellular component without making it soluble in the process. In any case, if the end product is soluble, or becomes soluble at some time during the procedure, the localization will not be valid. Solubility is also a very important consideration in the initial handling of the tissue. The fixative used, the method of dehydration, and the subsequent handling of the tissue must all be examined in the light of the solubility of the substance to be localized.

Adequate controls must be run at all times. In microscopic histochemical procedures every possible control must be used. The nature of the procedure will determine the number and types of controls necessary. The actual nature of the controls needed for the various techniques will be discussed under the histochemical techniques themselves. It is impossible to overemphasize the importance of controls in histochemistry. Whenever possible, two procedures should be used for the same substance. The best possible type of evidence for the identification of a site is to obtain the same localization using two techniques based on different principles.

Care and cleanliness are essential. A hastily done technique is usually worse than useless; it may be completely misleading. This should be kept in mind particularly where a histochemical technique forms only a part of a research project. Some kind of result is almost always obtained in the first attempt at a localization procedure (this is often not true in quantitative histochemistry); but whether this is the correct localization or merely an artifact will be apparent only after careful, thoughtful work. Cleanliness is an essential in histochemistry. Improperly cleaned slides may inhibit an enzyme reaction; impurities in the chemicals may result in false precipitates; and incorrectly made solutions may coat the slides with disfiguring films. After you have convinced yourself of the correctness of your data, you must still convince others, and dirty, clouded preparations do not help!

Equipment and Materials for Microscopic Histochemistry

General Equipment

The basic equipment necessary for microscopic histochemistry is the same as that used in traditional histology. A microtome, a paraffin oven, a slide warmer, Coplin staining jars, and an assortment of standard glassware form the core of a histochemical laboratory. In addition, a controlled-temperature water bath, a refrigerator, and a deep freeze are usually necessary. A freeze-dry apparatus (see Chapter 5) and a cold microtome may be needed for some histochemical procedures (see Chapter 6).

Microscopes

The basic piece of equipment in microscopic histochemistry is a microscope. A good microscope and a good light source are required. Time should be taken to become acquainted with the use of the microscope before beginning research in microscopic histochemistry. There are a number of excellent books on the use of the microscope, such as those by Barer (1953), Belling (1930), Freund (1960), and Needham (1958). An excellent treatment of photomicrography is given by Lawson (1960).

The usefulness of the light microscope for observations of living or unstained preparations was increased greatly by the invention of the phase microscope by Zernike in 1942. Since that time the use of the phase microscope has spread until it has become a common laboratory instrument. The phase microscope is based on the phase differences which are created in a beam of light passing through a piece of tissue. The optics in a phase microscope magnify these differences and develop contrasts, making visible structures which cannot be seen in ordinary light microscopes. All of the major microscope manufacturers produce phase contrast microscopes, and there are numerous excellent books and reviews on their use (Barer, 1959; Bennett, Osterberg, Jupnik, and Richards, 1951; Hale, 1959). Of particular interest to histochemists is the Hinne condenser, which can be easily adjusted to give bright field, phase contrast, or dark field illumination.

The interference microscope is based on the same general theoretical principle as the phase contrast microscope (Barer, 1959). But because of differences in construction, operation, and application, the interference microscope can be used to make mass determinations of microscopic objects, whereas the phase microscope cannot. At present the interference microscope has shown greatest application to problems involving single cell organisms or isolated cells or cell parts. However, the application of the interference microscope to biological problems continues to increase; among the kinds of work being undertaken are the analysis of mitosis in single living cells (Ambrose and Bajer, 1960), the study of the cell wall in algae (Green, 1960), and the analysis of enzyme histochemistry (Danielli, 1958). A particularly clear summary of the method of interference microscopy applied to biological systems is presented by Davies, Wilkins, Chayen, and LaCour (1954). Reviews of the operation and uses of the interference microscope are given by Barer (1959) and Hale (1958).

The polarizing microscope has long been a standard instrument in the study of cellulose, starch, and crystals present in plant cells. Since the use of the polarizing microscope is already widespread, and since numerous excellent articles are readily available on the principles involved (Barer, 1959; Oster, 1955), the polarizing microscope will not be discussed further.

Another microscope that can be used in some histochemical problems, but which will not be discussed here, is the ultraviolet microscope. The reason for this omission is that the ultraviolet microscope is a costly instrument with relatively narrow application. Ultraviolet light is absorbed by ordinary optical glass, and, as a result, quartz lenses must be used throughout the microscope. As regards work on plant tissue the ultraviolet microscope is of value primarily in the study of the nucleic acids and lignin. The reader interested in ultraviolet microscopy is referred to the excellent reviews by Nurnberger (1955) and Walker (1956).

Fluorescence microscopy, also based on the use of ultraviolet light, offers a much greater potential of use (Price and Schwartz, 1956;

Richards, 1955). In fluorescence microscopy, long-wavelength ultraviolet light is used to excite fluorescent materials to emit visible light. Although optical glass absorbs most ultraviolet light, particularly in the shorter wavelengths, it will transmit the long-wavelength ultraviolet used in fluorescence microscopy. As a result the standard light microscope can be used for fluorescence microscopy with relatively minor changes.

Fluorescence microscopy requires an intense source of ultraviolet light. The most frequently used source is a mercury arc lamp. Since silver does not reflect ultraviolet light well, the microscope mirror must be replaced with an aluminized, front-surface mirror. A filter must be placed between the source and the object to absorb any visible light emitted by the source. These filters are usually either gelatin or glass. The Corning Glass Works makes a number of ultraviolet transmitting filters. The choice of filter is often determined by the technique, and the type of filter to use will be suggested in the discussion of the various procedures. A second filter is placed between the object and the eye to absorb the longer wavelengths of ultraviolet light which may reach the eye or photographic emulsion and thus reduce the contrast in the image. A number of these ultraviolet absorption filters are available to be placed either in or on the ocular of the microscope. All of the accessory apparatus necessary for the techniques of fluorescence microscopy discussed here is readily available from the American Optical Co. or from Carl Zeiss, Inc.

The fluorescence microscope is often a monocular instrument, since the light emitted from the source is often of such low intensity that the loss of light involved in splitting the image in a binocular microscope would reduce the intensity such that accurate observation would not be possible. In working with a fluorescence microscope the observer should work in a darkened room and allow his eyes to become dark-adapted.

Fluorescence microscopy is still a relatively little used tool in histochemistry. However, owing to the diversity of its potential application, the future of fluorescence microscopy seems exceptionally bright. First, there is the observation of the natural fluorescence of substances within the cell, particularly the living cell. Various cell parts can be identified on the basis of fluorescence. Second, there is the use of fluorescent chemicals as specific histochemical reactants. This has proved particularly useful with regard to studies of callose. Finally, there is the use of fluorescence-labeled antibodies as extremely specific agents in the localization of various compounds within the cell (Mellors, 1959). In the labeled-antibody technique, an antibody to the substance to be localized is produced by injecting a highly purified sample of the substance into an animal. The antibody is extracted and labeled with a fluorescent group by conjugation. A sample or section of the tissue is then placed in a solution of the labeled antibody, which immediately combines with the substance to be labeled. The localization of the substance can then be studied in ultraviolet light. This approach is applicable to an almost endless list of biological compounds and offers great promise in the future.

Microspectrophotometry, or Cytophotometry

Twenty years ago microscopic histochemistry was an almost exclusively qualitative science with little prospect for quantitative measurement. Today, although the majority of the methods are still qualitative, an increasing number, particularly in protein and nucleic acid histochemistry, are yielding to quantitative measurement as a result of the development of microspectrophotometry, or cytophotometry (Pollister and Ornstein, 1959).

The microspectrophotometers used in this work are essentially the same as those discussed in Chapter 2; in that, they consist of a microscope, a monochromatic light source, and a photoreceptor. The problems involved in measuring the absorption of a dye bound to a nucleus and the absorption of a dye in solution are considerably different. These differences are pointed out by Pollister and Ornstein (1959) in an excellent review of the applications of microspectrophotometry to the study of cells. Such differences include the fact that because the geometry of the cell determines the absorption path, it is not readily adjustable by the investigator. Moreover, the absorption path is not a centimeter in length but only a few microns, necessitating a much greater color intensity if the measurement is to be made. Then, too, the investigator working with cells is always confronted with a situation in which the substance to be measured is not in solution but is in an essentially solid state and not necessarily uniform in distribution. Should this be the case, he has no standards for comparison, and his values become relative. He also has difficulty proving that his measurements obey the standard laws of absorption. Despite these difficulties, however, great strides are being made in the use of microspectrophotometric methods in microscopic histochemistry.

The theory of the use of a microspectrophotometer is straightforward. For example, a nucleus stained by the Feulgen reaction for DNA is brought under observation, and a measurement of the amount of light passing through it is made. Then the slide is moved, and the light passing through the cytoplasm is measured. The difference in the two measurements is proportional to the amount of color present and, hence, in the Feulgen reaction, to the amount of DNA present. By measuring the diameter of the nucleus and calculating its volume, the amount of DNA per nucleus can be determined. Such measurements are, of course, comparative and not absolute. For most purposes, however, this makes little difference.

The microspectrophotometric measurement of DNA has yielded very important information, such as the concept of DNA constancy (Swift, 1949, 1950). The application of the microspectrophotometer has been extended far beyond such simple measurements as are described here (Swift and Rasch, 1956). By using measurements at two wave lengths instead of one, the amount of dye present in irregularly shaped objects can be measured (Patau, 1952; Patau and Srinivaschar, 1960). Absorption curves for large numbers of substances in individual cells have been obtained by microspectrophotometric means (Pollister and Ornstein, 1959).

Although the theory is easily understood, a variety of practical problems arise, including those related to everything from the design of the apparatus through consideration of the laws of light absorption to light scatter and the determination of section thickness. However, the importance of the technique and the relative ease of obtaining the necessary equipment should encourage those considering its use. It is beyond the scope of this book to go into all the necessary considerations involved in microspectrophotometry. Good reviews abound in the literature; the interested reader is referred to two excellent ones by Swift and Rasch (1956) and by Pollister and Ornstein (1959).

Chemicals

The trend in histochemistry has been toward the development of techniques requiring increasingly sophisticated chemical reagents. Although many of these compounds can be synthesized without a great deal of elaborate equipment, they usually require a detailed knowledge of organic chemistry and often much time. Fortunately, the interest in histochemistry that has been shown by investigators using animal material, particularly by pathologists, has created a demand great enough to render practical the commercial production of the vast majority of histochemical reagents used. If such compounds are not readily available, there are commercial chemical laboratories which will make the compounds upon order. The materials specified in the procedures in this book may be obtained from the commercial chemical laboratories listed in Appendix A. For those who wish to synthesize their own chemicals, Gurr's *Methods of Analytical Histology and Histochemistry* is recommended as a source of many of the necessary procedures. The first paper in which a technique employing a new chemical is described usually gives the method for synthesizing the chemical.

Books on Microscopic Histochemistry of General Interest

Brachet, J. and A. E. Mirsky (Editors), 1959. *The Cell.* Vol. 1, Academic, New York. The first half of the volume is a collection of excellent review articles on a variety of quantitative and microscopic histochemical procedures.

Casselman, W. G. B., 1959. *Histochemical Technique.* Wiley, New York. An excellent small book of selected techniques.

Danielli, J. F., 1953. *Cytochemistry, A Critical Approach.* Chapman and Hall, London. One of the masters takes a thoughtful and critical look at the field.

―――― (Editor), 1958. *General Cytochemical Methods.* Vols. 1, 2, Academic, New York. An excellent review series covering selected topics.

Davenport, H. A., 1960. *Histological and Histochemical Technics.* Saunders, Philadelphia. This book is specifically designed for the beginning student studying animal tissues.

Glick, D., 1949. *Techniques of Histo and Cytochemistry.* Interscience, New York. One of the classics in the field; it covers both quantitative and microscopic histochemical procedures up to 1948.

Gomori, G., 1952. *Microscopic Histochemistry, Principles and Practice.* Univ. of Chicago Press, Chicago. A masterful summary of microscopic histochemical stain procedures up to 1951.

Grauman, W. and K. Newmann (Editors), 1959. *Handbuch der Histochemie.* Gustaf Fischer, Stuttgart. A collection of review papers in English, German, and French.

Gurr, E., 1958. *Methods of Analytical Histology and Histochemistry.* Williams and Wilkins Co., Baltimore. A large collection of microscopic histochemical stain procedures which includes directions for synthesizing many of the more special compounds.

Lillie, R. D., 1954. *Histopathologic Technic and Practical Histochemistry.* Blakiston, New York. A thorough, well-written presentation of histological and microscopic histochemical methods, primarily for animal tissues. One of the classics in the field.

Lison, L., 1960. *Histochimie et Cytochimie Animales, Principes et Methodes.* 3ᵉ ed. Gauthier-Villars, Paris. The third edition of one of the most important and influential books in histochemistry.

McManus, J. F. A. and P. B. Mowry, 1960. *Staining Methods, Histologic and Histochemical*, Hoeber, New York.

Mellors, R. C. (Editor), 1955 and 1959. *Analytical Cytology.* 1st and 2nd editions. McGraw-Hill, New York. An excellent collection of papers on a wide range of topics in microscopic histochemistry. The first and second editions differ considerably in content.

Oster, G. and A. W. Pollister (Editors), 1956. *Physical Techniques in Biological Research* (3 volumes). Academic, New York. Another fine collection of review papers on many special techniques in histochemistry. Pearse, A. G. E., 1960. *Histochemistry, Theoretical and Applied*, 2nd ed. J. and A. Churchill, London. A penetrating examination of the foundations of microscopic histochemistry. Rawlins, T. E. and W. N. Takahashi, 1952. *Technics of Plant Histochemistry and Virology*. National Press, Millbrae, California. This is the only histochemical book dealing with plant material written in recent years and is primarily a summary of microscopic histochemical procedures.

Journals which Regularly Publish Papers on Microscopic Histochemistry

Experimental Cell Research
Journal of Cell Biology (Journal of Biophysical and Biochemical Cytology)
Journal of Histochemistry and Cytochemistry

Stain Technology
Quarterly Journal of Microscopical Science

LITERATURE CITED

Ambrose, E. J. and A. Bajer, 1960. The analysis of mitoses in single living cells by interference microscopy. *Proc. Royal Soc.* B, **153**:357–366.

Baker, J. R., 1943. The discovery of the uses of colouring agents in biological micro-technique. *Jour. Quekett Microscop. Club.*, Ser. 4, **1**:256–275.

Barer, R., 1953. *Lecture Notes on the Use of the Microscope.* Blackwells, Oxford.

———, 1959. Phase, interference and polarizing microscopy, pp. 169–172. In *Analytical Cytology*, 2nd ed., R. C. Mellors (Editor). McGraw-Hill, Blakiston Div., New York.

Barrnett, R. J. and G. E. Palade, 1958. Applications of histochemistry to electron microscopy. *J. Histochem. and Cytochem.*, **6**:1–12.

Belling, J., 1930. *The Use of the Microscope.* McGraw-Hill, New York.

Bennett, A. H., E. Osterberg, S. Jupnik, and A. R. Richards, 1951. *Phase Microscopy, Principles and Application.* Wiley, New York.

Danielli, J. F., 1958. The calcium phosphate precipitation method for alkaline phosphatase. *Gen. Cytochem. Methods.* **1**:423–443.

Davies, H. G., M. H. F. Wilkins, J. Chayen, and L. F. LaCour, 1954. The use of the interference microscope to determine dry mass in living cells and as a quantitative cytochemical method. *J. Micros. Sci.*, **95**:271–304.

Freund, H., 1960. *Handbuch der Mikroskopie in der Technik.* Vol. 1, parts 1 and 2. Umschau. Verlog., Frankfort.

Green, P. B., 1958. Structural characteristics of developing *Nitella* cell walls. *J. Biophys. Biochem. Cytol.*, **4**:505–516.

———, 1960. Wall structure and laterial formation in the alga *Bryopsis. Am. J. Botany*, **47**:476–481.

Lawson, D. F., 1960. *Technique of Photomicrography*. George Newnes, Ltd., London.

Mellors, R. C., 1959. Fluorescent-antibody method, pp. 1–68. In *Analytical Cytology*, 2nd ed., Mellors, R. C. (Editor). McGraw-Hill, Blakiston Div., New York.

Needham, G. H., 1958. *The Use of the Microscope, Including Photomicrography*. Thomas, Springfield, Ill.

Nurnberger, J. I., 1955. Ultraviolet microscopy and microspectroscopy, pp. 4, 1–44. In *Analytical Cytology*, 1st ed., R. C. Mellors (Editor), McGraw-Hill, Blakiston Div., New York.

Oster, G., 1955. Birefringence and dichroism. In *Physical Techniques in Biological Research*. G. Oster, and A. W. Pollister (Editors). Academic, New York.

Patau, K., 1952. Absorption microphotometry of irregular-shaped objects. *Chromosoma*, 5:341–362.

Patau, K. and D. Srinivashar, 1960. A microspectrophotometer for measuring the DNA-content of nuclei by the two wave length method. *Cytologia*, 25:145–151.

Pollister, A. W. and L. Ornstein, 1959. The photometric chemical analysis of cells. In *Analytical Cytology*, 2nd ed., R. C. Mellors (Editor). McGraw-Hill, Blakiston Div., New York.

Price, G. R. and S. Schwartz, 1956. Fluorescence microscopy, pp. 91–148. In *Physical Techniques in Biological Research*. Vol. III. G. Oster and A. W. Pollister (Editors). Academic, New York.

Richards, O. W., 1955. Fluorescence microscopy. In *Analytical Cytology*, 1st ed. R. C. Mellors (Editor). McGraw-Hill, Blakiston Div., New York.

Swift, H. H., 1949. The desoxypentose nucleic acid content of animal nuclei. *Anat. Record*, 105:17.

————, 1950. The desoxyribose nucleic acid content of plant nuclei. *Physiol. Zool.*, 23:169–198.

Swift, H. H. and E. Rasch, 1956. Microphotometry with visible light, pp. 354–400. In *Physical Techniques in Biological Research*. Vol. III. G. Oster and A. W. Pollister (Editors). Academic, New York.

Walker, P. M. B., 1956. Ultraviolet absorption techniques, pp. 402–487. In *Physical Techniques in Biological Research*. Vol. III. G. Oster and A. W. Pollister (Editors). Academic, New York.

PART II

Preparation of the Tissue

CHAPTER 4

Histological
Procedures

Introduction

The methods of histology and histochemistry have a common origin and a core of similar procedures. The early histories of histology and histochemistry are one. Only in the late nineteenth century, after the introduction of aniline dyes and the development of interest in morphology, did the two fields separate. Botanical histological technique, frequently referred to as microtechnique, expanded rapidly at the turn of the century. The procedures of tissue fixation, dehydration, paraffin infiltration and embedding, sectioning, staining, and mounting were developed largely through empirical research. The preparations obtained by these methods are informative and are frequently objects of great beauty.

Microscopic histochemistry, particularly that of vascular plants, has incorporated many of these procedures. As will become evident when the various procedures of microscopic histochemistry are described, many are the same as standard histological methods up to the point at which the tissue is stained. Chemically fixed, dehydrated, paraffin-infiltrated, and sectioned material is used in many histochemical procedures. In others, different means are used to kill, dehydrate, and paraffin infiltrate the tissue, but the same means are used to section the tissue. Thus, the microscopic histochemist must be familiar with histological methods.

The quantitative histochemist must also be versed in histological procedures both because they may be necessary as the initial steps of a histochemical procedure and because they are frequently necessary to the understanding of tissue morphology. The major value of histo-chemical methods in botanical research is that they permit the recognition of the morphological complexity of plant tissue. This complexity can be appreciated and understood only through microscopic examination and analysis of the tissue.

The standard histological procedure involves the following steps:

1. The tissue is killed and fixed in a chemical fluid designed to preserve cell structure.
2. Water is removed from the cell by gradual replacement with alcohol. This step is termed tissue dehydration.
3. The tissue is infiltrated with paraffin and is then embedded in a block of the same material.
4. The infiltrated and embedded tissue is then sectioned on a micro-tome, and the sections are affixed to slides.
5. After the paraffin is removed, the tissue is stained.
6. Finally, the tissue is covered with a cover slip held in place with a permanent mounting medium.

Each step is important and essential if a satisfactory preparation is to be obtained. Many variations are possible at each step. For example, there are dozens of fixatives, several dehydration schedules, hundreds of stains, and several types of mounting media. In the Procedures section of this chapter I have presented a select group of methods which I feel, will have the greatest application and will give the most consistent results. It was not possible, however, to recommend only one fixative or one staining procedure, since different kinds of materials require different methods.

Before presenting the procedures, the various steps will be discussed. This discussion is intended not as a profound exploration of the bases of fixation and staining but as an introduction to the various aspects of botanical microtechnique. Detailed application of the procedures will be presented later in this chapter.

Fixation

The cell consists of a complex of substances in a highly organized state. Any disruption of this organization causes changes to occur which ultimately affect the morphology of the cell. The purpose of the fixative is to prevent these changes from occurring. The cell is killed and fixed in a solution designed to inhibit the vital processes of the cell, to prevent autolysis, and to change the physical properties of the chemical substances in the cell such that they will not be removed in subsequent handling. Ideally, the fixative would do this without changing the morphology of the cell from the living state. Such an ideal fixative has, needless to say, never been found, nor has one ever been closely approximated with chemical fixatives. The commonly used fixing solutions represent a compromise between the good and the bad features of several possible reagents.

The reagents most commonly used in botanical fixing solutions are alcohol, formalin, acetic acid, and chromic acid. Less frequently used in standard microtechnique are potassium permanganate and osmium tetroxide. The latter reagents are much more important to the electron microscopist.

Singly, each of the chemicals listed has properties that make it important as a fixative, yet no one is ideal. This can be seen from an examination of each chemical with regard to its effect on the cell.

Alcohol in the form of wine is one of the earliest fixatives. When used alone, usually at 50% or 70%, alcohol causes a coarse appearance in the cytoplasm and in the nucleus of the cell. Lipids remain soluble, and are either extracted in the fixative or in the subsequent handling of the tissue. Although alcohol penetrates the tissue fairly rapidly, it causes great shrinkage and considerable hardening. The use of a fixative to cause tissue-hardening is of historical interest. Many of the early fixatives were designed to harden soft tissue in order that the investigator could section the material with a straight-edged razor. However, the advent of paraffin infiltration and the modern microtome made extreme hardening a pronounced disadvantage.

Formalin, which was not used as a fixative until the 1890's, is one of the best. Formalin is formaldehyde dissolved in water. Commercial formalin usually contains 40% formaldehyde. Thus, a 10% solution of the commercial preparation results in a 4% solution of formaldehyde. This is the origin of 4% formalin fixative. Traditionally, the solution is adjusted to neutrality by storing it over marble chips. As a fixative, formalin preserves the fine structure of the cytoplasm. Moreover, it reduces the solubility of tissue lipids in the solvents used later in the dehydration procedure. Formalin causes little shrinkage of the tissue, but it does cause considerable hardening. The hardening of the cell walls, particularly in leaf tissue, is frequently so great that fragmentation of the wall occurs on sectioning. Formalin, however, is one of the best cytoplasm fixatives.

Acetic acid in the form of vinegar has been recognized as a tissue preservative for many centuries. The major feature of acetic acid as a fixative is its ability to preserve nuclear and chromosomal structure. It does not preserve cytoplasmic detail, nor does it prevent the loss of lipids. In addition, it removes mitochondria. Acetic acid moves rapidly into the tissue and may cause swelling or shrinkage of the cells. Moreover, it has a tendency to soften plant tissues and prevents the hardening of tissues by other fixatives.

Chromic acid, the dissolved form of chromium trioxide, has found wide application in fixatives used on plant tissues. It preserves both cytoplasmic and nuclear detail, although it does not preserve mitochondria. The relation of chromic acid to lipid solubility is rather complex in that it affects some but not others. In general, the penetration of chromic acid is slow. It causes little shrinkage or hardening of the tissue. The chromate ion apparently becomes tightly bound to the tissue, thus the tissue must be washed well if staining is to be effective.

Both potassium permanganate and osmium tetroxide are excellent fixatives of lipids and fats. They react chemically with these substances and reduce the solubility of lipids in organic solvents. Moreover, they appear to afford excellent preservation of the cytoplasm and the cytoplasmic particles of the cell. Tissues fixed with either potassium permanganate or osmium tetroxide do not respond well to paraffin infiltration or to staining. It was not until the development of the techniques associated with the preparation of sections for electron microscopy that the use of osmium tetroxide became widespread. Because of their importance in lipid histochemistry, both will be discussed in Chapter 12.

The difference between the appearance of cells treated with alcohol, formalin, acetic acid, and chromic acid is illustrated in Fig. 4-1. The cells in each preparation are from the same region of the onion root and are predominately cortical cells. From the comparison of these preparations it is clear that, although some chemicals act as good fixatives when used singly (formalin being the best), none are perfect. The natural inclination is to try mixtures of these chemicals to obtain a fixative that combines the good points of each while eliminating the bad. This was a major pastime of histologists for many years, with the result that there now exist hundreds of formulas for fixative mixtures.

Of these, the formulas most widely used to fix vascular plants are mixtures either of formalin, acetic acid, and alcohol or of formalin, acetic acid, and chromic acid. Mixtures of alcohol and acetic acid are particularly useful in chromosome studies. Chromic acid-acetic acid mixtures are widely used in studies on nonvascular plants, as is formalin alone.

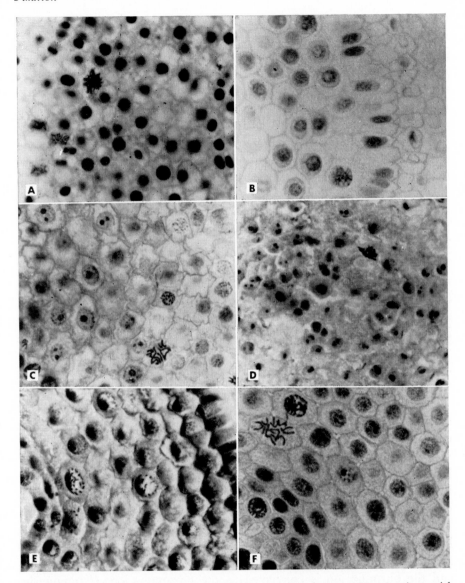

Figure 4-1. *Photomicrographs of sections of onion roots after fixation with various chemicals. All sections were taken the same distance from the root tip, and all were stained with Heidenhain's haematoxylin-orange G. A. 4% Formalin. B. 5% Chromic acid. C. 5% Acetic acid. D. 95% Ethyl alcohol. E. FAA. F. Navashin's fixative.*

A mixture of formalin, acetic acid, and alcohol (FAA) is probably the fixative used most extensively by botanists. The formula given in the Procedures section of this chapter is 90 ml of 50% ethyl alcohol, 5 ml of glacial acetic acid, and 5 ml of commercial formalin. The final

concentration of formaldehyde is thus approximately 2%. The tissue
is fixed in this mixture for a minimum of 4 hours and may be stored in
it indefinitely. Many variations of this fixative exist; thus if adequate
results are not obtained by using the suggested formula, the amounts of
the three components, as well as the concentration of the alcohol, can
be varied.

The logic behind the FAA mixture is this: the formalin counteracts
the coarse precipitation effect of the alcohol, whereas together they
"fix," or render insoluble, the proteins; neither of them adequately fixes
the nucleoprotein, hence acetic acid is added to preserve nuclear detail;
alcohol causes shrinkage of the protoplast, whereas acetic acid causes
swelling; together they would preserve the original shape of the cell;
finally, alcohol causes hardening, as does formalin, whereas acetic acid
helps prevent hardening. Together these three should provide excellent
fixation. Unfortunately, FAA is only a moderately good fixative for
most plant tissues. In most tissues, it causes considerable shrinkage,
hardens the cells, and occasionally makes sectioning difficult. In addition,
it frequently causes the cytoplasm to appear coarse and granular, and
it removes the mitochondria. However, FAA does give good chromosome fixation and is useful in morphological studies in which cell walls
are of principal interest. It readily penetrates most tissues and is easy to
use in the field. Tissue fixed in FAA is shown in Fig. 4-1.

The second group of fixatives widely used in botanical microtechnique
contains formalin, acetic acid, and chromic acid. A variety of fixatives
can be prepared from these chemicals. These fixatives are frequently
referred to as modifications of Navashin's fixative, or as CRAF fixatives,
from the abbreviation of the chemicals involved. All of the modifications
have the same components, and all are prepared from two solutions, one
containing the formalin, the second containing chromic and acetic acid.
The two solutions are mixed immediately before use, since formaldehyde is a strong reducing agent, and chromic acid is a strong oxidizing
agent. Thus, on standing, the formaldehyde is converted to formic acid,
and the chromic ion is converted to the chromous ion, changing the
action of the fixative. The formula given in the procedures section of
this chapter is a moderate-strength modification of Navashin's fixative.

The absence of alcohol and the addition of chromic acid in Navashin's
fixative results in less shrinkage and hardening than is found in FAA-
fixed material. In tissue treated with Navashin's fixative, the cytoplasm
appears fairly granular, and cytoplasmic particles are not well fixed, but
the nuclei and chromosomes are well preserved, and the general ap-

pearance of the tissue, particularly meristematic and reproductive structures, is excellent. Tissue fixed in Navashin's fixative is shown in Fig. 4-1.
The principal difficulty with this fixative is its slow penetration of the
tissue, which frequently necessitates the use of vacuum infiltration.

For research on the algae and fungi one of the most widely used
fixatives is a mixture of chromic acid and acetic acid. The concentration
of the two acids must frequently be adjusted by trial and error. The
formula given in the Procedures section is recommended for filamentous
algae, fungi, and other delicate material (Johansen, 1940). For larger,
coarser objects, higher concentrations of the acids should be used. For
marine algae, the solutions should be made up in sea water. Both FAA
and 4% formalin are useful with many algae and fungi.

All of the fixative mixtures discussed so far are good for preserving
nuclear and chromosomal detail. However, although these mixtures
preserve the cytoplasm, they do not preserve it in a lifelike manner.
Moreover, all of these mixtures remove the mitochondria. This type of
result is generally referred to as an acid fixation image. On the other
hand, there are fixatives that will preserve the mitochondria and other
cytoplasmic organelles but which do not preserve nuclear detail, thus
giving what is termed a basic fixation image. Since the fixatives giving
the basic fixation image have a pH of about 4, it is clear that the
terminology in this case is relative.

The fixative giving the best basic fixation image is Zirkle's modification of Erliki's fluid (Zirkle, 1934). This fixative is essentially a mixture
of bichromate and cupric ions and can give remarkable preparations.
Mitochondria and other cytoplasmic organelles, as well as nuclear detail, are preserved in both freeze-substituted and freeze-dried material,
discussed in the next chapter.

This discussion of fixation and fixatives has been oriented toward the
use of chemically fixed material as objects of morphological rather than
histochemical study. The problem of fixation in the microscopic histochemistry of the various cell constituents will be discussed in subsequent
chapters. For lists of other fixatives, the reader is referred to Baker
(1958), Johansen (1940), and Sass (1958).

However, the physicochemical action of chemical fixatives is not well
understood. Baker (1950, 1958) has done an impressive job in bringing
together a vast amount of data on both the fixing and staining of tissues.
He makes the excellent point that there should be greater use of single-
component fixatives in order that the investigator have the opportunity
to study the physicochemical action of the fixative. Baker terms the use

of such fixatives as the formalin-acetic acid-chromic acid mixture irrational, because a reducing and an oxidizing agent are mixed, and the investigator does not know the action of the mixture.

Unfortunately, little careful work has been done on the action of fixatives on plant tissues. The research of Ball (1941) and of Zirkle (1928, 1929) are outstanding examples of the type of work needed. More investigations of this type are needed before the action of various chemical fixatives on plant tissue can be understood. In the meantime the botanist will continue to rely on methods that are known to yield good preparations whether the methods are rational or not.

Tissue Dehydration and Paraffin Infiltration

Tissue may be sectioned with a straightedge razor either when fresh or after fixation, but it is far more commonly infiltrated with and embedded in paraffin and then sectioned on a microtome. The pioneering work on paraffin infiltration and embedding was carried out at the Zoological Station at Naples during the 1870's and was introduced into botanical microtechnique in the 1880's.

The major problem in paraffin infiltration is that paraffin and water are not miscible. This requires that the water be removed and replaced with an organic solvent compatible with paraffin. The solvent most commonly used is alcohol. Water must be removed from the tissue gradually, or physical changes will occur in the tissue, which may result in shrinkage or distortion of the cells. The gradual removal of water from the tissue is accomplished by placing the tissue in successively higher concentrations of ethyl alcohol. When most of the water is removed, tertiary butyl alcohol (TBA) is introduced into the mixture and is gradually increased in concentration. Dehydration is complete when the tissue is finally immersed in pure TBA.

Other dehydration methods are used for chemically fixed material, but the ethyl alcohol-TBA series is used by most botanists. In a simple variation of the method just discussed, normal butyl alcohol is used in place of tertiary butyl alcohol. In other respects, the method and the results obtained remain the same. For information on methods using dioxan, xylene, acetone, and other chemicals, see Johansen (1940) and Sass (1958). The point to remember is that dehydration can alter the tissue. Care should be taken to prevent extreme changes in alcohol concentration from one step to the next.

Paraffin is introduced into the tissue by placing the tissue and a small amount of TBA over a layer of solid paraffin, which is placed in the bottom of a small vial or dish. The vial (or dish) is placed in an oven at a temperature slightly above the melting point of the paraffin. Under these conditions the paraffin melts and displaces the TBA as it evaporates. Two changes of the molten paraffin are made in order that no trace of TBA will remain in the tissue or paraffin; the TBA must be removed, or sectioning will be difficult. Paraffin infiltration usually requires about 12 hours. For most soft or delicate materials, exposure to the hot paraffin should be limited to as short a period as possible. The temperature should be kept as low as possible to avoid cooking the material.

The last change of paraffin is frequently a mixture of paraffin, wax, and rubber. This can be made by heating together paraffin, small pieces of wax, and pieces of gum-rubber bands for several days and then decanting off the top of the mixture. Commercial preparations such as Tissuemat and Bioloid are more reliable. These are uniform, and are available in a range of melting points from 50–63°C. The choice of the correct melting point is dependent on several factors, such as the hardness of the tissue (the harder the embedding medium the higher the melting point) and the room temperature during sectioning (in summer, it may be necessary to use an embedding medium having a higher melting point). For many materials pure paraffin will work as well as, if not better than, special preparations. When working with new material it is often good practice to try both pure paraffin and a commercial preparation such as Tissuemat as the final embedding medium.

After the tissue is infiltrated with paraffin it must be embedded in a solid paraffin block. This is accomplished by simply pouring the molten paraffin and the tissue into a mold, arranging the tissue, and cooling the paraffin and tissue. The tissue is thus neatly embedded in a block of solid paraffin. Although the method is simple, the means of carrying it out are diverse. Two types of mold will be described here. One is a rectangular porcelain dish, usually termed an embedding boat. Such dishes are rigid and can be heated, facilitating the arrangement of the tissue in the paraffin by preventing too rapid hardening. However, the solid paraffin blocks are frequently difficult to remove from the boat, even if it has previously been coated with glycerine. The second type of mold is the paper boat, which is made by folding a piece of stiff paper into the form of a shallow dish. These are inexpensive to make, are unbreakable, and can easily be peeled away from the paraffin block. They cannot be heated directly, although they can be placed on a hot plate; they are not rigid, thus causing the tissue to become disarranged if moved; and they also require the time necessary to fold them.

Since paraffin is a crystalline substance, the size of the crystals present in the solid paraffin will influence the morphology and sectioning characteristics of the tissue. Since the best results are obtained if the crystals are small, the paraffin is rapidly cooled by placing the embedding boat in a dish of ice water. At first, only the bottom of the boat is placed in contact with the ice water, but as the paraffin hardens, the whole boat is submerged.

Care must be taken to arrange the tissue in the paraffin such that portions can be removed from the edge of the block, each portion containing a sample of the tissue. If a large quantity of material cannot all be arranged with adequate space between individual pieces, some should be arranged for sectioning, and the remainder should be pushed into one corner of the block. Later, if more material is needed, this segment of the block can be reheated and the samples can be rearranged for sectioning. Small objects can often be arranged and sectioned in groups of two or three or more to save time.

Paraffin-embedded material can be stored indefinitely in a cool location without changing the morphology of the tissue.

Other materials are used as infiltrating and embedding substances for special purposes. For light microscopy, the most important of these is celloidin. In botanical microtechnique, however, celloidin infiltration and embedding is an involved procedure, and serial sections can be obtained only with difficulty. For these and other reasons, the celloidin method is little used and will not be described here. Complete descriptions of the methods are available in Johansen (1940) and in Sass (1958).

Plastics have been used to prepare sections for the electron microscope. Since plastic-embedded material is of little value for routine light microscopy, these procedures are not included here. The interested reader is referred to Pease (1960).

Microtoming

Next, the paraffin-infiltrated and embedded tissue is sectioned on a microtome. A microtome is used in order that uniform sections can be obtained rapidly.

Two major types of microtomes are in use, the sliding microtome and the rotary microtome. The sliding microtome is the direct descendant of the cutting engines of the 1770's (Smith, 1915). In the sliding microtome, the tissue is held stationary, and the knife is moved in a plane at right angles to the tissue. This type of microtome is invaluable in the preparation of wood sections but is little used with paraffin-infiltrated tissue.

The rotary microtome, an American invention, was developed at the turn of the century (Smith, 1915). The knife of the rotary microtome is held stationary, and the tissue is moved vertically at right angles to the blade. The advantage in this arrangement with paraffin-infiltrated material is that the cut section adheres to the edge of the knife. As the next section is cut, the lower edge of this second section adheres to the upper edge of the first section. Thus, as more sections are cut, a ribbon of sections is produced. This means that sections can be handled in groups and that serial sections of an object can be obtained.

Many other types of microtomes have been designed, but aside from the sliding microtome, the freezing microtome (discussed in the next chapter), and the Cambridge rocking microtome (still used in England), the rotary microtome is the principal one in use today. There are two designs for rotary microtomes: (1) the Minot rotary microtome, in which the mechanism that moves the specimen forward is directly attached by gears to the drive mechanism; and (2) the Spencer rotary microtome, in which the mechanism that moves the specimen forward is separated from the drive mechanism. This separation is accomplished by having the drive mechanism move a cone-shaped arm against an inclined plane attached to the tissue holder. The actual mechanics of this separation are better seen by examining carefully a Spencer microtome. The object of this separation is to obtain a smoother, more uniform forward movement. However, both the Minot and the Spencer rotary microtomes are designed for paraffin work, and both are excellent precision machines.

The most important features to be considered in purchasing a microtome are that the machine be well-constructed, that the feed and drive mechanisms work smoothly, that the angle of the knife blade be adjustable, and that the tissue holder should be designed such that the tissue can be easily oriented in any plane in relation to the blade. The newer machines generally have all these features, whereas the older ones may lack one or more.

The choice of the blade to be used in the microtome is important. Two types of blades can be used: either a large, specially designed microtome blade or a razor blade held in an adapter designed to fit the usual microtome knife holder. There are adherents to both types of arrangement, and the problem of choice becomes a matter of personal preference.

To obtain good sections, the cutting edge of the microtome knife or razor blade must be sharp. If it is not, the sections may be excessively compressed or the ribbon may be torn, if it forms at all. The proper way to sharpen microtome knives has long been a favorite topic of discussion among histologists. Many hours are also spent over a carefully selected stone, sharpening the knife. This chore has been made much less arduous by the development of the automatic microtome knife sharpener. For those who prefer to sharpen their knives by hand or to use razor blades, directions are provided at the end of the Procedures section of this chapter.

In the rotary microtome, the angle at which the knife is adjusted also determines the quality of section obtained. When a tissue block is sectioned, it is forced downward over the edge of the knife. The downward motion of the block continues for some distance after the block has cleared the edge of the blade. The block is then moved upward past the knife edge. If the angle of the blade with respect to the surface of the block is very small, the block will rub against the back of the blade, causing compression of the block. The next section that is cut will thus either be too thin or, in extreme cases, it will not be cut at all. Excessively large angles will also cause trouble.

The proper blade angle can be found quickly and easily by trying various settings of the blade holder and by observing which angle gives the best sections. Different materials may require different angles. Richards (1959) has given a means of calculating this angle.

The shape of the paraffin block is another extremely important factor in obtaining good sections. To understand why, it is necessary to mention certain details involved in preparing a block of embedded tissue for microtoming. After a piece of tissue has been cut from the large block obtained at the end of the embedding procedure, it is mounted on a holder that can be inserted into the microtome. The microtome is equipped with several metal tissue holders, in the form of pedestals, on which the embedded tissue can be mounted. More commonly, however, wood blocks are used. These are first cut to fit in the microtome and are then soaked in molten paraffin for several days in order that the paraffin will infiltrate at least the outer layers of the wood. Although this paraffin treatment of the wood is not essential, it aids in the next step—the attachment of the tissue to the wood block.

The block to be sectioned is now mounted on the wooden or metal holder by melting the bottom of the paraffin block and the paraffin coating of the holder with a hot needle and pressing the two molten surfaces together immediately. They will then fuse and solidify. To hasten the solidification of the paraffin the block and holder may be placed in ice water or in a refrigerator. This practice is recommended, since cold blocks section better.

Before the block is placed in the microtome, it is trimmed in order to remove excess paraffin from around the tissue and to make the faces of the block that are going to strike the knife (*i.e.*, the horizontal faces) parallel to one another. If these faces are not parallel, the ribbon that is produced will curve. This is to be avoided at any cost, because curved ribbons are extremely difficult to handle in the subsequent steps. The two vertical sides of the block (*i.e.*, those not hitting the cutting edge of the knife directly) may also be trimmed parallel to one another. This keeps the edge of the ribbon even but does not influence the curvature of the ribbon. Frequently, however, if the tissue is the same general color as the paraffin, as are many root tips for example, it is better to trim one of the sides at an angle. This will result in a saw-toothed appearance and is helpful in determining where to cut the ribbon for mounting on slides.

The mounting and trimming of the paraffin block are important. Time and care should be invested at this point, since it will save time and trouble later. Always mount the tissue such that the long axis is parallel to the cutting edge of the knife. Sometimes, if the tissue is of uneven hardness, an even, straight ribbon is obtained only if the faces of the block hitting the knife are not parallel. In general, experience is the key to successful trimming and microtoming.

After the block is trimmed, the block and holder are placed in the microtome. The holder is secured to the microtome by a vise-like clamp. The newer microtomes have a type of universal joint which can be adjusted by a set of three screws. The universal joint also holds the vise and the tissue holder. This arrangement allows the operator to align the face of the paraffin block parallel to the knife and to make fine adjustments on the orientation of the cutting plane of the tissue. Care should be taken in these adjustments both because they affect the success of the final preparation and because the knife is a considerable hazard to the fingers.

When the block is in place and is correctly oriented, sectioning can begin. The first few sections formed will be incomplete and will not form a ribbon. The next sections will form a ribbon, however, and if it is not straight, judicious trimming of the block while still in the microtome will frequently result in a straight ribbon. Not infrequently, the ribbon will be straight until the tissue is reached, at which point it will curve. Again, careful trimming of the block will eliminate the curvature.

The pressure with which the tissue strikes the blade will result in compression of the sections. This can be partially corrected in the next step, when the sections are mounted on slides, but it is important, particularly in histochemical work, to minimize this compression. The factors influencing this compression are several, and have been studied in some detail by Shields and Dean (1949). They found that a cutting speed of one section per second was best and that compression variations resulting from melting point variation of the Tissuemat used (52–62°C) were insignificant if the blocks were chilled. Section thickness, however, had a great effect on compression. In a 5-μ section the compression was 26.5%; in a 15-μ section, 7.4%; and in a 25-μ section, 2.0%. An even rate of sectioning, a chilled block, and a sharp knife appear to be the requirements for the best results.

Many factors influence microtoming. Even experienced operators are not always assured of success. Several common sources of trouble are listed below.

(1) The condition of the cutting edge of the knife has been discussed already.

(2) If paraffin adheres to the back of the blade, this may cause the block to pick up the ribbon on the upswing.

(3) Lint or dirt on the cutting edge of the knife may tear the ribbon.

(4) The tissue may be too hard to section or may fragment when it hits the knife edge.

(5) The sections may become statically charged, causing them to adhere to the knife, the block, the operator, or to float in the air.

Static electricity can be eliminated in a number of ways, but none works very well. One method involves increasing the humidity in the room by boiling water; another requires grounding the microtome; and another involves the use of a commercial device that contains a source of radioactivity, which ionizes the air in the vicinity of the tissue and blade. The latter method is one of the best; the apparatus, called a Neutra-Stat, can be obtained from Gardner Laboratory, Inc., Bethesda 14, Maryland, or from laboratory supply houses in general. It should not be used, however, when sectioning material for autoradiographs, since it represents a source of contamination of radioactive matter.

The thickness at which the tissue should be sectioned is an important consideration and depends completely on the nature of the material and on the subject of the investigation. For example, if root tips are to be used in a study of mitochondrial morphology, 1- to 2-μ sections would be cut. The same type of root tip may be used in a study of general cell development and, in this case, may be sectioned at 10–15 μ. For a chromosome study, in which the object would be to obtain uncut chromosomes all from one cell in the same section, the root tip may be sectioned at 15–20 μ. At this thickness the probability of obtaining favorable results is increased. Megagametophytes and reproductive organs in general are frequently sectioned at 25–35 μ. The majority of plant material, however, can be sectioned at 10–20 μ when used for morphological studies, although it is only possible to determine the precise thickness after a trial run.

The final question with regard to microtomy is whether or not the sections obtained are of the thickness indicated on the microtome setting. The work of Shields and Dean (1949) indicates that they are not. They found that at a setting of 5 μ the sections obtained were actually 6.05 μ and that at a setting of 25 μ the sections were 25.6 μ thick. Thus, the error decreased with the increase in section thickness. This problem has not been considered by many workers other than those interested in microspectrophotometry, in which section thickness becomes critical. The measurement of section thickness is by no means easy (Pollister and Ornstein, 1959), and the use of calibrated fine adjustments offers only a partial, inaccurate measure. For this reason, the histochemist should always keep in mind that his sections may not be of the thickness indicated by the microtome setting.

For a more complete discussion of microtoming, see the work of Gettner and Ornstein (1956), Richards (1959), and Sjöstrand (1956). The books on botanical microtechnique by Johansen (1940) and by Sass (1958) contain many practical suggestions on the handling of plant tissue during dehydration, embedding, and microtoming.

Affixing the Tissue to the Slide

Sections are affixed to slides by the use of an adhesive. The adhesive contains a protein which, upon denaturation, seals the tissue to the slide. There are roughly half a dozen adhesives in use today, and all are relatively similar in composition. Two adhesives are described in the section on Procedures. One is Haupt's adhesive, which is probably the adhesive used by more botanists than any other. The second, similar to Haupt's, has found wide use in autoradiographic work in which Haupt's adhesive cannot be used (Ficq, 1959).

Haupt's adhesive contains gelatin and glycerine. It is spread on the slide immediately before the sections are to be mounted. Next, a 4% formalin solution is placed on the slide, and the tissue is floated on the formalin. The slide is then placed on a slide warmer set at a temperature several degrees below the melting point of the paraffin. The heat and the surface tension of the solution cause the tissue to expand; thus the compression that resulted from sectioning is almost eliminated. After the tissue has resumed a nearly normal shape, most of the formalin is drained off, and the slide is allowed to dry on the slide warmer.

The autoradiographic adhesive contains gelatin and chrome alum. The slides are dipped in the adhesive, drained, and allowed to dry, after which they may be stored in a refrigerator for several weeks before use. The tissue is placed on the slide and floated with distilled water. The same procedure is then followed as with Haupt's adhesive.

After the slides are dry, in either case, they may be stored indefinitely if they are to be used in histological work. However, if the tissue is to be used in a histochemical test, it should be used as soon as possible.

It is in this step—the mounting of the sections on the slide—that the importance of a straight ribbon becomes clear. Curved ribbons will cause no end of trouble and can never really be satisfactorily straightened during the mounting procedure.

For many microscopic histochemical methods it is undesirable to have the tissue floated with either water or formalin. If this be the case, the tissue is simply pressed on the slide with a rolling motion of the finger, either by placing the finger directly on the tissue or on a piece of flat Teflon plastic laid over the tissue.

Staining

The staining of sections is the most fascinating part of histological technique. No one can fail to delight in the spectacle of the colorless and nearly invisible tissue taking on the vivid hues of the artist's palette. A. S. Foster likes to tell of the student who came to him after a laboratory period in an elementary course and told him how she admired the people who made the slides; imagine painting pictures that small! As naïve as such a statement is, it does reflect the impression that a carefully prepared specimen can give. It also reflects the art that is a very real part of staining, and which makes the staining of botanical material a highly individualized matter.

The interesting history of biological staining techniques is almost as long as the history of the microscope. Indeed, a history of cytology and histology shows how closely developments in these fields are associated with the improvement of microscopes and of dyes and staining methods (Hughes, 1959). The dyes available to the histologist were limited in number until Perkin discovered aniline dyes in 1856. Not long after their discovery, aniline dyes were introduced into histological research, greatly increasing the range of color available to the histologist (Conn, 1933). By 1900, between the older natural dyes and the more recently developed synthetic dyes, hundreds of dyes were available and in use. Of these, few have achieved wide use; fewer still have been adapted to use in routine botanical microtechnique. Among the dyes most commonly used in botanical microtechnique are safranin, fast green, haematoxylin, orange G, and aniline blue.

The basis of dye selection is the ionic binding of the dye to the structure stained. Dyes owe their color to the presence in their molecules of specific groups called chromophores. The two most important chromophore groups are quinonoid rings and azo linkages. Of the dyes mentioned above, safranin, haematoxylin, fast green, and aniline blue are quinonoid-ring dyes, whereas orange G is an azo dye. In solution, dyes act either as positive or as negative ions. Those that have positive charges are called basic dyes (e.g., safranin); those that have negative charges are termed acid dyes (e.g., orange G and fast green). The various chemical constituents of the cell have net electrical charges that are often dependent on the pH of the containing solution or on the nature of their fixation. Proteins are examples of molecules having both positive and negative charges and whose net charge is dependent on the pH. This characteristic is used in a histochemical test for basic proteins. The nucleic acids, on the other hand, are strongly negatively charged due to the presence of phosphate groups in the molecule and therefore bind basic dyes readily. Cells or parts of cells that stain heavily with basic dyes are termed basophilic; those that stain heavily with acid dyes are termed acidophilic. For a much more detailed discussion of stains and dye action, the reader should consult Baker (1958).

Before the tissue can be stained the paraffin must be removed by placing the slide in xylene. Only a few minutes are required to remove the paraffin. The slide is then transferred to a 1:1 solution of xylene and alcohol; then to absolute alcohol; and is then hydrated by passing it through an alcohol series of 95%, 70%, 50%, 30% alcohol and, finally, into water. If the first dye is an aqueous solution, it is necessary to pass the slide into water before placing it in the dye solution. If, however, the dye is in an alcoholic solution, the tissue can be transferred directly from the 50% alcohol solution of the dehydration series into the dye.

Dyes are used singly and, more frequently, in combinations of two, such as safranin-fast green, haematoxylin-orange G, haematoxylin-safranin. The first stain applied to the tissue is termed the primary stain; the

second is called the counter stain. Thus, in the safranin-fast green combination, safranin is the primary stain and fast green the counter stain,
whereas in the haematoxylin-safranin combination, the haematoxylin is
the primary stain; safranin, the counter stain.

The stain used depends on the structures to be observed. Safranin-fast
green is a good general combination. The safranin stains the chromosomes, nucleoli, and lignified cell walls red; the fast green stains the
rest of the cell structures. Tannic acid-ferric chloride-safranin is particularly good for staining meristematic tissues. The tannic acid-ferric
chloride stains cell walls black and the cytoplasm blue-gray; the safranin
stains the chromosomes, nucleoli, and lignified cell walls red. Haematoxylin-orange G is excellent for cytological detail; chromosomes and
mitochondria are stained blue-black by the haematoxylin, and the cytoplasm and cell wall are stained by the orange G. There are many other
stains which are particularly good for certain studies. Various stains
should be tried on the same material in order that the best one may be
selected. The stain azure B (Chapter 11) is a good general stain as well
as a specific nucleic acid method. Similarly, the periodic acid-Schiff's
reaction (Chapter 9) is an excellent cell wall stain.

The detailed schedules for a set of the most useful and generally
applicable staining methods are given in the Procedures section of this
chapter. Before presenting these schedules, however, the chemical bases
of some of the procedures will be discussed.

Safranin-Fast Green

In the safranin-fast green combination, the tissue is first overstained
with safranin. All the dye-binding sites are filled, and unbound dye is
absorbed at the tissue surfaces. The tissue is then washed to remove the
unbound dye. Next, the tissue is destained in acid alcohol, which removes the dye not tightly bound, namely, the dye bound by the cytoplasm, cellulose, and nuclear material other than the nucleolus and the
chromosomes. The lignin in the cell wall, the nucleoli, and the chromosomes hold the dye tightly. The acid alcohol is not particularly selective,
and will effectively remove all of the stain if applied long enough. When
most of the color has left the cytoplasm, however, the tissue is dehydrated by rapid transfer through a series of alcohols of increasing concentration (in which safranin is soluble) to fast green. The fast green
stains the cytoplasm and cellulose, which now act as positive dye-binding
sites. Absorbed, excess fast green is removed with a differentiating solution consisting of clove oil, absolute alcohol, and xylene, in which the
dye is slightly soluble. Finally, the tissue is placed in xylene after which

a cover slip is mounted with a permanent mounting medium. Aniline blue may be used in place of fast green, a substitute frequently used in work on wood.

Iron Haematoxylin-Orange G

Haematoxylin is one of the most important dyes used in botanical microtechnique. The procedure is not easy, but should be learned. The mode of action of haematoxylin is considerably different from that of safranin.

First, haematoxylin is the colorless form of the dye haematein. For a solution of haematoxylin to act as a dye it must first be oxidized to haematein by exposure to air. This period of oxidation is usually referred to as the ripening period. The length of time required to ripen the dye solution varies, depending on the composition of the dye solution and the conditions of the ripening period. In the iron haematoxylin (Heidenhain's haematoxylin) the ripening is very rapid, whereas in Delafield's haematoxylin the ripening takes weeks.

Second, even a fully ripened solution of haematoxylin will not stain the tissue. Only after the tissue has been placed in a solution of an iron salt can the haematein be bound to the tissue via the iron. The iron, in the form of ferric ions, acts as a mordant, and is attached to the negative binding sites in the tissue. Then the iron chelates the haematein, firmly binding the dye to the structure. Since most of the negative sites in the cell are associated with chromosomes, this is an excellent stain for chromosomes. Proteins, however, will also stain with haematoxylin.

Tissues to be stained with Heidenhain's haematoxylin are placed in a solution of ferric chloride. After a suitable period the slide is washed and placed in the haematoxylin solution. After a period in the dye the tissue is washed and destained. The destaining agent is the same chemical as the mordant. The mordant destains by forming a soluble complex with the dye and thus breaks down the tissue-mordant-haematoxylin complex. The amount of destaining depends upon the structures to be observed. If the mitochondria are to be studied, less destaining is carried out than if the chromosomes are to be observed.

The tissue is next washed, dehydrated, and counterstained with orange G, which acts in the same manner as fast green. Safranin may replace orange G as a counter stain, as may a 1% aqueous solution of Bismarck brown. For many types of materials no counterstain is used.

Delafield's haematoxylin is similar in behavior to Heidenhain's haematoxylin except that the mordant is combined with the dye. This combination of the mordant and the dye simplifies the staining procedure, although it frequently results in a loss of detail. In autoradiography, Delafield's haematoxylin is frequently used to stain tissue through the photographic emulsion.

Both Heidenhain's and Delafield's haematoxylin work well with algae and other nonvascular plants, as well as with vascular plants. Heidenhain's haematoxylin is particularly good for both mitochondria and chromosomes in all plant groups.

Tannic Acid-Ferric Chloride-Safranin

In the tannic acid-ferric chloride-safranin combination, it is tannic acid which acts as the mordant. Tannic acid combines with proteins but, more important for the use of this stain, also combines with pectic substances and with other carbohydrates in the primary cell wall. The ferric ion forms a complex with the tannic acid, and the blue-black color that results is due to this ferric complex. The safranin acts in the same manner as in the safranin-fast green combination, but here it is used as the counter stain instead of as the primary stain.

This stain, which is frequently referred to as Foster's stain (Johansen, 1940), is an excellent one for meristematic regions. It stains the developing primary walls black, the secondary walls red, the cytoplasm gray, and the nucleoli and chromosomes red.

Aniline Blue

This stain may be used as a counter stain to safranin or as a primary stain for algae. As a stain for algae it acts as an acid dye and becomes bound to the cytoplasm but does not stain the nuclei clearly (Norris, 1957). Iron haematoxylin, however, is a good nuclear stain for algae and fungi, as are various modifications of the acetocarmine techniques used on higher plants (Cave and Pocock, 1951; Stein, 1958).

Mounting the Cover Slips

After the tissue has been stained, it is dehydrated, and a cover slip is mounted over it. The cover slip makes the preparation permanent. The cover slip is held in place with a mounting medium. The medium should have the same refractive index as the glass slide (1.518) and should not affect the stained tissue. The traditional mounting medium is Canada balsam dissolved in xylene. In recent years a whole family of synthetic media has been developed with properties similar or superior to Canada balsam. Among these media are Clarite, Harleco Synthetic Resin, Kleermount, and Piccolyte.

When mounting cover slips with Canada balsam or one of the synthetic resin media, the tissue must be dehydrated completely and placed in xylene. The slide is then taken from the xylene, and the side of the slide not carrying the tissue is wiped with a cloth. A few drops of the medium are then placed over the tissue, and a completely clean cover slip is gently lowered over the tissue and medium. Care must be taken to avoid trapping air bubbles in the tissue or under the cover slip. The slide is then placed on a slide warmer, and the mounting medium is allowed to harden. With experience, it becomes possible to judge the proper amount of medium to use such that the area under the cover slip will be filled without excess medium accumulating around the edge. If there is an excess, it can be removed best by letting the slide dry and then cutting the unwanted material from the edge of the cover slip with a sharp razor blade.

In addition to Canada balsam and the similar synthetic resins, several other mounting media exist. Diaphane, a permanent medium that is soluble in alcohol rather than xylene, has found wide use in research on algae. A medium similar to diaphane is euparal.

A number of mounting media are also available that can be used directly on tissues in aqueous solution. The simplest of them is Karo syrup. This sugar mixture is actually a fine mounting medium, and will not crystallize or dry if the blue label type is used. Karo can be used directly from the bottle without dilution.

Another mixture used on tissue in water or alcohol solutions is glycerine jelly. This is a combination of gelatin and glycerine, with phenol added as a preservative. Glycerine jelly is frequently used as a mounting medium for temporary histochemical preparations.

Cover slips are available in varying thicknesses ranging from very thin (No. 00) to thick (No. 3). The thick cover slips are generally used for fresh mounts, whereas the very thin ones are used for cytological studies. The focal distance of an oil immersion objective is in some cases so short that, unless a very thin cover slip is used, there is not enough room left to focus. For most purposes, including most oil immersion work, a No. 1 cover slip is best.

Squashes and Smears

The preceding methods have dealt with tissues that have been sectioned. Other means are used to handle certain types of materials. One of these is the squash or smear method, used primarily for chromosome studies. In this method a naturally soft piece of tissue (such as an anther) or a piece of softened tissue (such as a root tip treated with acid) is pressed between the slide and the cover slip. This results in the mechanical separation of the cells. The cells are then stained, usually by using dyes that color only the chromosomes. The resulting preparations frequently show with startling clarity chromosome detail not readily seen in slides prepared by other methods. Squash preparations are widely used in chromosome counting work, since all the chromosomes of a cell are visible in the same field.

Two famous and widely used stains are used for smears or squashes. These are the acetocarmine and Feulgen stains. A third, less generally used stain is the iodine-crystal violet stain, which, although not easy to use, yields fine preparations. These three stains will be discussed here and will be employed in methods given in the section on procedures.

The acetocarmine method, developed by Belling (1926) for chromosome work, combines the killing, fixing, and staining solutions. In its simplest form the procedure involves merely placing the fresh tissue on the slide with a drop of the acetocarmine solution, teasing the tissue apart with an iron needle, placing a cover slip over the preparation to squash the tissue flat, heating the slide gently with an alcohol lamp, and examining it under a microscope. The chromosomes appear dark red; the cytoplasm, either pink or colorless. Tissue fixed in alcohol-acetic acid (3:1) may also be used.

The acetocarmine solution consists of 1% of carmine in 45% acetic acid. The iron needle that is used to tease the tissue apart adds a small amount of iron. The fixation is provided by the acetic acid and is excellent for chromosomes. The carmine acts as a basic dye, and the iron may be involved in some way as a mordant. Orcein may be substituted for carmine, and stains some chromosomes better.

The ease of obtaining good preparations with the acetocarmine method has made it one of the most widely used staining procedures for chromosomes. Acetocarmine has also been used to stain the chromosomes of various algae (Cave and Pocock, 1951).

The Feulgen stain is actually an excellent microscopic histochemical test for DNA, and, as such, will be discussed in detail in Chapter 11. It is also one of the best chromosome stains available, because it colors only the chromosomes. The cytoplasm remains clear, since it contains no DNA.

Tissue to be stained by the Feulgen method is fixed in alcohol-acetic acid (3:1) or in a similar fixative. The tissue is then subjected to acid hydrolysis. This treatment reveals an aldehyde associated with chromosomal DNA. The acid treatment also partially macerates the tissue. The tissue is then placed in Schiff's reagent. This contains the dye fucshin in the leuco- form. The dye combines with the aldehyde, forming a fucshin-DNA complex which is red-violet. The tissue is placed on a slide, teased apart, and is squashed with a cover slip to separate the cells and to make the chromosomes clearly visible. Azure A may be substituted for the Schiff's reagent. This colors the chromosomes blue. In some tissues, Azure A yields much more deeply stained chromosomes than does the fucshin.

The iodine-crystal violet stain works on quite a different principle. Crystal violet is a typical basic dye, and thus becomes bound to the cytoplasm as well as to the chromosomes, as do most basic dyes. The iodine becomes associated with the chromatin, and acts as a trapping agent for the crystal violet. During differentiation with alcohol the crystal violet absorbed by the cytoplasm is extracted rapidly, whereas that associated with the iodine and chromatin is extracted slowly (Baker, 1958). As a result, the cytoplasm remains clear, and the chromosomes are stained violet to black. The technique is not very easy, but the preparations are frequently so clear that it is worth attempting, particularly for chromosomes during meiosis.

Both the Feulgen and the iodine-crystal violet stains can be used on sectioned material as well as on squashes.

Squash preparations are usually temporary in nature unless given further treatment. This treatment may consist of removing the cover slip from the slide, dehydrating the cells, and then using a permanent mounting medium to remount the cover slip. When material is scarce, and if it is undesirable to remove the cover slip, other methods can be used for making permanent mounts. These methods involve moving materials under the cover slip. One such method is given in the section on procedures.

Chromosomes frequently require special pretreatments and other refinements of technique to yield the data required. For such special methods, as well as for an excellent treatment of chromosome techniques, see Darlington and LaCour (1960).

Note to the Novice

Botanical histological technique is laborious, time-consuming; it requires experience, but it is not difficult, and the rewards are great. The preparation of a well-stained section of tissue gives a real sense of personal achievement.

The person inexperienced in these techniques is advised to start by fixing samples of an herbaceous stem, a soft leaf, and some root tips in FAA and in Navashin's fixative; dehydrating and paraffin-infiltrating these by means of the TBA series; sectioning them at various thicknesses in different orientations; and staining the sections, trying several different combinations. From these he will be able to determine which fixatives and stains are best for his problem and will gain experience in their use.

Procedures

I. Preparation of the Tissue

A. Cut the tissue into pieces several mm in diameter or thickness immediately before being placed in the fixative. It is advisable to dissect in the case of large stem tips, flower buds, and similar materials before they are fixed. Excessively hairy tissue will cause difficulty in both fixation and sectioning. The hairs slow the penetration of the fixative and break during sectioning, causing tears. Little can be done to improve the situation except to remove as many of the hairs as possible by dissection. The tissue must be free of dirt, sand, or other materials that will cause grave difficulties in sectioning.

B. Prepare a small label, approximately 5 x 30 mm, made of high quality bond paper. Use a hard pencil or india ink to write all the pertinent data about the tissue on the label. These data should include the date the tissue was fixed and the fixative used. Place the label in the fixative with the tissue, and keep the two together at all times.

II. Chemical Fixatives

A. GENERAL USE OF FIXATIVES

1. Place the fixative and the tissue in small vials provided with cork stoppers or in screw-top bottles (Fig. 4-2). Use tight fitting stoppers or caps if the tissue is to be stored for more than a few days.

2. Always use a large volume of fixative in relation to the volume of the tissue.

3. If the tissue does not sink immediately (or after a short time in the fixative) place the bottle containing the tissue and fixative under reduced pressure. A practical setup consists of an aspirator, vacuum pump, or vacuum line attached to a vacuum desiccator in which the bottles are placed.

4. Leave the tissue in the fixative for a minimum of 4 hours (as a

general rule). The tissue can be stored indefinitely in most of the fixatives given below.

5. Remember to place the label in the fixative with the tissue and to fix the tissue in as fresh a state as possible.

B. FIXATIVE FORMULAS

1. Formalin-acetic acid-alcohol (FAA)

Ethyl alcohol, 50%	90 ml
Glacial acetic acid	5 ml
Commercial formalin (40% formaldehyde)	5 ml

2. Navashin's solution

Solution A:

Chromium trioxide (chromic acid)	5 g
Glacial acetic acid	50 ml
Distilled water	320 ml

Solution B:

Commercial formalin	200 ml
Distilled water	175 ml

Mix equal volumes of solutions A and B immediately before placing the tissue in the fixative. Navashin's fixative does not penetrate as well as FAA, thus vacuum infiltration is usually necessary. Recommended for general use.

3. Karpechenko's solution, Papenfuss' modification (Papenfuss, 1946)

Solution A:

Chromium trioxide (chromic acid)	1 g
Glacial acetic acid	5 ml
Sea water	65 ml

Solution B:

Commercial formalin	40 ml
Sea water	35 ml

Use as Navashin's solution, of which it is a modification. Specifically recommended for marine algae, including calcareous species because it dissolves out the calcium salts.

4. Chrom-acetic solution (Johansen, 1940)

10% Aqueous chromic acid		2.5 ml
10% Aqueous acetic acid		5 ml
Distilled water	to 500	ml

This is a weak chrom-acetic acid mixture, and both acids may be varied if the results from this formula are not satisfactory. Recommended for fresh water algae and for fungi.

5a. Carnoy's solution (Johansen, 1940)
    Absolute alcohol   15 ml
    Glacial acetic acid   5 ml
5b. Carnoy's solution
    Absolute alcohol   30 ml
    Glacial acetic acid   5 ml
    Chloroform   15 ml

Both of these fixatives are recommended for chromosome studies. Both give poor fixation of tissue morphology. Do not leave the tissue in these solutions for more than 48 hours. Less than an hour is frequently sufficient.

6. Erliki's fluid, Zirkle's modification (Zirkle, 1934)
    Potassium bichromate   1.25 g
    Ammonium bichromate   1.25 g
    Cupric sulphate   1   g
    Distilled water   200   ml

This fixative gives a basic image, thus nuclear detail is lacking. It is recommended particularly for mitochondria. Fix the tissue for 48 hours, and then wash it in running water. Erickson and Rosen (1949) recommend the addition of 0.3 ml of pyridine and the reduction of the cupric sulphate to 0.5 g.

7. Formal calcium   (See page 263)
8. Lewitsky's fluid   (See page 263)

III. Dehydration: Alcohol Series

A. To wash tissue that has been fixed in alcohol-containing fixatives, run it through several brief changes of alcohol of the same concentration as that present in the fixative.

B. Wash tissue that has been in fixatives containing chromic acid or other heavy metals in running water for 4–24 hours (Fig. 4-2). When thoroughly washed, leave the tissue for 1–2 hours in each of the following ethyl alcohol series: 5%, 10%, and 30%.

C. The tissue is now ready for complete dehydration in the TBA series. This consists of mixtures of tertiary butyl alcohol (TBA), ethyl alcohol, and water; the ethyl alcohol and water being replaced by TBA in the higher members of the series. The series consists of the following mixtures:

50   50 ml H_2O, 40 ml 95% alcohol, 10 ml TBA
70   30 ml H_2O, 50 ml 95% alcohol, 20 ml TBA
85   15 ml H_2O, 50 ml 95% alcohol, 35 ml TBA

95   45 ml 95% alcohol, 55 ml TBA
100   25 ml absolute alcohol, 75 ml TBA
TBA   100% TBA

The number of the series (50, 70, . . . TBA) indicates the total alcohol concentration of each member. Each solution may be used repeatedly except the final 100% TBA, which is used only once and is then used to make up the other lower members of the series. Pure TBA has a freezing point slightly below room temperature. When the tissue is in pure TBA it must be stored in a warm place at night. Normal butyl alcohol may be used in place of TBA, and has the advantage of possessing a lower freezing point.

Leave the tissue in each solution of the TBA series for a minimum of 2–4 hours (a maximum of several days is usually permissible). Leave the tissue in TBA 8 hours to overnight. Repeat this step three times. The tissue is now completely dehydrated and ready for paraffin infiltration and embedding.

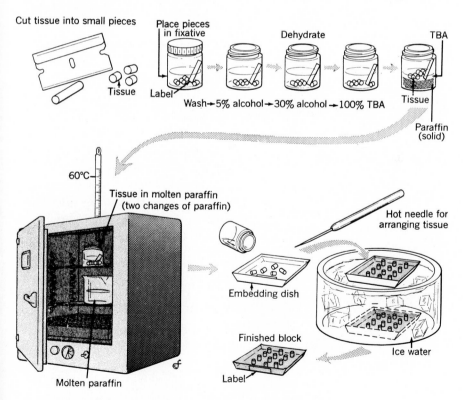

Figure 4-2. *Fixation, dehydration, and paraffin embedding.*

IV. Paraffin Infiltration and Embedding

A. Place the tissue, and just enough TBA to cover it, in a small dish or bottle half filled with solid paraffin (Fig. 4-2). Place the dish in an oven at a temperature 5° higher than the melting point of the paraffin used.

B. Approximately 4 hours after the paraffin has melted, pour off the paraffin, taking care not to lose the tissue, and replace it with fresh molten paraffin.

C. Repeat the above procedure once more, replacing the paraffin with fresh paraffin, Tissuemat, or a similar embedding medium.

D. Carefully coat the inside of a clean, dry porcelain embedding dish with a thin layer of glycerine. If the solid paraffin sticks to the bottom of the dish after embedding, add a few drops of detergent to the glycerine, or apply it directly to the dish. Warm the embedding dish by holding it in the flame of a Bunsen burner or by placing it on a hot plate. Paper boats can also be used for embedding (Fig. 4-3). To make one of these, cut a stiff piece of paper (file cards work well) into a rectangle. Next, fold the two longer sides (a) in for a distance equal to the final desired depth of the boat, or about one-half inch. Now, fold the two shorter sides in (b) approximately twice this distance. Next, unfold and flatten the paper. Bring the sides together (Step 1, Fig. 4-3), and at the corners (C) fold back the overlap onto the shorter sides (Step 2) and turn the projecting part of the end wall (B) over to hold the corners in place (Step 3). Paper boats are not coated with glycerine, since they can be peeled away from the paraffin or Tissuemat after it has solidified. They are less rigid than the porcelain dishes and are harder to use in aligning many small pieces of tissue. However they are easier to use when embedding large pieces of tissue. For general use, the porcelain dishes are recommended.

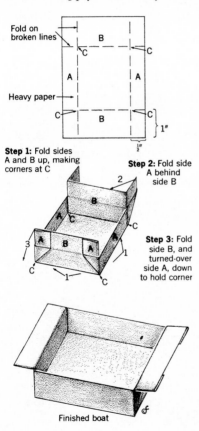

Figure 4-3
Construction of paper embedding boats.

E. Take the dish containing the tissue and the paraffin or Tissuemat from the oven. Swirl the contents and pour them into the embedding dish (or boat). Use enough paraffin or Tissuemat to cover the tissue adequately.

F. Use a warm needle to arrange and orient the tissue such that individual pieces can be cut easily from the finished block (Fig. 4-2). Place the label such that it can be read when the block is solid.

G. Carefully lift the embedding dish, and place it on the surface of a dish of ice water. After the surface of the paraffin has solidified, plunge the dish under water and leave it there. If a porcelain embedding dish is used, the paraffin will contract slightly as it cools and will pull away from the dish and float to the surface of the water. If it fails to do this, loosen the block with a razor blade. If a paper boat is used, allow the block to completely harden, and then peel away the paper from the block.

H. After the block has completely cooled, remove it from the water, dry it, and wrap it in a sheet of paper or aluminum foil, and store it in a refrigerator.

V. Sectioning (Rotary Microtome)

A. Carefully remove from the paraffin block a piece of paraffin containing the tissue to be sectioned. Use a razor blade to cut V-shaped grooves on opposite sides of the block along the lines at which you want the piece to break (Fig. 4-4). With thin blocks it is easy to cut through the block in making the grooves, but with thick blocks it is best to break the piece from the block cautiously, allowing the grooves to determine the location of the break.

B. Mount the piece of paraffin containing the tissue on a wooden peg or block about one-half inch in diameter and 2 inches long. Soak new blocks in molten paraffin for several days before using them. This need only be done once. It is easiest to soak a number of blocks at one time. They can then be drained on paper toweling and stored until used. Each block can be used repeatedly.

C. To mount the embedded tissue on the wooden block, carefully heat the bottom of the paraffin and the top of the wooden block. While still molten, press the two surfaces together, and allow them to solidify. Use a warm needle to build up a mound of paraffin at the base of the piece to add strength. When small pieces of paraffin are involved, the bottom may be difficult to heat. If this be the case, warm only the wooden block. Then quickly press the piece of paraffin containing

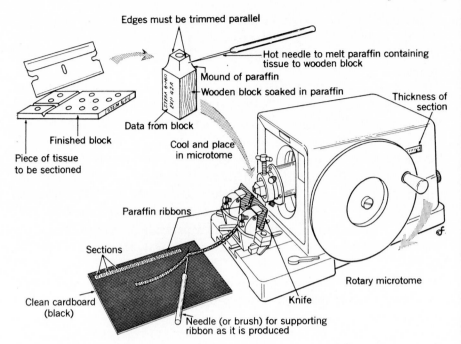

Figure 4-4. *Sectioning with a rotary microtome.*

the tissue against the block, and use a warm needle to melt the bottom of the paraffin and seal the union.

D. In either case chill the paraffin by placing it in a dish of ice water or in a refrigerator.

E. When the paraffin is completely cool, trim the piece, using a sharp, single-edged razor blade. Remove excess paraffin from around the tissue, but leave the base as broad as possible. Next, make the surfaces of the piece that will be parallel to the knife blade parallel to each other. Often, with tissue which is irregular in shape or consistency, a straight ribbon can be obtained only if the surfaces are not parallel. Only experience, however, can guide the trimming of such pieces. Finally, trim the piece such that its surfaces lie close to the embedded tissue. In general, the surfaces should be parallel to one another, although it is frequently an advantage to cut one surface at an angle. Thus, the ribbon will have a saw-toothed appearance, which will aid in the visual delimitation of the sections. This is important when working with tissue that is nearly colorless.

F. Put the trimmed block in the ice water or refrigerator until shortly before it is to be sectioned in the microtome.

G. Place the block in the microtome. Be sure the safety catch of the microtome is in place, since the aligning of the tissue must be done with the knife in place. The following directions are for the Spencer rotary microtome. The block is secured in the microtome by a vise-like arrangement that is held in a universal joint regulated by three screws. First, place the block in the vise, and orient the block with relation to the knife. As yet, this orientation is not precise. Next, secure the block in place by turning the screw which activates the vise. Carefully align the tissue in relation to the blade by adjusting the three screws on the universal joint. Keep the following two points in mind with regard to this final alignment: (1) the edge of the block that hits the knife should be parallel to the knife edge; (2) the block must be oriented in relation to the knife such that the tissue will be sectioned along the desired plane. Make sure all the screws are tight and that the block is held firmly before starting to section.

H. Set the microtome to the desired section thickness, and release the safety catch. Cut a few trial sections. These will probably not be complete. Continue sectioning until a ribbon begins to form. If the ribbon starts to curve, stop sectioning, and judiciously trim the paraffin block with a razor blade without removing it from the microtome.

I. When it becomes evident that a straight ribbon will form, and that the plane of the sections is as desired, begin sectioning at an even rate of about one section per second, stopping as little as possible.

J. As the ribbon forms, slip the end of a dissecting needle, forceps, or brush under it, and guide it away from the knife (Fig. 4-4). When the ribbon is long enough, carefully lay it on a piece of black, lint-free poster board, and cut the ribbon a few inches from the knife edge. Another line of sections can then be cut and placed on the board parallel to the first. Only when the ribbon is finished is the last section disengaged from the knife.

K. There are a number of conditions which lead to difficulties during sectioning. Some of the more common difficulties are listed here. For a more complete list see Richards (1959).

1. *Sections tear.* This may result from a nick in the blade, and can be remedied by using a different part of the knife. It may also be caused by lint or dirt on the blade. This can usually be removed by running a finger up the back of the blade to its edge. If the tear is not across the entire section but starts at the tissue, it may be that the tissue is so hard that it is fragmenting. The fragments cause the tearing. Frequently, there is little that can be done about this last condition, although soaking the block in water or 60% alcohol with 10% glycerine may help (Baker, 1941).

2. *Ribbon does not form.* This alarming event often occurs when a block has been too thoroughly chilled before sectioning. If this is be-

lieved to be the case, allow the block to warm up to room temperature, or warm the block by breathing on it or by moving a gooseneck lamp close to it. Another cause may be that the paraffin is of too high a melting point for the sectioning conditions. If this be the case, melt the paraffin, and embed the tissue in paraffin or Tissuemat having a lower melting point. Static electricity, which is the cause of several other unpleasant occurrences in microtoming, may also be the cause of the failure of sections to form a ribbon. To reduce static electricity the microtome may be grounded, the humidity in the room may be increased by heating water, or the commercial ionizing apparatus discussed earlier may be used (page 68). To avoid static electricity, sectioning is frequently best in the morning. Finally, a dull knife may prevent ribbon formation.

3. *Sections are excessively compressed.* This is a common difficulty in thin sections, and may be caused by a dull blade. If the paraffin is too soft, either because it has too low a melting point or because it is too warm, this, too, will result in excessive compression. To reduce compression in thin sections it is often necessary to section in a cold room.

4. *Block picks up ribbon on return stroke.* Static electricity or a dull knife may be the cause. Frequently, however, this difficulty is caused by the angle of the knife, which should be readjusted, or by paraffin on the back of the knife, which can be removed with a piece of xylene-soaked cloth.

5. *Sections are of uneven thickness.* Again, the blade may be at the wrong angle; the blade should be adjusted if necessary. The microtome may be at fault, and should be examined with care. Always keep the microtome well lubricated and clean.

6. *Sections fly around or stick to everything.* This remarkable phenomenon is caused by static electricity. See item 2 above for possible corrective measures.

When difficulty is encountered in sectioning, first check the condition of the blade, then check the blade angle, and, finally, check the temperature and condition of the block; always make the easiest adjustments first. Some days, however, it is best simply to give up attempts at microtoming and do something else.

N. The ribbons may be stored for a few days in shallow boxes at below room temperature. Normally, however, they should be mounted on slides as soon as possible.

O. Microtome knives can be sharpened by hand according to the following directions (Gettner and Ornstein, 1956; Richards, 1959).

1. Each microtome knife comes with a sharpening back that raises the

knife and establishes the angle of the cutting facets. Keep this back with the knife; do not exchange it with other backs.

2. To sharpen the knife, attach the handle to the end of the knife, and slip on the back.

3. Examine the knife under the low power of a microscope; note any nicks, and check the general condition of the blade.

4. For honing, use a fine-grained sharpening stone lubricated with soapstone. Hold the knife at an angle to the long axis of the stone, and move it forward against the stone in such a manner that the entire edge moves across the stone. Apply enough pressure to the knife such that it will ride evenly and firmly as it moves along the stone. At the end of the first forward stroke, turn the knife over by rotating it on the back, and reverse the direction of the movement. Thus, first one side and then the other of the knife is polished against the stone. The knife is sharp when the cutting facets and edge, as viewed under the low power of the microscope with strong reflected light, appear as a narrow, straight, and unbroken bright line.

5. An alternate method is to use a glass plate ($\frac{3}{16}$ inch or thicker, 12–14 inches long, and an inch wider than the blade) and abrasives suspended in water. Use Corundum 303 or 304 to remove nicks, levigated alumina and Corundum 305 for ordinary sharping, and Linde A and B powder for final polishing. The motion of the knife is the same as in D except that a diagonal movement is not necessary, since the glass plate is wider than the stone. The same criteria for sharpness are used.

6. Strop the sharpened blade on a rigid strop. (This is optional.) If a strop is used the blade is drawn (*not* pushed) lightly across the surface of the strop.

7. Finally, clean and dry the blade well before storing. In some laboratories, and in some climates, it is necessary to oil the blade before storing it.

P. Razor blades may be used in place of knives in microtomy. They are most effective when used and sharpened according to the following directions.

1. When razor blades are used in place of microtome knives, it is best to use the thicker kind of blade, such as a Schick blade. These are held in a specially designed holder, the newest model produced by American Optical Co. being highly recommended. These holders are designed for wider, thinner blades than the Schick blade, thus it is necessary to use two blades if Schick blades are used. One is placed cutting-edge down in the bottom of the holder; the second is placed above it with the cutting edge up and projecting above the edge of the

holder. This prevents the top blade from slipping and falling into the holder.

2. For fairly thick sections, new razor blades may be used without further treatment. Thin sections (less than 10 μ) are best cut on sharpened razor blades.

3. To sharpen razor blades it is necessary to construct the holder shown in Fig. 4-5. This holder is a slight modification of one designed by Sjöstrand (1956) for the sharpening of razor blades used in electron microscopy. The angle of the cutting facets is determined by the knob on the back, and should be 28 to 30°.

4. After the blade is in the holder, sharpening is done using a glass plate and a solution of 10 ml of Linde B, 8 ml of glycerine, 2 ml of acetone, and 10 ml of water (Gettner and Ornstein, 1956). Push the blade first in one direction and then in the other. Only a few minutes of sharpening are necessary. Keep all equipment and solutions free of dust.

5. Store the sharpened blades in a desiccator.

VI. Affixing Sections to Slides

A. First clean the slide. For most uses it is merely necessary to soak the slides in alcohol and to dry them with a clean, lint-free cloth. In some cases, particularly when the slides are reused or dirty, it is necessary to soak the slides in a standard cleaning solution, rinse them well in running water, soak them in alcohol, and let them dry. For general use, frosted-end slides work well, since the data concerning the ribbon may be written in pencil on the slide. If unfrosted slides are used, use

Figure 4-5. *Razor blade holder used in sharpening blades.*

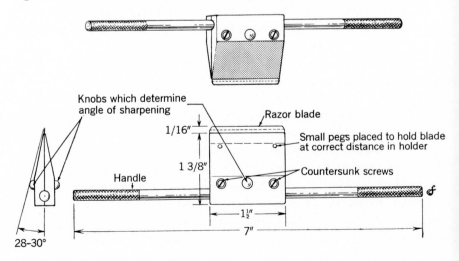

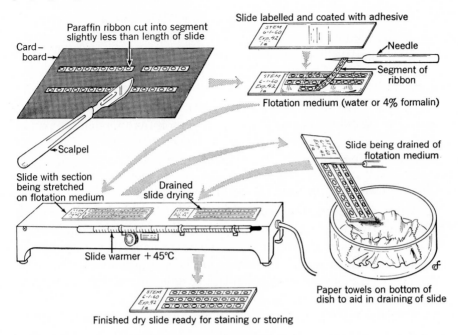

Figure 4-6. *Mounting paraffin sections on slides.*

a diamond point or a carborundum pencil to write the data on the slides.

B. Cut the paraffin ribbon into shorter units which are approximately two-thirds to three-fourths the length of the cover slip to be used (Fig. 4-6).

C. Cover the upper surface of the slide with a thin coating of Haupt's adhesive. To make Haupt's adhesive, dissolve 1 g of gelatin in 100 ml of H_2O at 90°C. Cool this mixture to 30°C, and then add 15 ml of glycerine. Finally, stir and filter the adhesive, and store it in a refrigerator. As a preservative, 2 g of phenol may be added. (See page 199 for another excellent adhesive.)

D. Add a few drops of 4% formalin to the slide, and float the segments of the ribbon on the formalin by means of a needle, brush, or tooth pick. Arrange the ribbon segments neatly and compactly on the slide.

E. Transfer the slide to a slide warmer several degrees lower than the melting point of the paraffin or Tissuemat used. Add more 4% formalin to permit the tissue to stretch as it warms. When the tissue is fully extended, carefully remove the slide from the slide warmer, and allow it to cool.

F. When the slide is cool drain most of the formalin solution off the slide onto a paper towel folded in a Petri dish, and use a needle to prevent the sections from floating off the slide. Arrange the tissue with two dissecting needles, and remove the remaining liquid from the slide. Using a clean cloth, carefully wipe the surface of the slide not covered by the sections.

G. Replace the slide on the slide warmer, and allow it to dry overnight. The slides may be stored in this condition for an indefinite period.

VII. Staining

A. SAFRANIN-FAST GREEN

1. Remove the paraffin from the sections by placing the slide in xylene for 5 minutes and then in a 1:1 mixture of xylene and absolute alcohol for another 5 minutes. The xylene and all other solutions discussed in these histological procedures are kept in Coplin stain jars or in some other type of container in which the slides are held such that they will not move against one another.

2. Partially hydrate sections by passing through a series of alcohols of decreasing concentration: absolute, 95%, 70%, and 50% (5 minutes in each).

3. Stain in safranin 1 to 24 hours. Make a stock solution of safranin (1% safranin in 95% alcohol), and dilute with an equal amount of distilled water before use.

4. Wash in water, pass briefly through acidified 70% alcohol to destain, and then pass rapidly through 95% and absolute alcohol.

5. Counterstain with fast green (0.5% solution in 50% clove oil, 50% alcohol) for 30 seconds to 4 minutes.

6. Differentiate the fast green by placing it in a mixture of 50% clove oil, 25% absolute alcohol, and 25% xylene. Use two changes, 5 to 15 minutes each.

7. Place the sections in xylene, making three changes of at least 15 minutes each, and mount cover slip with balsam or other mounting medium.

Nucleoli, chromosomes, cuticle, and lignified cell walls stain red; the remaining structures stain green. This is a very easy and useful stain combination.

B. SAFRANIN-ANILINE BLUE

Steps 1–3 are identical to the first three steps in the preceding procedure.

4. Wash sections in water and destain, if necessary, in acidified water.

5. Counterstain with aniline blue (saturated solution of aniline blue in absolute alcohol, diluted 50% with clove oil before use) for 1 minute.

6. Place in a mixture of 50% clove oil, 25% absolute alcohol, and 25% xylene or in pure methyl salicylate.

7. Finally, place in three changes of xylene for 15 minutes each, and mount with cover slip.

This is a particularly fine stain for gymnosperm tissue, although it can be used for most other tissues as a substitute for fast green. The color combination is similar to the safranin-fast green, with blue replacing green.

C. TANNIC ACID-FERRIC CHLORIDE-SAFRANIN

1. Deparaffinize sections, and hydrate completely by passing through absolute, 95%, 70%, 50%, and 30% alcohol to water.

2. Mordant by placing sections in a 1% aqueous solution of tannic acid for 10 minutes.

3. Wash in running water for 5 minutes.

4. Stain in a 3% aqueous solution of ferric chloride for 5 minutes.

5. Wash in running water for 5 minutes. If the color is not dark enough, repeat steps 2, 3, and 4.

6. Counterstain with safranin as described above.

7. Dehydrate by passing through 95% and absolute alcohol.

8. Place in 3 changes of xylene, and mount with cover slip.

This stain is particularly good for shoot and root apical regions; it colors the nucleoli, chromosomes, cuticle, and lignified cell walls red and colors the remainder of the cell blue-black and gray. The primary wall stains clearly. For other versions of this procedure see Northern (1936).

D. HEIDENHAIN'S IRON HAEMATOXYLIN-ORANGE G

1. Deparaffinize sections, and bring to water.

2. Mordant in either 3% ferric chloride or ferric ammonium sulfate for $\frac{1}{2}$–2 hours.

3. Wash thoroughly.

4. Stain in 0.5% aqueous haematoxylin $\frac{1}{2}$–2 hours or longer. (Prepare a 10% aqueous solution of haematoxylin in absolute alcohol. Add 5 ml of this stock solution to 100 ml of distilled water, and add a trace of sodium bicarbonate. The solution should acquire a rich wine red color.)

5. Wash with running water.

6. Destain in 2% ferric chloride or ferric ammonium sulfate. The

time for destaining can be determined only by observing the cells under the microscope. Use a glass plate over the stage of the microscope. Watch particularly the chromatin-containing bodies, and remember that the preparation will appear more gray in water than in the final mounting medium.

7. Wash thoroughly in running water.

8. Dehydrate to absolute alcohol.

9. Counterstain for 1–5 minutes with orange G (0.5% in clove oil; prepare by shaking 4 hours and then filtering or by dissolving first in methyl cellosolve). The use of a counter stain with Heidenhain's iron haematoxylin is not always desirable.

10. Differentiate in a solution of equal parts clove oil, absolute alcohol, and xylene for 5–15 minutes.

11. Place in 3 changes of xylene (15 minutes each), and mount.

Chromosomes, nuclei, nucleoli, mitochondria, and plastids stain dark blue; the cytoplasm and the cell walls stain light orange. This procedure is particularly useful in studying cytoplasmic particles. Although the procedure is not easy, it is an excellent one to learn.

E. IRON HAEMATOXYLIN-BISMARCK BROWN

Steps 1–7 are identical to the corresponding steps in the preceding procedure.

8. Counterstain with a 1% aqueous solution of Bismarck brown for 2–4 hours.

9. Wash with water.

10. Dehydrate through alcohol series, using 2 changes of absolute alcohol in final step.

11. Place in 3 changes of xylene, and mount cover slip.

This combination is especially useful for woody tissue and is a modification of a stain designed for work with phloem (Harrar, 1928).

F. DELAFIELD'S HAEMATOXYLIN (JOHANSEN, 1940)

1. Remove the paraffin, and hydrate through alcohol series to water.

2. Place in Delafield's haematoxylin for 5 to 30 minutes. To make Delafield's haematoxylin, add 4 g of haematoxylin to 25 ml of 95% alcohol, and carefully add this to 400 ml of a standard aqueous solution of ammonium aluminum sulfate. Expose this solution to light and air for 4 days to a week. After exposure add 10 ml of glycerine and 100 ml of methyl alcohol. Allow to stand exposed to air for several months until the color is a dark wine shade. Filter, and use.

3. Wash in running tap water for 5 minutes.

4. Place in water acidified with a few drops of HCl for 1 to 2 minutes. Do not allow sections to remain in this solution for a long time.

5. Return the sections to tap water, and wash until they turn purple. If this does not occur, add a small amount of sodium carbonate to the water.

6. Dehydrate rapidly through the alcohol series (a few minutes in each member of the series).

7. Place in 3 changes of xylene, and mount with the cover slip.

Chromosomes, nucleoli, resting nuclei, mitochondria, and other cytoplasmic particles will appear deep blue-black; cytoplasm, blue-gray. Orange G may be used as a counter stain, but it is not generally recommended. Safranin and Delafield's haematoxylin are frequently used together. In this combination the safranin is used first, and the Delafield's haematoxylin is used as a counter stain. If this stain is desired, follow steps 1 through 3 in the safranin-fast green procedure; wash; destain with acidified 50% alcohol; and then proceed with steps 2 through 7 of the present method. Delafield's haematoxylin is recommended for general cytological investigations and for use with algae and fungi.

G. ANILINE BLUE (PAPENFUSS, 1937)

1. This stain is recommended specifically for algae and can be used either with fixed whole material or with sections.

2. For fixed whole specimens in glycerine, use the following method.

(a) Place material in a 1% aqueous solution of aniline blue for 2–3 minutes.
(b) Wash in water for a few seconds to remove excess stain.
(c) Add a few drops of 1% HCl to the water to fix the stain.
(d) Wash in running water for a few minutes to remove acid.
(e) Mount in 50% glycerine containing a few drops of 1% HCl.

3. For sections use the following method.

(a) Remove paraffin, and bring to 80% alcohol.
(b) Stain in a 1% solution of aniline blue in 80% alcohol.
(c) Wash in 80% alcohol for a few minutes.
(d) Add a few drops of 1% HCl to the alcohol to fix the stain.
(e) Wash in fresh 80% alcohol to remove acid.
(f) Dehydrate, and mount.

The cell walls and cytoplasm appear blue; the nuclei do not stain clearly. If the nuclei are to be stained, use Delafield's haematoxylin.

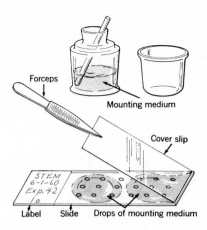

Forceps

Mounting medium

Cover slip

STEM
6-1-60
Exp.42
la

Label   Slide   Drops of mounting medium

Figure 4-7
Mounting the cover slip.

VIII. Mounting the Cover Slip

A. Clean a number of cover slips by placing them in alcohol and drying them with a lint-free cloth. In drying cover slips hold them between two pieces of cloth, rub both surfaces with thumb and forefinger, exerting equal pressure with each.

B. Remove the slide from the xylene, and hold it such that the tissue is on the upper surface. Wipe the lower surface with a cloth.

C. Place 1–3 drops of Canada balsam, Clarite, or other mounting medium on the slide.

D. Pick up the cover slip with a pair of forceps, and hold the cover slip such that the right edge touches the slide just to the right of the tissue (Fig. 4-7). Now, lower the other end of the cover slip until the cover slip makes contact with the mounting medium. Continue to lower, taking care to keep bubbles from being trapped in or around the tissue, until the cover slip rests completely on the slide.

E. Use enough mounting medium to fill the entire area under the cover slip, not so much that it overflows the top of the cover slip.

F. Place the slide on a slide warmer for at least 24 hours before microscopic examination under oil.

IX. Coating Sections

During the course of certain histochemical procedures, there is a great danger that the sections may become loosened from the slide and be lost. This can be avoided by coating the sections with celloidin. The celloidin coating will not interfere with the reactions and will usually keep the sections on the slide.

A. Remove the paraffin from the sections in the usual manner, and place the slides in 95% alcohol.

B. Dip the slide in a 0.5% solution of celloidin or paralloidin in alcohol-ether.

C. Allow the slide to drain for a moment, and place it in 95% alcohol to harden the celloidin.

X. *Smears and Squashes* (DARLINGTON AND LACOUR, 1960; JOHANSEN, 1940)

A. ACETOCARMINE METHOD

1. Make acetocarmine by mixing 55 ml of distilled water, 45 ml of acetic acid, and 0.5 g of carmine. Boil gently for 5 minutes, shake, cool, and filter.

2. Use of acetocarmine with soft tissue, such as anthers.
(a) Place a drop of acetocarmine on a clean slide, and add the tissue.
(b) With a pair of iron needles tease the material apart and place a cover slip over the preparation.
(c) Heat gently with an alcohol lamp.
(d) Apply pressure to the cover slip to flatten the material.
(e) The preparation is now ready for examination. The edges of the cover slip may be sealed with wax. With some tissues it is best to smear the tissue out on the slide with the blade of a scalpel before adding the acetocarmine.

3. Use of acetocarmine with rigid tissue, such as root tips and leaves.

(a) Place tissue directly in a small test tube containing a few milliliters of acetocarmine, and heat at 60°C for 15–20 minutes.
(b) Remove material from the test tube, and place on a clean slide in a drop of acetocarmine.
(c) Follow steps (b) through (e) in the procedure given above.

4. Use of acetocarmine with fixed tissue.

(a) Fix tissue in a 3:1 mixture of alcohol and acetic acid for half an hour.
(b) Transfer to 70% alcohol. The tissue may remain here indefinitely.
(c) Place tissue in a drop of acetocarmine on a slide.
(d) Repeat steps (b) through (e) of the first acetocarmine method.

5. Use of acetocarmine with microscopic algae, and fungi. (Cave and Pocock, 1951; Stein, 1958).

(a) Pick up cells or colonies with a capillary pipette, and place on a clean cover slip in a drop of the following fixative: 0.5 g of iodine, 1 g of potassium iodide, 4 ml of glacial acetic acid, 24 ml of commercial formalin and 400 ml of distilled water.
(b) Add a drop of solution composed of one part 0.4% ferric hydroxide in propionic acid and two parts absolute alcohol.

(c) Allow to act for 2–5 minutes, and remove excess solution.

(d) Invert cover slip on a drop of acetocarmine on a clean slide.

(e) Heat gently over an alcohol lamp.

(f) Preparation is ready for microscopic observation.

B. FEULGEN METHOD

1. Fix tissue in a 3:1 mixture of alcohol and acetic acid for 30 minutes at room temperature.

2. Place tissue in 70% alcohol.

3. Transfer to 1 N HCl at 60°C for 15 minutes.

This not only hydrolyzes but partially macerates the tissue, thus careful handling of the tissue is required after this stage.

4. Wash in distilled water.

5. Stain in Schiff's reagent (see page 199) for 30 to 60 minutes or longer in the dark. Several hours may be necessary.

6. Wash in distilled water.

7. Bleach in a mixture of 1 part sodium metabisulfite, 3 parts 1 N HCl, and 3 parts distilled water. Use 2 changes of 10 minutes each.

8. Wash in tap water for 30 minutes.

9. Place the material on a slide in a drop of 45% acetic acid, and tease into very small fragments with a needle. Cover with a cover slip.

10. Heat gently, and flatten by pressing on cover slip.

11. Seal edges of cover slip with wax.

The chromosomes should appear red violet in perfectly clear cells.

A solution of 0.25% Azure A, to which 1 drop of thionyl chloride per 10 ml has been added, may be used in place of the Schiff's reagent (De Lamater, 1951). In this case merely wash the slides in water, and dehydrate.

C. CRYSTAL VIOLET METHOD (BAKER AND JORDAN, 1953)

1. Smear soft material, such as anthers, on a clean slide with a scalpel.

2. Immediately fix by placing slide, face down, in a dish of alcohol and acetic acid (3:1) or in a similar fixative.

3. After 10–20 minutes wash in water.

4. Place in 1% aqueous crystal violet for 15 minutes.

5. Rinse in distilled water.

6. Place in 1% solution of iodine in 2% aqueous potassium iodide.

7. Rinse in distilled water.

8. Dehydrate in 70%, 90%, and absolute alcohol, leaving slide in each solution for 10 seconds.

9. Place in absolute alcohol for 1 minute, and then in 2 changes of xylene.

10. Mount in permanent mounting medium.

The chromosomes will be a beautiful dark violet in a crystal clear cytoplasm. This stain is highly recommended for sectioned material. Remove paraffin, hydrate, and start at step 4 in the above schedule. For another, more traditional crystal violet method, see Darlington and LaCour (1960).

D. METHODS FOR MAKING TEMPORARY MOUNTS PERMANENT

1. Methods based on removing the cover slip (Darlington and La Cour, 1960)

(a) After an acetocarmine procedure, invert slide in a Petri dish containing 10% acetic acid. Cover slip will drop free in 5–10 minutes. Pass slide and cover slip through a 3:1 mixture of alcohol and acetic acid for 2 minutes; then pass through two changes of absolute alcohol for 2 minutes each. Remount cover slip with Euparal or Diaphane.

(b) After Feulgen method place slide face down in a dish of 40% alcohol. In a few minutes the cover slip will fall off. Place slide and cover slip in 80% alcohol for 2 minutes; then place in 2 changes of absolute alcohol for 2 minutes each. Remount cover slip with Euparal or Diaphane.

(c) After Feulgen method lay slide on block of dry ice, making certain good contact is made. Freeze for 30 seconds to several minutes, and then pry off the cover slip with razor blade while slide is still on dry ice. Immediately place slide and cover slip in 95% alcohol, and leave 5 minutes. Then place in absolute alcohol for 5 minutes or longer, and remount cover slip with Euparal or Diaphane. Immersion of the slide in liquid nitrogen may be used as an alternate freezing method.

2. Method based on not removing the cover slip (Bradley, 1948; Cave and Pocock, 1951)

(a) Draw the following solutions under the cover slip by placing a drop along one edge of the cover slip and a piece of filter paper on the opposite edge: (1) 45% acetic acid, (2) 1 part 95% alcohol to 2 parts 45% acetic acid, (3) 2 parts absolute alcohol to 1 part glacial acetic acid, (4) absolute alcohol, (5) absolute alcohol.

(b) Next, ring cover slip with Euparal or Diaphane, and place in the bottom of a flat, tightly covered tin box. Cover the bottom of this box with a piece of filter paper wetted with absolute alcohol.

(c) After 24 hours place the slides on top of a paraffin oven, and dry overnight.

(d) The cover slip may be cleaned with absolute alcohol.

LITERATURE CITED

Baker, J. R., 1941. A fluid for softening tissue embedded in paraffin wax. *J. Roy. Microscop. Soc.*, **61**:75–78.

———, 1950. *Cytological Technique.* 3rd ed. Meuthen, New York.

———, 1958. Principles of Biological Microtechnique, Meuthen, London.

Baker, J. R. and B. J. Jordan, 1953. Miscellaneous contributions to microtechnique. *Quart. J. Microscop. Sci.*, **94**:237–242.

Ball, E., 1941. Microtechnique for the shoot apex. *Am. J. Botany*, **28**:233–243.

Belling, J., 1926. The iron-acetocarmine method of fixing and staining chromosomes. *Biol. Bull.*, **50**:160–162.

Bradley, M. V., 1948. A method for making aceto-carmine squashes permanent without removal of the cover slip. *Stain Technol.*, **23**:41–44.

Cave, M. S. and M. A. Pocock, 1951. The aceto-carmine technic applied to the colonial Volvocales. *Stain Technol.*, **26**:173–174.

Conn, H. J., 1953. *The History of Staining.* Biol. Stain Comm., Geneva, New York.

Darlington, C. D. and L. F. LaCour, 1960. *The Handling of Chromosomes.* Macmillan, New York.

De Lamater, E. D., 1951. A staining and dehydration procedure for the handling of microorganisms. *Stain Technol.*, **26**:199–204.

Erickson, R. O. and G. U. Rosen, 1949. Cytological effects of protanemonion on the root tip of *Zea mays. Am. J. Botany*, **36**:317–322.

Ficq, A., 1959. Autoradiography, pp. 67–90. In *The Cell.* Vol. I. J. Brachet and A. E. Mirsky (Editors). Academic, New York.

Gettner, M. E. and L. Ornstein, 1956. Microtomy. In *Physical Techniques in Biological Research.* G. Oster and A. W. Pollister (Editors). Academic, New York.

Harrar, E. S., 1928. A stain combination for phloem tissues of woody plants. *Botan. Gaz.*, **86**:111–112.

Hughes, A., 1959. *A History of Cytology.* Abelard-Schuman, London and New York.

Johansen, D. A., 1940. *Plant Microtechnique.* McGraw-Hill, New York.

Norris, R. E., 1957. Morphological Studies on the Kallymeniaceae. *Univ. of Calif. Publ. Botany*, **28**:251–334.

Northern, H. T., 1936. Histological applications of tannic acid and ferric chloride. *Stain Technol.*, **11**:23–24.

Papenfuss, G. F., 1937. The structure and reproduction of *Claudis multifida, Vanvoorstia spectabilis,* and *Vanvoorstia coccinea. Symb. Botan. Uppsal.*, **2**:1–66.

———, 1946. Structure and reproduction of *Trichogloea requienii* with a comparison of the genera of *Helminthocladiaceae. Bull. Torrey Botan. Club*, **73**:419–437.

Pease, D. C., 1960. *Histological Tech-*

niques for Electron Microscopy. Academic, New York.

Pollister, A. W. and L. Ornstein, 1959. The photometric chemical analysis of cells, pp. 431–518. In *Analytical Cytology*. 2nd ed. R. C. Mellors (Editor). McGraw-Hill, New York.

Richards, O. W., 1959. *The Effective Use and Proper Care of the Microtome*. American Optical Co., Buffalo.

Sass, J. E., 1958. *Botanical Microtechnique*. 3rd. ed. Iowa State College Press, Ames, Iowa.

Shields, L. H. and H. L. Dean, 1949. Microtome compression in plant tissue. *Am. J. Botany*, 36:408–416.

Sjöstrand, F. S., 1956. Electron microscopy of cells and tissues, pp. 241–298. In *Physical Techniques in Bio-*

logical Research. G. Oster and A. W. Pollister (Editors). Academic, New York.

Smith, G. M., 1915. The development of botanical microtechnique. *Trans. Am. Microscop. Soc.*, 34:71–129.

Stein, J. R., 1958. A morphological study of *Astrephomene gubernaculifera* and *Volvulina steinii*. *Am. J. Botany*, 45:388–397.

Zirkle, C., 1928. The effect of hydrogen ion concentration upon the fixation images of various salts of chromium. *Protoplasma*, 4:201–227.

———, 1929. Fixation images with acetates and chromates. *Protoplasma*, 5:511–534.

———, 1934. Amines in cytological fixing fluids. *Protoplasma*, 20:473–482.

CHAPTER 5

Freeze-substitution
and Freeze-drying

Introduction

For many, indeed most, histochemical procedures, chemically fixed and dehydrated tissue cannot be used. The reason is that chemical fixation and dehydration profoundly alter the condition of the tissue from that present in the living state; proteins are denatured, lipids are extracted, water-soluble substances are lost, enzymes are inactivated, and other drastic changes may occur. Yet, for many histochemical methods the tissue must be dehydrated and paraffin infiltrated. Autoradiography, for example, requires thin sections of tissue. For some types of autoradiographic studies chemically fixed and dehydrated tissue may be used (Woods and Taylor, 1959). For other types of autoradiographic work, however, chemically fixed and dehydrated tissue is unsuitable. Research on the distribution and translocation of water soluble substances, for example, cannot be determined through autoradiographs of chemically fixed and dehydrated tissue (Gage and Arnoff, 1960; Perkins, Nelson, and Gorham, 1959).

There are alternate methods to chemical fixation and dehydration which yield paraffin-infiltrated and embedded tissue. These are the methods of freeze-substitution and freeze-drying.

In both methods the initial step consists in rapid freezing the tissue. However, the next step—tissue dehydration—differs between the two methods. In freeze-substitution, the ice formed in the initial freezing is dissolved by cold alcohol, whereas in freeze-drying, the ice is removed by evaporation at low temperatures in a vacuum. The mode of paraffin infiltration also differs between the two procedures. In freeze-substitution, the alcohol is replaced with toluene, and the tissue is paraffin infil-

100

trated by methods similar to those used with chemically fixed and dehydrated tissue. In freeze-drying, the tissue is paraffin-infiltrated under vacuum.

The condition of freeze-substituted and freeze-dried material is not identical. The effect of these procedures on the state of the tissue will be discussed more fully later, but a general statement can be made here. In both methods the proteins remain in a relatively native state. Some enzymes survive both procedures; however, more of them are active after freeze-drying than after freeze-substitution. Water soluble materials are present in both freeze-dried and freeze-substituted tissue, although they are probably less distorted in freeze-dried material. The major difference in tissue prepared by the two methods is the loss, in freeze-substituted tissue, of substances soluble in alcohol and other organic solvents. These materials, which include the lipids and the pigments, are for the most part absent in freeze-substituted tissue, whereas they are present in freeze-dried tissue. An example of the difference between freeze-substituted and freeze-dried tissue can be seen in Fig. 5-1; sections of two onion roots, one prepared by freeze-drying and the other by freeze-substitution, are shown under phase and fluorescence microscopy. The loss of fluorescent materials from the freeze-substituted tissue, but not from the freeze-dried tissue, is apparent.

Thus, freeze-dried tissue more closely resembles fresh material than does either freeze-substituted or chemically fixed and dehydrated tissue. Freeze-substituted tissue, however, is considerably less altered than chemically fixed and dehydrated tissue, and since the procedure of freeze-substitution requires considerably less equipment and skill than does freeze-drying, freeze-substituted tissue is recommended for many histochemical methods.

In this chapter, the problem of freezing the tissue, common to both methods, will be discussed first. This will be followed by a discussion of freeze-substitution and of freeze-drying.

Freezing

The initial step in both freeze-substitution and freeze-drying consists of the rapid cooling of the tissue. The object of this step, which is of critical importance to both methods, is to freeze the water in the tissue and produce ice crystals below the resolution of the light microscope (Bell, 1952). This is accomplished by freezing small pieces of tissue at a temperature approximating that of liquid nitrogen. This step is of

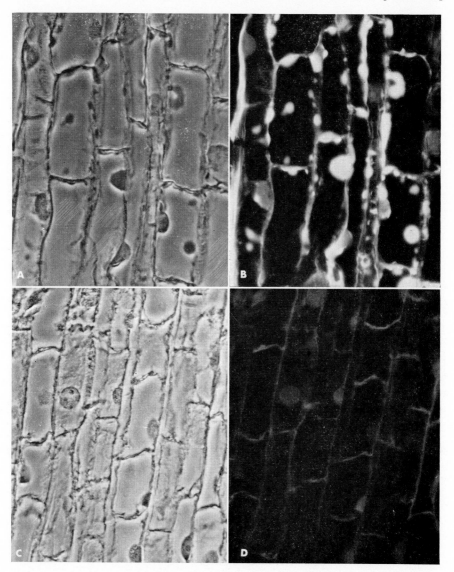

Figure 5-1. *A comparison of freeze-dried (A and B) and freeze-substituted (C and D) tissue. In each example the same tissue has been photographed with phase (A and C) and in the ultraviolet (B and D). From such comparisons it is clear that material present in freeze-dried tissue is removed from freeze-substituted tissue.*

great importance, because if large ice crystals are formed, a number of artifacts may be produced which may ruin the tissue. One of these ice crystal artifacts is shown in Fig. 5-2; the megaspore mother cell in the center of the photograph froze slowly enough such that fairly large ice crystals formed, compressing the cytoplasm and nuclear material between them. This deformation of the cell persists even after the ice is removed, giving the cell a striated appearance. Ice artifacts may be much more severe than the one illustrated and may completely disrupt thin walled cells.

To obtain small ice crystals the tissue should be frozen as rapidly as possible. The size of the tissue and the nature of the cooling bath are both important factors in rapid freezing. For good preparations the pieces of tissue must be as small as possible, preferably no thicker than 1 to 2 mm. Such pieces will freeze more rapidly and uniformly than larger ones. They will also show fewer tears, since tearing is the result of stresses produced by unequal contraction of various parts of the tissue during cooling.

The cooling bath, usually an organic solvent having a low freezing point and a high heat capacity, is cooled with liquid nitrogen. The two most commonly used compounds are isopentane (2-methyl-butane) and propane. These have freezing points of $-165\,°C$ and $-185\,°C$ respectively, whereas the temperature of the liquid nitrogen is $-195\,°C$. Since the object is to cool the tissue as rapidly as possible, why is the tissue not placed directly in liquid nitrogen? The nature of liquid nitrogen provides the answer. When tissue is placed in liquid nitrogen, the latent heat in the tissue is sufficient to cause the formation of an envelope of gaseous nitrogen around the tissue. This envelope greatly decreases the rate of

Figure 5-2. *An example of ice crystal artifacts in a section of a freeze-dried megaspore mother cell of* Lilium. *The arrow points to the striations caused by the formation of ice crystals.*

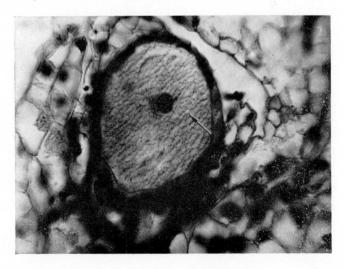

heat loss and increases the size of the ice crystals formed. Fernandez-Morán (1960) has circumvented this difficulty by using helium II at 1–2°K. Liquid helium II has super heat conductivity, and this feature, combined with its low temperature, results in the very rapid freezing of tissue. Because only extremely small pieces of tissue can be used, and because the method is both difficult and expensive, it would appear that this elegant method has limited importance in general histochemistry. Until the availability of liquid helium becomes greater, its price less, and the equipment necessary for its use common, isopentane or propane, cooled with liquid nitrogen, will remain the principal cooling baths used in freeze-substitution and freeze-drying.

Both isopentane and propane are widely used for freezing. Isopentane has been in use longer and is probably the more widely used. It has the advantage of being a liquid at room temperature and is not as inflammable as propane. Isopentane, however, freezes at a higher temperature than propane and becomes difficult to work with near its freezing point. The addition of methylcyclohexane to the mixture both depresses its freezing point (to −175°C) and alters its consistency at low temperatures, making it easier to use. Propane offers the advantage of having a lower freezing point and has better physical properties at low temperatures than pure isopentane. Since it is a gas, however, it must first be liquified before it can be used, thus requiring additional equipment and an added step. The highly inflammable nature of propane also requires added precautions and often results in trouble.

Isopentane and propane give similar end results in terms of tissue morphology when used with liquid nitrogen in freeze-substitution and freeze-drying, thus the choice between the two is a matter of personal preference. Isopentane with methylcyclohexane added is more easily used and is highly recommended.

When the isopentane or propane is cooled as near its freezing point as possible without complete solidification, the tissue is plunged beneath the surface of the liquid. This may be accomplished by throwing the tissue into the liquid or by attaching the tissue to a piece of gauze or very thin metal foil and plunging this into the mixture with forceps. Other methods are also possible. The all-important point is that the tissue must enter the freezing bath rapidly and must not be caught in the surface tension of the solution. Any pieces caught at the surface even momentarily should be discarded, because their rate of cooling will be drastically prolonged. In such material, pronounced ice crystal artifacts will be present.

The physiochemical aspects of the rapid freezing of tissue are complex and not clearly understood. Some practical features of the problem have been briefly presented here. For a discussion of the theoretical and experimental aspects of the problem see Rey (1960) and Stephenson (1960).

Another method for freezing tissue consists in using relatively warm temperatures (from −40 to −64°C), thus freezing the tissue more slowly. This method is suggested by Chayen *et al.* (1960a,b) and is based on the use of slow freezing methods to preserve the viability of sperm and other types of cells. In this procedure, closed vials are cooled overnight in dry ice, and pieces of tissue are frozen by pressing them against the side of the vial. This method of freezing has been used only in connection with sectioning the tissue in a cryostat (Chayen *et al.*, 1960b) and has not been used in either freeze-substitution or freeze-drying. The possibility exists that the method of freezing which gives the best results in terms of preservation of cell viability is not the best method for obtaining accurate localizations of compounds in cells. Until careful comparative studies are made of the different methods of freezing and of their effects on the morphology and chemistry of the cell, the rapid method freezing of material is recommended.

Freeze-substitution

Freeze-substitution was devised by Simpson in 1941, making it the newest of the major methods of tissue preparation. In this method the ice is removed from the tissue by dissolution in cold alcohol. The procedure is straightforward and requires little equipment, yet it was not widely used until recently and is still almost unknown to botanists.

In freeze-substitution the frozen tissue is placed in alcohol at −30°C or lower. The temperature is not as critical here as in freeze-drying, but it still must be considered. If the temperature rises much above −30°C, changes may occur in the crystals. They may fuse and increase in size, causing artifacts, or they may melt and give the tissue the appearance of a poorly chemically fixed preparation.

The basic principle involved in this technique for tissue dehydration is that the ice in the tissue is dissolved by the alcohol. The rate of dissolution and the amount of the ice dissolved are temperature dependent. This is because the determining factor is the establishment of an equilibrium in a diphase system consisting, on one side, of an alcohol-water mixture, which results from the dissolution of some of the ice, and on the other side, of the remaining ice. As the temperature is lowered, the equilibrium shifts, with the result that the alcohol-water phase contains

less and less water; consequently, a decreasing amount of the ice is dissolved in the alcohol.

Fortunately, if the tissue is placed in absolute alcohol between −30°
and −40°C, the equilibrium is such that the ice present in the tissue will
dissolve in 24–48 hours. A large volume of alcohol in relation to the
volume of the tissue must always be used, because this will clearly effect
the amount of ice dissolved. The usual procedure consists in placing
the frozen tissue in absolute ethyl or methyl alcohol and in keeping the
tissue and alcohol between −30° and −40°C for 24 hours. The alcohol,
which now contains most of the water from the tissue, is replaced with
fresh, cold absolute alcohol and is allowed to remain in contact with the
tissue for another 24 hours. Usually two, or at most three, alcohol
changes are necessary, although more can be made.

For paraffin infiltration, the alcohol is replaced by toluene, and the
tissue is then brought to room temperature. Paraffin infiltration, with
one change of paraffin, can be accomplished in 4–6 hours. When it has
been paraffin infiltrated, the tissue can be handled by the standard
procedures.

The question now arises as to when the tissue is fixed in freeze-substitution. The mere freezing of proteins and nucleoproteins does not
cause denaturation, nor is it caused by alcohol at low temperatures.
Toluene is not a protein precipitant, although it is a good lipid solvent
and does remove lipids from the tissue. The heat applied during infiltration may cause some denaturation, but this is probably minimal,
owing to the dehydrated state of the proteins. Therefore, the tissue in
paraffin sections probably contains relatively undenatured proteins and
nucleoproteins and probably has lost most of its readily soluble lipids,
as well as other substances soluble in organic solvents.

The fixation picture obtained in the final preparation is the one produced by the first chemical which comes in contact with the tissue and
is a fixative (Hancox, 1957). If Haupt's adhesive is used, and if the
sections are floated on formalin, the picture will be predominately determined by formalin. Thus, the results of freeze-substitution as evi-
denced by the final preparation will vary depending on the handling of
the dehydrated tissue. A procedure that has been recommended to
insure uniform results consists in floating the tissue on a slide with 95%
alcohol (Hancox, 1957).

The tissue may also be fixed with alcohol between the stages of dehydration and paraffin infiltration. Woods and Pollister (1955) obtained
excellent preservation of cytological detail by using warm 75% ethyl
alcohol or acidified alcohol at room temperature after the substitution

phase. Their work illustrates the fine preservation of cytological detail that can be achieved by freeze-substitution. Alcohol, which is a poor fixative of fresh tissue, appears to fix dehydrated tissue adequately. The effect of the alcohol on the chemistry of the cells, however, has not been fully investigated. Tissue fixed in this manner should be excellent for protein and nucleic acid studies, but probably is not suitable for all enzyme localizations. Zalokar (1960) found that after freeze-substitution, *Neurospora* hyphae no longer showed cytochrome oxidase and succinic dehydrogenase activity. On the other hand, acid and alkaline phosphatases were completely unaffected, and β-galactosidase was only partially inactivated.

An interesting approach to the problem of fixing freeze-substituted tissue has been supplied by Feder and Sidman (1958). They have shown that the addition of osmium tetroxide, mercuric chloride, or picric acid to the solvent used during the substitution phase results in the fixing of the cells even at −70°C. One of the problems in using osmium as a fixative when working with fresh tissue is its very poor penetration into the tissue. This difficulty is overcome when the osmium is used during the substitution phase. The removal of the ice is slow enough such that the penetration rate of the osmium is not a limiting factor. This procedure has been used only with animal tissue, but the potential of the technique is so great that it is included among the procedures given. There are some indications that certain enzymes may remain active after osmium fixation (Novikoff, 1959). Additional work on the effect of the fixatives used during dehydration is needed; particularly in the light of Bell's (1959) observation that in cells fixed during substitution with mercuric chloride, the mercury combined with cytoplasmic, but not nuclear, ribonucleic acid.

There is a great need for careful studies of the effect of freeze-substitution (with and without subsequent fixation) on the chemistry of cellular constituents.

Freeze-substitution, however, offers an excellent starting point for histochemical procedures. It is one of the easiest ways to preserve tissue, and will become increasingly important to the botanical histochemist.

Freeze-drying

The Incas are reported to have dried frozen potatoes on the slopes of mountains where cold drafts of air constantly moved over the potatoes. This appears to have been the earliest use of freeze-drying as a means of preserving biological material. As a scientific procedure, it was introduced by Altman in 1890, but received only sporadic use until 1932, when Gersh designed the first of the modern freeze-drying methods. Since then, a wide range of apparatus and approaches has been developed, making available to the investigator a considerable selection of procedures.

The freeze-drying technique provides a good example of the kind of difficulty which can be encountered when methods developed for animal tissue are applied to plant material. Goodspeed and Uber, in 1934, were the first to apply the technique to plant tissue. They found that the tissues took considerably longer to dry and that, when dry, they were extremely difficult to paraffin infiltrate. In the pieces which were infiltrated, the preparations were excellent (Goodspeed and Uber, 1934). Freeze-drying was not used again with plant tissue until 1954, when Jensen used an improved apparatus which decreased the drying time but did not markedly improve the paraffin infiltration of the tissue. For Goodspeed and Uber (1934) and for Jensen (1954a), the procedure followed gave good results when used with animal material. By modifying the basic approach to the drying of the tissue, Jensen (1954b) reduced the drying time further and somewhat improved the paraffin infiltration of the tissue. Satisfactory paraffin infiltration was obtained only after Branton realized that the characteristics of the cell wall changed during drying and that the method which gives the best results with animal tissue gives the poorest results with plant tissue (Branton and Jacobson, 1961; Jensen and Branton, 1962). These conditions will be fully discussed in this section. The basic point, however, is that the use of this valuable technique in botany was delayed because the unique properties of the plant cell were not fully appreciated.

In freeze-drying, the frozen tissue is dehydrated at $-30°C$, either in a high vacuum or in a partial vacuum, with a stream of moving gas. When the tissue is dry it is infiltrated with paraffin under vacuum. Thus, the tissue is ready for sectioning without being subjected to an organic solvent. The principal problem in freeze-drying is how to increase the rate of water loss from the ice phase in the tissue. Four main factors are involved: (1) the temperature, (2) the vacuum, (3) the water gradient, and (4) the nature of the tissue. The relation of temperature to evaporation is such that the lower the temperature, the slower will be the rate of water loss, but the temperature must be kept below $-30°C$ because of the possibility of the ice melting and of subsequent crystal growth. As the water molecules escape from the ice in the tissue, they enter an atmosphere composed of other water molecules and gas molecules. If there are a large number of such molecules present there is a reasonable possibility that the escaping water molecules will be reflected back to the ice and be recaptured. Dehydration under such conditions would be very slow. But if the gas molecules are removed by employing a vacuum, and if the water molecules are removed by using a desiccant, the rate of water loss should be increased. This is indeed the case, for the higher the vacuum, the longer will be the mean free path of an escaping water molecule and the smaller the possibility of recapture. Further, the more effective the desiccant, the fewer water molecules there will be available in the system for recapture. Hence, very high vacuum systems and extremely efficient desiccants are employed in freeze-drying apparatus. But the tissue must still be considered. Ice in the cells on the surface of a block of tissue may act as free ice; but ice in the interior of the block presents a different problem. From the interior the water molecules must pass through a surface shell of already dehydrated tissue before they are free of the tissue. In this passage there are numerous occasions for recapture, which will decrease the rate of water loss. Thus, the vacuum may be very high and the desiccant very efficient, but the drying rate may still be a function of the size and characteristics of the tissue.

Another important consideration with regard to the rate of drying of plant tissue is the effect of drying on the cellulose of the cell wall (Branton and Jacobson, 1961). The speed at which water can diffuse through cellulose decreases very rapidly with decreasing moisture content of the cellulose. Therefore, the most rapid rate of drying of plant material was obtained by the use of a stream of gas with a controlled moisture content. Certain effects of this controlled drying on other properties of the dried plant tissue will be discussed later.

Although there are numerous variations on the high vacuum freeze-drying apparatus, there are three main types (Fig. 5-3) which may be designated by the name of the principal designer: (1) the Gersh apparatus (Gersh, 1932; Gersh and Stephenson, 1954); (2) the Glick apparatus (Glick and Malstrom, 1952; Glick and Bloom, 1956); and (3) the Stowell apparatus (Stowell, 1951).

The Gersh apparatus (Fig. 5–3A) consists of a dehydration chamber (a) kept at $-30°C$ or below by a cooling bath or a refrigeration unit. A chemical desiccant, normally phosphorus pentoxide, is placed between the dehydration chamber and the vacuum pump. A mechanical vacuum pump is usually employed. The tissue, when dry, is removed from the dehydration chamber and placed in degassed, molten paraffin and placed under vacuum. There are a great many possible variations of this design (see Gersh and Stephenson, 1954).

Animal tissue will dry in a few days to a week, depending upon the

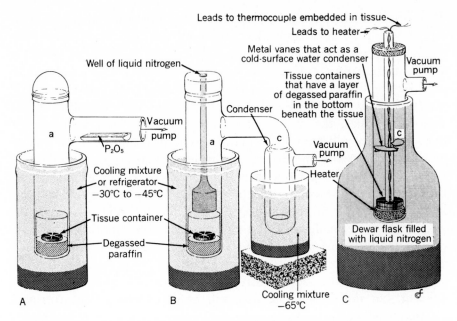

Figure 5-3. *High-vacuum freeze-drying systems. A. Gersh apparatus. B. Glick apparatus. C. Stowell apparatus.*

tissue and the size of the piece. Goodspeed and Uber (1934), only a year after the publication of Gersh's work, used such an apparatus on plant tissue. They found that most plant tissue took 1 to 3 weeks or more to dry.

The Glick apparatus (Fig. 5-3B) consists of a dehydration chamber (a) kept at −30°C. In place of a chemical desiccant a cold-finger condenser (c) cooled with liquid nitrogen is inserted. A well of liquid nitrogen may be introduced directly over the tissue. Glick also introduced an oil diffusion pump into the system to augment the mechanical vacuum pump. Degassed paraffin is placed in the bottom of the dehydration chamber. When the tissue is dry, the chamber is removed from the cooling bath and warmed until the paraffin melts. The tissue sinks into the paraffin and is infiltrated in the original vacuum. The proximity of the desiccant to the tissue in this apparatus tends to decrease the number of water molecules in the space around the tissue, and decreases the drying time.

This apparatus was used on plant tissue by Jensen, who found that, although animal tissue took several hours to 2 days to dry (Glick and Malstrom, 1952), plant tissue required 1 to 6 days to dry (Jensen,

1954a). Only leaves would dehydrate in 1 day, whereas most other kinds of tissue took 2 to 4 days.

The Stowell apparatus (Fig. 5-3C) introduced a new idea into the design, for here the cooling bath used in the dehydration chamber is liquid nitrogen. The liquid nitrogen keeps the tissue cold and also cools 3 metal vanes at c, which act as the desiccant and which are analogous to the liquid nitrogen well of the Glick apparatus. However, the temperature of the dehydration chamber approaches that of the liquid nitrogen and is far too low for the tissue. To correct this condition, a small electrical heater is placed below the tissue at b to keep the tissue between $-30°$ and $-40°C$. A layer of degassed paraffin can be placed between the tissue and the heater; thus, when the tissue is dry, the paraffin can be heated and melted, allowing paraffin infiltration.

No reports have been published on the use of this equipment with plant tissue. Animal tissue, however, drys only slightly better in this apparatus than in the Glick apparatus, and it would be expected that the drying times for plant tissue would be the same with this apparatus as with the Glick type.

In all the above designs, if only physical principles were to be considered, the highest vacuum and the best desiccant should always be employed. Work by Stephenson (1953), however, has reenforced the belief of many workers that the tissue is the major limiting factor. Although a good vacuum is necessary, there is little to be gained in using both an oil diffusion pump and a mechanical pump. Similarly, a water trap cooled with a mixture of dry ice and either acetone or methylcellosolve at $-65°C$ is almost as efficient as one cooled with liquid nitrogen at $-195°C$ and is easier to work with (Gustafson, 1954).

There are several commercial, high vacuum, freeze-drying apparatus available. One of the best, easiest to use, and cheapest is the Vitris Histological Freeze-Dryer (available from such supply houses as Aloe Scientific, St. Louis, Mo. and Arthur La Pine and Co., Chicago, Ill.). A more elaborate and expensive apparatus is the Leybold Freeze-Dryer (Arthur La Pine and Co., Chicago, Ill.).

A second approach to the drying of tissues at low temperatures consists in employing a partial vacuum and a stream of gas (Branton and Jacobson, 1961; Jensen, 1954b; Jensen and Kavaljian, 1956; Treffenberg, 1953). The design for such an apparatus is shown in Fig. 5-4. Here the tissue is held in small baskets having wire mesh tops and bottoms; the baskets are placed on a layer of paraffin in the bottom of the dehydration chamber. The gas is introduced by a tube connected to the outside

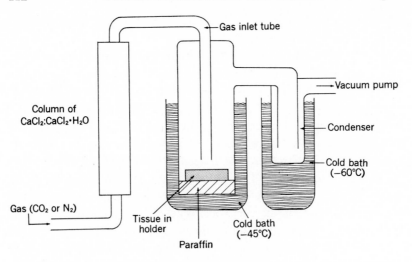

Figure 5-4. *Schematic diagram of the moving gas freeze-drying apparatus.*

through the top. It is not cooled before being admitted to the dehydration chamber because it was found that using uncooled gas increased the temperature in the dehydration chamber only a few degrees. A mechanical vacuum pump is used, and a partial pressure of approximately 1.5 cm of Hg is maintained by leaking gas into the system. The dehydration chamber is surrounded by a cold bath at −45°C. At the end of a run, the gas flow is stopped, the pressure is allowed to increase, the cold bath is removed, and a bath at 60°C is placed around the bottom of the dehydration chamber. The paraffin then melts, and the tissue is paraffin-infiltrated in a very short time.

With a moving gas apparatus having a relatively low vacuum, plant tissue can be dried in much shorter times than in the high vacuum machines. A comparison of drying times obtained by measurement of water loss is shown in Fig. 5-5 (Branton and Jacobson, 1961). The tissue dried in maximum vacuum took longest to dry. Tissue dried in a partial vacuum using a stream of very dry gas (10^{-3} μg H_2O/liter) took longer to dry than tissue dried in gas that contained more moisture (4.0 μg H_2O/liter). The moving gas appears not only to sweep the water molecules away from the surface of the tissue but also to maintain the cellulose in such a condition that water vapor will readily pass through the cell walls. It is apparent that the water content of the gas becomes a critical factor in the drying of plant tissues.

The moisture content of the gas is also important in the problem of paraffin infiltration of the freeze-dried tissue. Little difficulty is encountered in infiltrating animal tissue with paraffin at the end of the drying period. Great difficulty, however, is encountered when attempts are made to paraffin-infiltrate plant tissue that has been dried in a high vacuum or in dry gas. Plant material dried with moist gas, however, is easily infiltrated with paraffin. The poor paraffin infiltration obtained in the past was a major deterrent to the use of freeze-dried plant tissue. By controlling the moisture content of the drying gas, excellent paraffin infiltration can be obtained in every run. The explanation for the increased efficiency of paraffin penetration after drying in moist gas is probably again dependent on the nature of the dried cellulose of the wall.

The water content of the gas that is most effective in drying the tissue is between 2.6 and 4.0 μg H_2O/liter (Branton and Jacobson, 1961). The best method of obtaining gas of the desired water content is to pass the gas through a column of a mixture of $CaCl_2$ and $CaCl_2 \cdot H_2O$. Such a column acts to dehydrate gas that contains more than the desired amount of water and to hydrate gas that contains too little water. Various factors affect the operation of the column, such as the length of the column, the pressure of the gas in the column, and the capacity of the pump. Directions for the preparation of such a column are given later in this chapter.

The amount of water in the gas is so critical that careful determinations of the water content must be made in order to obtain adequate paraffin infiltration of the tissue. Procedures for such determinations are not difficult; one method is given in detail here. Differences in drying characteristics of various tissues can be expected, and some experimentation will probably be necessary to determine the optimal water content of the gas stream for more unusual materials. Various drying temperatures may require slightly different moisture contents.

Owing to the undenatured state of the proteins, the pres-

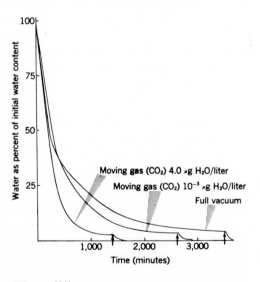

Figure 5-5
Effect of moving gas and of the moisture content of the gas on the drying time of barley roots. Arrows indicate time at which the cooling bath was replaced with water at 60°C. [Redrawn from Branton and Jacobson, Exp. Cell Research. 22, 1961.]

ence of lipids, and the retention of active compounds when in paraffin, freeze-dried tissue must be handled differently than tissues embedded in paraffin after preparation by other techniques. Dry tissue that has not been paraffin infiltrated appears life-like in form but has a slightly whitish cast. After infiltration the tissue regains its original color. If the paraffin block has been allowed to absorb water after embedding, or if the block is stored where it can accumulate moisture, particularly at room temperature, the tissue will turn brown, probably indicating the occurrence of oxidation reactions and enzyme activity. It is therefore desirable not to submerge the paraffin in water during embedding. The paraffin-embedded material should be wrapped in aluminum foil stored in a vacuum desiccator in a refrigerator.

The question of when fixation of the cell constituents occurs is as applicable to freeze-drying as it is to freeze-substitution. With freeze-dried material, the presence of lipid material is an added consideration. It would seem that with freeze-dried material, more than with freeze-substituted material, the possibility of fixing the tissue during the stretching procedure should be exploited. Very little work has been done on this particular problem. The method of handling the tissue after sectioning is of great importance. The difference in morphology of root cells that were freeze-dried under the same conditions but mounted differently on the microscope slide can be seen in Fig. 5-6. The section pressed on with a finger shows very excellent detail, whereas the section floated on with water shows great distortion.

Freeze-dried material, particularly if handled with some care, can yield remarkable preparations. Both mitochondria and chromosomes are excellently preserved and may be seen in great detail in the same cell. The unique advantage in using freeze-dried material is that precise data

Figure 5-6. *Effect of differences in mounting procedure on the morphology of freeze-dried plant tissue. The tissue in A was mounted on the slide with water. The tissue in B was pressed onto the slide with a finger. Barley root (900×).*

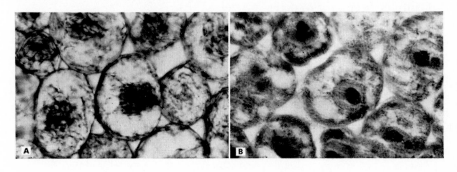

can be obtained from localization procedures for enzymes and other cell constituents. After the tissue has been sectioned it can be mounted on a slide coated with adhesive by pressing with the forefinger; the enzyme localization can then be made while the paraffin is still in the tissue. Only after the localization procedure is completed is the tissue subjected to an organic solvent. In the work of Uber and Goodspeed (1935), in which microincineration was used to localize various minerals, the only liquid in contact with the tissue was molten paraffin.

Until recently the difficulties in both drying and paraffin infiltrating plant material have been so great that the usefulness of freeze-drying in botanical histochemistry seemed limited. The successful resolution of these problems promises much greater application of freeze-drying in the future. However, systems of the moving gas type, in which gases of controlled moisture content are used, are clearly the most satisfactory for plant tissue and are highly recommended.

Procedures

1. Freezing

A. Cut the tissue into pieces 1 to 5 mm thick. Small pieces that are difficult to handle may be affixed by the cell sap at their cut ends to squares of cotton gauze or aluminum foil from cigarette wrappers. Cut leaves into small discs or squares.

B. Either liquid air or liquid nitrogen is usable, and should be stored in narrow-necked Dewar flasks. A cork stopper may be placed lightly in the neck opening but it *must* be loose to allow gas to escape. The isopentane (2-methyl-butane) to which is added 8% methylcyclohexane must be stored in a refrigerator and should be removed only when needed.

C. Fit a small beaker with a fairly long wire handle, and pour about $\frac{1}{2}$–1 in. of isopentane into it.

D. Pour liquid nitrogen into a small, wide-mouthed Dewar flask until the violent bubbling stops, and lower the beaker containing the isopentane into the liquid nitrogen. Stir the isopentane until it becomes fairly viscous, indicating that the temperature is between $-165°$ and $-175°C$. The arrangement shown in Fig. 5-7 facilitates raising and lowering the beaker of isopentane.

E. Lift the beaker just above the surface of the liquid nitrogen, and stir the isopentane for a moment to be certain that it is not about to solidify completely. The isopentane is now ready to be used for freezing the tissue.

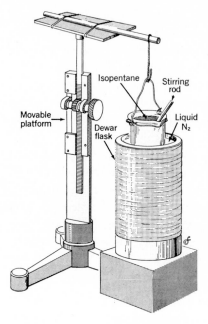

Figure 5-7
Apparatus used in freezing tissue for either freeze-substitution or freeze-drying.

F. The tissue must be plunged beneath the surface of the isopentane. The larger pieces can be thrown in forcibly. The smaller pieces attached to gauze can be submerged by gripping the edge of the gauze with a forceps and plunging both gauze and tissue. A few moments in the cold isopentane are sufficient.

G. Used isopentane can be placed in a bottle containing granular calcium chloride; do not pour it into the bottle of unused reagent. Liquid nitrogen can best be disposed of by pouring it on the floor; *never* pour it down a drain.

H. If propane is used in place of isopentane, construct a coil of copper tubing. Attach one end of the coil to a tank of propane by means of a rubber tube. Bend the other end of the tubing into a hook that will go over the edge of a small beaker. Submerge the beaker and coil in liquid nitrogen, and pass propane into the coil. The propane will condense in the coil and drip into the beaker. When an adequate amount of liquid propane is present in the bottom of the beaker, turn off the flow of gas into the condensing coil. The liquid propane must be further cooled before it is ready for use in freezing tissue. Perform all of these operations in a hood.

II. *Freeze-substitution: Dehydration* (JENSEN AND ASHTON, 1960; WOODS AND POLLISTER, 1955)

A. Prepare a cold chamber. This may consist of any arrangement that will maintain a temperature of $-30°C$ or lower. Several commercial brands of deep freezes can be adjusted to maintain temperatures of about $-35°C$. A large, wide-mouthed Dewar flask half filled with a methylcellosolve or an acetone-dry ice bath at approximately $-60°C$ may also be used. A more elaborate device is recommended by Woods and Pollister (1955). A large Dewar flask is filled $\frac{2}{3}$ full of powdered dry ice. A metal disc slightly smaller than the inside of the flask is placed on top of the dry ice. On top of the metal disc are placed one or more cardboard discs, and on top of these is placed a 400 ml beaker. Surrounding the beaker is a layer of insulation that fills the area between the beaker and the flask but does not prevent the beaker from sliding down into the flask as the dry ice evaporates. Next, 200 ml of 65% alcohol are poured into the beaker. This alcohol-water mixture will maintain a temperature between $-41°$ and $-45°$C as a partially frozen slush. The amount of freezing is controlled by the number of cardboard discs placed between the beaker and the metal disc above the dry ice. Vials containing the substitution solvent and the tissue are placed in the bath, and the beaker is covered with a tightly fitting cover of plastic sheeting. A thermometer is projected through the cover into a vial of absolute alcohol placed in the bath. According to Woods and Pollister (1955), a stable temperature can be maintained for as long as five days.

B. Place test tubes or vials half full of methyl or ethyl alcohol in the cold bath or deep freeze. Fit these with stoppers, and label them.

C. Allow 15 minutes to cool, and place the frozen tissue in the cold alcohol, taking care to use a cold pair of forceps in handling the material.

D. After 24 hours replace the alcohol with fresh, cold alcohol. After another 24 hours replace the alcohol with cold pure toluene.

E. Wait an hour, and remove the tubes from the cold. After another hour replace the toluene with fresh toluene at room temperature.

F. Wait 2 to 4 hours, and place the tissue and a covering layer of toluene on solid paraffin in the bottom of vials, and place the vials in an oven. Change the paraffin after 4–8 hours, and embed 2–4 hours later.

G. Longer times in the alcohol or lower temperatures may be necessary for larger pieces.

H. If fixation of the tissue after dehydration is desired the following two procedures are recommended by Woods and Pollister (1955): (1) replace the absolute alcohol with 75% ethyl alcohol, warm slowly to 60°C, and hold at that temperature for 1 hour; (2) replace the absolute alcohol with acidified 95% ethyl alcohol (100 ml of 95% ethyl alcohol plus 0.3 ml of glacial acetic acid), warm slowly to room temperature, and hold for 30 minutes. In both procedures, the tissue is then dehydrated in absolute alcohol and embedded in paraffin.

III. Freeze-substitution: Fixation During Dehydration
(FEDER AND SIDMAN, 1958, BELL, 1959)

A. Place the frozen tissue into any one of the following solutions that has been precooled to less than $-30°$C: 1% mercuric chloride in absolute ethyl alcohol; 1% picric acid in absolute ethyl alcohol; 1%

osmium tetroxide in acetone. The first two solutions can be made at room temperature and then cooled. The osmium solution must be made with acetone at −70°C. Great care should be taken when handling osmium tetroxide, and the work should be done in a hood.

B. Keep the tissue in these solutions for 3–7 days.

C. After this time transfer tissue that has been fixed in mercuric chloride or picric acid to the refrigerator, and wash it for 12 hours in three changes of absolute ethyl alcohol. Then place it in chloroform for 6–12 hours. Wash tissue fixed in osmium 2 or 3 times with acetone at the low temperatures, and transfer it to the refrigerator. Then follow the same procedure as for the other tissues.

D. After fixation bring the tissue to room temperature, transfer it to xylene, and embed it in paraffin.

E. This procedure has been used only on animal tissue. Osmium is recommended by Feder and Sidman (1958), but mercuric chloride and picric acid are also reported as excellent. Methyl alcohol has also been used with 1% mercuric chloride (Bell, 1959).

IV. Freeze-drying: Vacuum Method, Glick Apparatus
(GLICK AND MALSTROM, 1952, JENSEN, 1954a)

A. The apparatus recommended is a Glick type B apparatus, which consists of a dehydration chamber with a well (see Fig. 5-3B). The dehydration chamber is connected to a cold-finger condenser which is in turn connected to a vacuum pump. If both a mechanical pump and an oil or mercury diffusion pump are used, the diffusion pump is placed between the condenser and the mechanical pump. There are many possible ways in which this type of apparatus can be constructed. These points, however, should be kept in mind: the diameter of the tubing used should be as large as possible; and all joints should be of fine ground glass sealed with silicone grease, with as few joints as possible. Before each run, paraffin is placed in the bottom of the dehydration chamber and melted, and the system is sealed and evacuated. The paraffin will bubble until the trapped gas has been removed. When the bubbling stops, the paraffin is solidified with cold water. The paraffin is now considered degassed.

B. The tissue is handled and frozen as for freeze-substitution except that a wire basket is placed in the isopentane, cooled, and left in the isopentane. The tissue is then dropped into the basket.

C. Remove the basket containing the tissue from the isopentane, and quickly transfer it to the cooled dehydration chamber. The dehydration chamber may be cooled either in a refrigeration unit or in a methylcellosolve-dry ice mixture at $-30°$ to $-40°C$. Because this temperature is above the equilibrium temperature of the mixture, which is $-65°C$, it can be maintained only by adding pieces of dry ice at intervals.

D. Seal the system; place a methylcellosolve-dry ice bath at $-65°C$ or liquid nitrogen around the condenser (c) and in the center well; and start the mechanical pump. If an oil diffusion pump is used, allow the mechanical pump to run for a half hour before starting the diffusion pump. Be sure to have water flowing through the jacket of the oil diffusion pump before it is started. Keep both pumps operating for the entire period during which the tissue remains in the apparatus (1 to 6 days, depending on the tissue).

E. When dehydration is believed to be complete remove the cooling bath, and use warm water to melt the paraffin in the bottom of the dehydration chamber.

F. The tissue will sink in the paraffin and become infiltrated with a minimum of bubbling, although some bubbling inevitably occurs with plant material. Ideally, the tissue will sink in the paraffin when completely infiltrated. The tissue, however, will often fail to sink yet still be useful.

G. Stop the pumps, and open the system.

H. Remove the tissue, and embed it in blocks.

V. *Freeze-drying: Moving Gas Method* (JENSEN AND KAVALJIAN, 1956, BRANTON AND JACOBSON, 1961)

A. The moving-gas freeze-dry apparatus (Fig. 5-8) described here employs CO_2. The amount of moisture in the gas must be between 2.6 and 4.0 μg H_2O/liter at $-45°C$. This moisture content is maintained by passing the gas through a column of $CaCl_2$ and $CaCl_2.H_2O$. This mixture is prepared by placing anhydrous $CaCl_2$ (8 mesh) in a large vacuum desiccator around a beaker containing enough water to monohydrate 60% of the $CaCl_2$ The desiccator is connected to a vacuum pump, and the air is removed. The water will evaporate and combine with the $CaCl_2$. If a large enough column is used (3–4 in. $\times$ 2–5 ft), it will be good for many months of constant use. The rate at which the gas passes through the column is important in establishing the moisture content. If the rate is too rapid or the column too small, an equilibrium will not be reached during the time the gas is in the column. The amount of moisture that remains in the gas after it has passed through the particular column used must be determined when the apparatus is first assembled. Directions for making these determinations are given at the end of this section.

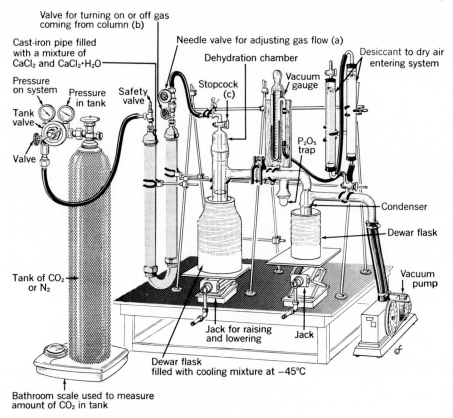

Figure 5-8. *Improved moving-gas freeze-drying apparatus.*

The moving-gas freeze-dry apparatus consists of a dehydration chamber surrounded by an alcohol (65% v/v)-dry ice bath. A dehydration chamber with a diameter of 2 in. is recommended under the conditions outlined here. A tube enters the top of the dehydration chamber and terminates about 1–2 in. above the top of a layer of degassed paraffin that is in a glass liner (Fig. 5-9). The inlet tube is connected to the column of $CaCl_2$ and $CaCl_2 \cdot H_2O$ by a piece of heavy-walled tubing. A needle valve (a, Fig. 5-8) regulates the flow of CO_2 completely when desired. A stopcock (c) is placed in the inlet tube at the top of the dehydration chamber and is used to seal the chamber during the paraffin infiltration stage.

The dehydration chamber is connected by a side arm to a cold finger condenser. This condenser is surrounded by a cooling mixture at $-65\,^{\circ}C$. A P_2O_5 trap may be inserted between the chamber and the condenser. Such a trap will remove most of the water from the system and is easier to clean than the condenser. A vacuum gauge is placed in the system, and a column of desiccant is connected to a stopcock which acts as a general air intake for the system. Almost any type of mechanical vacuum pump can be used. Tubing of large diameter should be used between the dehydration chamber and the pump. The tank of CO_2, which is equipped with a reduction valve, is placed on a small bathroom scale in order that the amount of CO_2 in the tank can be measured by its loss of weight, because the scale on the valve will not function until only a few pounds of pressure remain. A cold bath surrounding the dehydration chamber should be mounted on a laboratory jack or similar movable platform in order that it can be lowered after the drying period.

The tissue is held in containers made of fine wire mesh and fitted with covers. One design for tissue containers is illustrated in Fig. 5-10. Such containers are held in a metal rack which is placed with the containers into the isopentane freezing bath. Loose covers, held in place by a ring and a nut, are placed over the tops of the containers. A small funnel can be used to fill the containers. The tops, ring, and nut can all be handled easily in the freezing bath by using forceps. There are many ways in which the tissue can be held; this is but one type of container. The only precaution that must be taken is to make the containers of some porous material.

The cooling bath recommended for surrounding the dehydration chamber is an alcohol-water-dry ice mixture. This mixture, suggested by Branton and Jacobson (1961), maintains a remarkably steady temperature. The temperature that the bath will have depends on the amount of water present. A 65% alcohol-water (v/v) mixture will maintain a temperature of $-45\,°C$ in solid CO_2. Some care, however, must be used in preparing the mixture. Powdered dry ice should be added slowly until the mix-

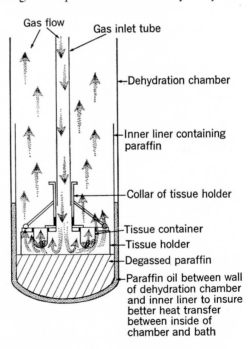

Gas flow

Gas inlet tube

Dehydration chamber

Inner liner containing paraffin

Collar of tissue holder

Tissue container

Tissue holder

Degassed paraffin

Paraffin oil between wall of dehydration chamber and inner liner to insure better heat transfer between inside of chamber and bath

Figure 5-9
Detail of the bottom of the dehydration chamber in the moving-gas freeze-drying apparatus.

Figure 5-10. *Construction of tissue containers used in the moving-gas freeze-drying apparatus.*

ture freezes into a slush; then small pieces of solid dry ice should be added. The dry ice should float in the mixture and not be allowed to settle to the bottom of the Dewar flask. The best baths take a day or more to prepare, but they can be kept for weeks by adding pieces of dry ice from time to time. Use as large a volume of the mixture as possible; the larger the volume, the more constant the temperature. Other cooling baths may be used, but this one is recommended.

Cover the cooling bath with an insulating material such as plastic foam or layers of paper, cloth, or aluminum foil. The better the cover, the more constant the temperature.

B. Place the rack holding the stainless steel tissue containers into the beaker of isopentane, and cool both the isopentane and containers by lowering the beaker into liquid nitrogen. Freeze the tissue by dropping it into the containers. Next, place the covers on the containers. Put the ring in position, and screw the collar down, holding the covers firmly. Transfer the rack to the bottom of the dehydration chamber.

C. Seal the top of the chamber, close the stopcock, and start the vacuum pump. Allow the vacuum pump to run a few minutes with the stopcock shut to achieve a fairly good vacuum. Then, open the stopcock, and adjust the pressure to 1.5 cm Hg by means of the needle valve. The pressure can be adjusted by using only the stopcock, but this is more difficult and far more tedious than by using the needle valve. Leave the needle valve in place from one run to the next; use the stopcock and coarse adjustment valve to open and shut the system. In this way, only minor adjustments will be necessary from one run to the next.

D. Most tissue will dry in less than 24 hours, but the usual practice is to allow the run to go 2 or 3 times longer than the drying time.

E. At the end of the run close the stopcock, and allow the pressure in the chamber to drop as far as possible. Then lower the cooling bath, and allow the tissue to warm. If the tissue is visible, it should appear life-like in form and whitish in color. If it appears either shrunken or brown, there is little point in continuing. Next, place a waterbath at 60°C, or a small electric heating mantle, around the dehydration chamber to melt the paraffin. Let the tissue containers and the tissue sink into the molten paraffin. Most tissue will be infiltrated rapidly, but leaves may require several hours.

F. Turn off the vacuum pump, and open the system. Remove the top of the dehydration chamber, and lift the cup containing the liquid paraffin and the tissue containers out of the chamber. The tissue should not be floating in the paraffin; if it is, paraffin infiltration is probably not complete. Finally, embed the tissue in paraffin, wrap the block in aluminum foil, and store in a vacuum desiccator in a refrigerator.

The apparatus described here is designed for routine use and is rather elaborate. A moving-gas freeze-dry apparatus can be very simple (Fig. 5-11). All that is essential is a column of $CaCl_2$, a side-arm test tube, and a Dewar flask. Rubber stoppers may replace the glass joints. Branton has used this type of apparatus effectively.

III. Determination of Water Content of Gas

A. Assemble the tank of gas and the $CaCl_2$ column as shown in Fig. 5-12.

B. Set the pressure on the tank valve between 25 and 40 lb, and adjust the rate of flow of gas from the $CaCl_2$ column to 1.5 liters/min by means of a needle valve. The flow rate is determined by water displacement from a 2-liter graduate cylinder filled with water and inverted in a container.

C. The gas coming from the $CaCl_2$ column is passed through a series

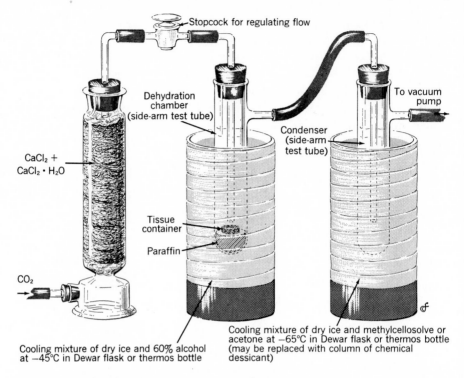

Figure 5-11. *Simplified moving-gas freeze-drying apparatus.*

of three or more **U**-tubes filled with a P_2O_5-glass wool mixture. The tubes must have stopcocks on each arm. To prepare the tubes (1) cut glass wool into fine pieces, and mix with P_2O_5; (2) insert this mixture into the tubes by means of a wide mouth funnel, taking care that no P_2O_5 touches the side-arm of the tubes; (3) wipe off the tubes with a damp cloth, dry with a slightly damp cloth, and weigh each tube carefully by suspending it from the balance. Note: Just before weighing, open one of the stopcocks for a second to equalize the pressures inside and outside the tube.

D. After a known amount of gas (100 liters) has passed through the tubes, they are again weighed.

E. The results are expressed as μg H_2O/liter and should be within 2.6–4.0 μg H_2O/liter. It is recommended that a range of pressure settings on the tank valve be tried because this pressure is a significant factor in determining the water content of the gas. The lower the pressure, the faster will be the passage of the gas through the $CaCl_2$ column and the less time there will be for establishing an equilibrium between the gas and the $CaCl_2$-$CaCl_2 \cdot H_2O$ mixture. The higher the pressure, the longer the gas will be in contact with the $CaCl_2$ mixture and the better will be the equilibrium. Thus, within a certain range of pressures (25–40 lb in our apparatus), the setting is directly related to the moisture content of the gas. However, the range of this relationship must be established for each assembly.

IV. Handling Freeze-dried Tissue

A. Do not immerse the paraffin block in water during embedding. Cool in a refrigerator.

B. Store the blocks, wrapped in aluminum foil, in a vacuum desiccator in a cold place.

C. If the tissue is to be used for enzyme work it should not be stored for more than several months before use, although this time period varies with the enzyme.

D. If the tissue is to be used in a histochemical localization procedure, the sections should be affixed to the slide as follows: place a section, or a small group of sections, on a clean slide or on a slide lightly coated with Haupt's adhesive; press the sections onto the slide with a firm

Figure 5-12. *Apparatus for moisture determination of gas used in freeze-drying apparatus.*

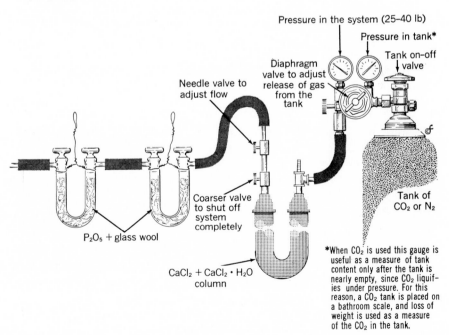

Pressure in the system (25–40 lb)

Pressure in tank*

Tank on–off valve

Diaphragm valve to adjust release of gas from the tank

Needle valve to adjust flow

Coarser valve to shut off system completely

Tank of CO_2 or N_2

P_2O_5 + glass wool

$CaCl_2$ + $CaCl_2 \cdot H_2O$ column

*When CO_2 is used this gauge is useful as a measure of tank content only after the tank is nearly empty, since CO_2 liquifies under pressure. For this reason, a CO_2 tank is placed on a bathroom scale, and loss of weight is used as a measure of the CO_2 in the tank.

rolling motion of the forefinger; place the slide on a slide warmer; and use no later than the next day.

LITERATURE CITED

Bell, L. G. E., 1952. The application of freezing and drying techniques in cytology, pp. 35–62. In *International Review of Cytology*. Vol. I. G. H. Bourne and J. F. Danielli (Editors). Academic, New York.

———, 1959. The combination of a portion of the cytoplasmic ribonucleic acid compounds with mercury. *Exptl. Cell Research*, 16:615–623.

Branton, D. and L. Jacobson, 1961. Freeze-drying of plant material. *Exptl. Cell Research* 22:559–568.

Chayen, J., G. J. Cunningham, P. B Gahan, and A. A. Silcox, 1960a. Life-like preservation of cytoplasmic detail in plant cells. *Nature*, 186:1068–1069.

———, 1960b. Newer methods in cytology. *Bull. Research Council of Israel*, 8D:273–284.

Feder, N. and R. L. Sidman, 1958. Methods and principles of fixation by freeze-substitution. *J. Biophys. Biochem. Cytol.*, 4:593–602.

Fernandez-Morán, H., 1960. Low temperature preparation techniques for electron microscopy of biological specimens based on rapid freezing with liquid Helium II. *Ann. N. Y. Acad. Sci.*, 85:689–713.

Gage, R. S. and S. Arnoff, 1960. Radioautography of tritiated photosynthate arising from HTO. *Plant Physiol.*, 35:65–68.

Gersh, I., 1932. The Altman technique for fixation by drying while freezing. *Anat. Record*, 53:309.

Gersh, I. and J. L. Stephenson, 1954. Freezing and drying of tissues for morphological and histochemical studies, pp. 329–385. In *Biological Applications of Freezing and Drying*. R. J. C. Harris (Editor). Academic, New York.

Glick, D. and D. Bloom, 1956. Studies in histochemistry. XXXIX. The performance of freeze-drying apparatus for the preparation of embedded tissue and an improved design. *Exptl. Cell Research*, 10:687–696.

Glick, D. and B. G. Malstrom, 1952. Studies in histochemistry XXIII. Simple and efficient freezing-drying apparatus for the preparation of embedded tissue. *Exptl. Cell Research*, 3:125–137.

Goodspeed, T. H. and F. M. Uber, 1934. Application of the Altman freezing-drying techniques to plant cytology. *Proc. Nat. Acad. Sci.* (US), 20:495–501.

Gustafson, B. E., 1954. Theoretical considerations on the freeze-drying of tissues. K. Fysiograf. Sällskapets Lund, Forhandl., 24:12–20.

Hancox, N. M., 1957. Experiments on the fundamental effects of freeze-substitution. *Exptl. Cell Research*, 13:263–275.

Jensen, W. A., 1954a. The application of freeze-dry methods to plant material. *Stain Technol.*, 29:143–150.

———, 1954b. A new approach to freezing-drying of tissue. *Exptl. Cell Research*, 7:572–574.

Jensen, W. A. and M. Ashton, 1960.

The composition of the developing primary wall in onion root tip cells. I. Quantitative analyses. *Plant Physiol.*, **35**:313–323.

Jensen, W. A. and D. Branton, 1962. Recent progress in freeze-drying plant tissues. *Proc. 1st Int. Congress of Histochemistry.* Pergammon. In Press.

Jensen, W. A. and L. G. Kavaljian, 1956. The cytochemical localization of ascorbic acid in root tip cells. *J. Biophys. and Biochem. Cytol.*, **2**: 87–92.

Novikoff, A. B., 1959. The intracellular localization of chemical constituents, pp. 69–168. In *Analytical Cytology.* 2nd ed. R. C. Mellors (Editor). Mc-Graw-Hill, Blakiston Division, New York.

Perkins, N. J., C. D. Nelson, and P. R. Gorham, 1959. A tissue autoradiographic study of the translocation of C^{14}-labelled sugars in the stems of young soybean plants. *Can. J. Botany*, **37**:871–877.

Rey, L. R., 1960. Thermal analysis of eutectics in freezing solutions. *Ann. N. Y. Acad. Sci.*, **85**:510–534.

Stephenson, J. L., 1953. Theory of the vacuum drying of frozen tissues. *Bull. Math. Biophys.*, **15**:411–429.

———, 1960. Ice crystal formation in biological materials during rapid freezing. *Ann. N. Y. Acad. Sci.*, **85**: 535–540.

Stowell, R. E., 1951. A modified freeze-drying apparatus for tissues. *Stain Technol.*, **26**:105–108.

Treffenberg, L., 1953. A method of freezing-drying of histological preparations. *Arkiv. Zool.*, **4**:295–296.

Uber, F. M. and T. H. Goodspeed, 1935. Microincineration studies. II. Localization of ash yielding substances during meiosis and its possible significance in X-irradiation phenomena. *Botan. Gaz.*, **97**:416–420.

Woods, P. S. and A. W. Pollister, 1955. An ice-solvent method of drying frozen tissue for plant cytology. *Stain Technol.*, **30**:123–131.

Woods, P. S. and J. H. Taylor, 1959. Studies of ribonucleic acid metabolism with tritium-labeled cytidine. *Laboratory Invest.*, **8**:309–318.

Zalokar, M., 1960. Cytochemistry of centrifuged hyphae of *Neurospora Exptl. Cell Research*, **19**:114–132.

CHAPTER 6

Fresh and Frozen Sectioning

Introduction

"I took a good clear piece of cork and with a pen-knife sharpen'd as keen as a razor, I cut a piece of it off. . . ." Thus, Robert Hooke, in 1665, described a method of tissue sectioning still widely used at the present time, namely the cutting of unfixed tissue with a knife or razor blade. This procedure and a series of others involving fresh, fixed, or frozen material are of great importance in both branches of histochemistry. These procedures are separated from those given in the preceding two chapters by the absence of dehydration and paraffin infiltration. For the solution of many histochemical problems, particularly determinations of enzyme activity, they are the procedures of choice.

These sectioning methods fall into two groups: (1) those which involve sectioning either fresh or fixed tissue with a razor or microtome at room temperature, and (2) those which involve sectioning either fresh or fixed tissue with a microtome after freezing.

Fresh Sectioning

Free-hand sectioning is a simple technique and requires only a sharp razor, or a specially sharpened knife, and a steady hand. For best results, a good straightedge razor made of steel which is not excessively brittle should be used. Single-edged razor blades, however, are equally acceptable for most work. In cutting fresh tissue, wedge-shaped sections frequently yield the best results. With practice, relatively thin sections $(15-20\,\mu)$ can be obtained from free-hand sectioning.

The importance of this simple technique to histochemistry, par-

128

ticularly microscopic histochemistry, should not be overlooked. Van Fleet (1954) has used fresh hand-cut sections in his enzyme studies. Similarly, a great deal of the microscopic histochemistry of lipids and cell wall materials is based on hand-cut fresh sections.

Free-hand sectioning is most successful with material that is firm but not hard. Some woody materials can be cut this way, but the sliding microtome offers a more sophisticated means of sectioning them. This machine, beloved by wood anatomists, has been little used in histochemistry. As the methods of both microscopic and quantitative histochemistry are applied to a wider range of plant material, woody tissues must be included in botanical histochemical research. For sectioning woody material, the sliding microtome offers distinct advantages in that it enables the investigator to secure uniform, relatively thin sections of tissue which has not been dehydrated or paraffin infiltrated.

In the sliding microtome the tissue is held stationary in a metal clamp. The blade is held in a holder which moves back and forth on a carefully machined horizontal surface. The microtome is usually constructed such that the tissue and clamp are raised a given amount each time the knife makes a complete cutting cycle.

With both free-hand sectioning and the sliding microtome, the tissue is generally cut without a supporting matrix unless some material such as pith is used for support. A number of procedures have been developed that use a surrounding matrix for fresh tissue. In none of these is the tissue infiltrated with the matrix material.

One procedure of this type was developed by Sunderland and Brown (1956) for sectioning fresh shoot apices to be used in quantitative histochemical determinations. In their work, clay was used to support the tissue firmly while it was sectioned by hand under a dissecting microscope. The principal difficulties found in this procedure are the irregularity of the sections and the possibility of carrying clay into the determinations.

Another example of the use of such a matrix is found in the method developed by Jensen (1955) for the sectioning of roots. In this method the tissue is placed in a hole made in a solid paraffin block. The paraffin adjacent to the hole is carefully melted with a warm needle to hold the tissue in place. The tissue is then sectioned on a rotary microtome at room temperature. Fresh sections over 100 μ thick can be obtained easily. For material such as roots, the method is of considerable value.

Still another method employs carbowax (polyethylene glycol) as a matrix in conjunction with a freezing microtome. In other methods that utilize the freezing microtome, the cooling process (obtained by the expansion of CO_2) is used to freeze the tissue before it is sectioned. However, in this method the cooling is used only to solidify the carbo-wax surrounding the tissue. Thus, the tissue is sectioned without freezing. Good preservation of enzyme activity has been reported by the use of this procedure (McLane, 1951). The major difficulty experienced in using this method lies in the unreliability of section thicknesses obtained.

Frozen Sectioning

The cutting of frozen tissue is not as old a method as fresh sectioning; it was first proposed by Raspail in 1825 (Baker, 1950). The methods of cutting frozen tissue form a broad spectrum, with the freezing microtome at one end and the special refrigerated microtome at the other. Frozen sections have not been important in either plant histology or histochemistry. The successes obtained, however, by the use of frozen sections in animal histochemistry, particularly enzyme histochemistry, will force plant histochemists to examine more closely the recent developments made by animal workers in the sectioning of fresh frozen tissue.

The freezing microtome is the poorest means of sectioning plant tissue. The general principle on which the freezing microtome is designed is the cooling of the tissue holder, and sometimes the knife, by the expansion of compressed CO_2. The tissue is placed on the tissue holder with water or a mounting medium and is frozen with bursts of CO_2. The temperature of the tissue and its surrounding ice is only slightly below zero, and unless the blade is specially cooled, the tissue thaws during or shortly after cutting. In most freezing microtomes the tissue is held stationary, and the knife moves. The general principle is similar to that of the sliding microtome, although the movement of the knife is substantially different. Some modern freezing microtomes, designed for routine clinical pathological use, have refrigeration units which replace CO_2 as the means of cooling.

In general, sections of plant material obtained by use of the freezing microtome are not useful in plant cytology or histochemistry, although they may be helpful in some types of plant histology (Johansen, 1940). The slow freezing and rapid thawing result in the disruption of cell detail and in the loss or movement of various cell constituents. Thin sections are difficult to cut, and the older model freezing microtomes are notorious for the inaccuracy of section thickness. The freezing microtome is not recommended for general use in histochemical procedures, with the exception of cell wall studies, or when used with carbowax as described earlier (p. 129). An example of the successful use of the freezing microtome, however, is the work of Abbe (1946), who used it on a study of latex distribution in roots.

Most of the objections to the freezing microtome are overcome by cold microtome or cryostat procedures. These methods involve freezing the tissue as for freeze-drying or freeze-substitution and then sectioning the frozen tissue on a microtome held between $-5°$ and $-20°C$ in a cold box or refrigerator. Consequently, the tissue, microtome, blade, and surrounding air are at a low temperature, and the difficulties encountered with the freezing microtome are avoided.

The basic principle in the cold microtoming of frozen tissue is that only a small portion of the section thaws during cutting, and this immediately refreezes (Thornburg and Mengers, 1957). These conditions are met by keeping the tissue, the knife, and the surrounding air at temperatures considerably below zero. The knife in particular is frequently cooled to temperatures below that of the tissue by a special attachment containing dry ice (Pearse, 1960). The temperature of the tissue, determined largely by the temperature of the surrounding air, is adjusted such that flat, thin sections may be obtained. In general, animal tissue can be sectioned best between $-10°$ and $-20°C$.

The method was developed by Linderstrøm-Lang and Mogensen (1938) at the Carlsberg Laboratory, and except for a few scattered studies (Wanner and Leupold, 1947; Chayen, Cunningham, Gahan, and Silcox, 1960; Fried and Franklin, 1961), the method has not been used extensively with plant tissue. Investigators working with animal tissue, however, have shown considerably more interest in the procedure. They have advanced the design of the equipment such that sections can be cut thinner, more easily, more rapidly, and in greater comfort than in the original machine (Pearse, 1960).

The original cryostat of Linderstrøm-Lang and Mogensen (1938) consists of a specially constructed wooden box which holds a rotary microtome (Fig. 6-1). The box is equipped with a window and two hand holes,

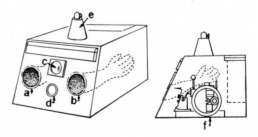

Figure 6-1
Cryostat. a, b. Openings with lambskin leather gloves attached. c. Observation window. d. Extra hole. e. Lamp. f. Microtome. [Redrawn from Linderstrøm-Lang and Mogensen, Compt. rend. trav. lab. Carlsberg, Sér. Chim. 23, 1938.]

as well as a container for dry ice and a means of adjusting the temperature. The tissue is frozen rapidly and sectioned without embedding at −10° to −20°C in the cryostat. Uusually the sections curl as they are cut. To prevent curling, a glass plate is fixed on the knife in order that the cut sections will slide between the blade and the glass and remain flat. Although perfectly acceptable sections can be cut with this apparatus, it is not easy to use. Heavy gloves must be used, and the microtome must be continually cleaned and oiled.

A number of important modifications in the original Linderstrøm-Lang and Mogensen design were made by Coons, Leduc, and Kaplan (1951). They replaced the dry ice with a refrigeration unit and changed the arrangement used to prevent the sections from curling, making the microtome considerably easier to use. Gloves still must be used, however, and the rotary microtome must still be operated from within the box. Further changes were made by Pearse (1960), who uses a Cambridge rocker-type microtome in a refrigerated box. All microtome controls are external to the low temperature portion of the unit, making the operation of the microtome easier. Pearse also designed a new mechanism to prevent section curling and provided a stainless steel chute for the delivery of the sections and a means of cooling the knife below the temperature of the unit and the tissue. Additional changes were proposed by Chang, Russel, Moore, and Sinclair (1961); these were further improved by Chang, Russel, and Moore (1961). Their cryostat has an open top and employs a rotary microtome. The control of the microtome is external to the refrigerated unit. This feature, plus the open top, makes the use of the apparatus relatively simple. Chang and his associates also have abandoned the use of section anti-curling devices in favor of a camel's-hair brush.

All of the modifications listed above have increased the ease of operation of the original Linderstrøm-Lang and Mogensen apparatus. Commercial models of the three refrigerated units are available (Coons type, from Harris Refrigeration Co., Cambridge, Mass.; Pearse type, from National Instrument Laboratories, Inc., Washington, D.C.; Chang type, from International Equipment Co., Boston, Mass.) and appear to be a wise investment if the work contemplated involves fresh frozen tissue. So little work with plant tissue has been done on these machines that a specific recommendation as to type cannot be made.

There are also a number of intermediate types of apparatus between the freezing microtome and the cold microtome, such as those using a sliding microtome with specially cooled tissue holder and knife (Adamstone and Taylor, 1948) or a similarly equipped microtome in a modified refrigerator (Thornburg and Mengers, 1957).

Handling Frozen Sections

The use of a refrigerated or cold microtome involves freezing the tissue, affixing the tissue by freezing it to the tissue holder, and sectioning the frozen tissue in the cold. For plant tissue, it has been recommended that the tissue be frozen while it is surrounded by gelatin (Fried and Franklin, 1961). Chayen, Cunningham, Gahan, and Silcox (1960) recommend that plant tissue be frozen slowly after treatment with polyvinyl alcohol.

After the sections are cut they may be handled in many ways. The sections may be mounted either on slides or on cover slips, which may be either cold or warm. They may then be immersed in a fixative when thawed (Adamstone and Taylor, 1948; Fried and Franklin, 1961) or they may be thawed, dried, and then fixed (Pearse, 1960). Alternatively they may be simply thawed and dried (Pearse, 1960) or dried without thawing at −20°C in a vacuum desiccator (Chayen, Cunningham, Gahan, and Silcox, 1960).

The sections may be placed directly in a reaction mixture for either quantitative (Linderstrøm-Lang, 1952) or microscopic (Pearse, 1960) histochemistry. Freeze-drying of the frozen sections is frequently useful, particularly in quantitative histochemistry (Glick, Swigart, Nayyar, and Stecklein, 1955; Lowry, 1953); freeze-substitution of the frozen sections may also be performed (Chang and Hori, 1961).

Thus, fresh, frozen tissue sectioned on a refrigerated microtome can be used as the starting point for many procedures. However, so little work has been done with fresh, frozen plant material sectioned in this way that it is not possible to recommend a best procedure for handling the sectioned tissue. A great deal of work in using these techniques with plant tissue must be done. The work of Chayen, Cunningham, Gahan, and Silcox (1960) and Fried and Franklin (1961) is only the beginning. Comparative studies involving the various methods and a wide range of plant tissues are clearly needed.

Procedures

1. Use of the Sliding Microtome (JOHANSEN, 1940; RICHARDS, 1959)

A. The tissue may be either fresh or fixed. Many woody tissues section well after having been fixed for several days in 50% ethyl alcohol. The tissue must be rigid enough to be held firmly in the clamp on the microtome. Softer material can sometimes be cut if it is surrounded by pieces of pith.

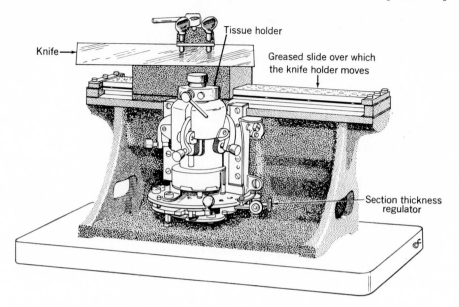

Figure 6-2. *Sliding microtome.*

B. Place the blade in the microtome (Fig. 6-2). The blade and holder should slide back and forth smoothly and easily on the greased horizontal track. The blade passes at an oblique angle to the tissue, which is held vertically in the tissue holder. The angle of the blade in relation to the tissue should be such that a large section of the cutting surface of the blade is used as the knife passes through the tissue. This is done to facilitate the sectioning of hard materials, to keep the wear on the blade even, and to keep the blade as sharp as possible. The cutting angle of the blade is generally slightly more than that used with the rotary microtome.

C. Using a camel's-hair brush, moisten the surface of the tissue with water, with the fixative used, or with a glycerine solution.

D. As the knife cuts through the tissue, hold the brush lightly over the top of the tissue and the section, to help prevent the section from curling.

E. With the camel's-hair brush, remove the section from the blade, and place it in a small dish of water or fixative.

F. The thickness of the section is determined by how far the material is moved up. This movement is automatic on the newer sliding microtomes, hence it is only necessary to set the marked gauge to the desired thickness. Some older microtomes are semiautomatic. On these the operator sets the distance and then pulls a small handle to raise the tissue by this amount. On the oldest microtomes, the distance the material moves is determined merely by turning the screw that supports the tissue. A wheel that is calibrated to indicate microns of vertical movement is usually attached to the base of the screw, thereby providing a measure of movement and, consequently, section thickness.

G. The best sliding microtomes are precise instruments which yield uniform sections. The sections obtained are usually fairly thick (more than 20 μ), owing primarily to the nature of the material. Serial sections are difficult to obtain on a sliding microtome.

II. Paraffin Embedding of Fresh Tissue (JENSEN, 1955)

A. Firmly attach a block of paraffin to a standard tissue block used with the rotary microtome (Fig. 6-3).

B. Using a warm needle, make a hole in the block about twice the diameter of the tissue.

C. If the tissue is white or near white, make a very small mark with India ink on its extreme apex.

D. Place the tissue in the hole such that the apex is up, and carefully melt the paraffin to make it flow around the tissue. Use a warm needle for this, but take care that the paraffin is not too warm when it comes in contact with the tissue. It is important that there be no air bubbles between the paraffin and the tissue.

E. After the paraffin has solidified completely, section the tissue on a rotary microtome. The nature of the tissue will determine the thickness at which sections can be cut. Usually, sections can be cut no thinner than 100 μ.

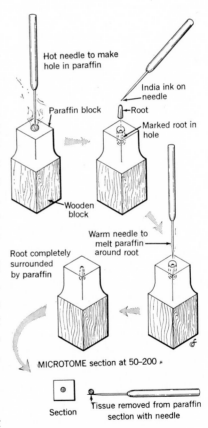

Figure 6-3
Paraffin embedding method of preparing fresh section.

III. Clay Support (SUNDERLAND AND BROWN, 1956)

A. Place a small mound of moist clay on a microscope slide, and gently press the tissue into it until it is half surrounded.

B. Cut the tissue under a dissecting microscope into the necessary pieces. Use a knife made by affixing a razor-blade fragment to a wooden handle. The tissue is best cut by starting the cut in the clay and drawing the blade across the tissue.

IV. Carbowax Embedding on a Freezing Microtome (MCLANE, 1951)

A. Use the higher-molecular-weight polyethylene glycol (Carbowax 4000), which has a melting point of about 50°C. Melt a small amount of this material in a beaker on a hot plate, taking care that the temperature does not rise more than a few degrees above the melting point.

B. Pour enough carbowax onto the stage of a freezing microtome to coat roughly two-thirds of the surface (see Procedure V).

C. Place the material to be sectioned in the hardening wax, and arrange as desired. Add more wax to support and cover the material.

D. Allow the wax to harden. This may be hastened by using small bursts of CO_2, but the tissue must not be allowed to freeze.

E. Between cuts, brush the surface of the material with a moist brush. This prevents the flaking of the wax and greatly facilitates sectioning.

F. Wash the sections with water to remove any particles of wax clinging to them.

V. Use of the Freezing Microtome (RICHARDS, 1959)

A. The freezing portion of this microtome consists of a vertical tissue holder in the form of a chamber connected to a tank of compressed CO_2. A needle valve regulates the flow of gas to the chamber, the roof of which forms the platform on which the tissue is placed. Releasing the compressed gas cools the chamber and freezes the tissue resting on the top. The knife is moved across the tissue, which is held stationary. The mechanism for moving the knife is connected to the tissue holder in such a way that the tissue is moved up a predetermined amount each time the knife makes a complete cycle.

B. Place the tissue, either fresh or fixed, in a drop of water or gum sugar (100 ml of H_2O, 100 g of cane sugar, 35 g of gum acacia, and 0.1 g of thymol) on the tissue platform. Place additional water or gum sugar around the edge of the tissue, and freeze the tissue and the surrounding medium by emitting bursts of CO_2 into the chamber beneath the tissue platform. When the tissue and surrounding medium are frozen they are ready to be sectioned.

C. Cut the tissue by moving the knife across the tissue. If the tissue is frozen too hard, it will crumble or curl; if the tissue is not frozen hard enough, sections will not form. When sectioning is good, cut rapidly.

D. Use a camel's-hair brush to transfer the sections from the knife to a dish of water or sugar solution.

E. Plant tissue is not easily sectioned on a freezing microtome. The material frequently fragments during sectioning, even under the best conditions, and cytological detail is generally lost. For morphological studies and research on the cell wall, frozen sections can be useful.

VI. Use of the Cold Microtome

A. ROTARY MICROTOME IN CRYOSTAT COOLED WITH DRY ICE (LINDERSTRØM-LANG AND MOGENSEN, 1938)

1. Construct a wooden box, two layers in thickness, along the general lines of the box shown in Fig. 6-1. The box must be well made and large enough to hold a Minot type rotary microtome in the front half and a dry ice chamber in the rear. Construct a sloping front, and provide two openings that can be connected to lined gloves (a and b). Place a one-inch thick lucite or plexiglas window at c. To remove the sections, make a hole at d, and provide a suitable movable cover for the hole. Place a light over a window in the top of the chamber. Cover the dry ice chamber in the rear of the box with a well-insulated lid. To prevent the microtome from moving, fix two guide rails to the floor of the front compartment. To prevent the microtome from becoming frosted, place an electric heater, capable of holding the microtome at 5°C, between the rails. Use a small blower actuated by a thermo switch to maintain the temperature of the chamber at −20°C. Use only light oils to lubricate the microtome.

2. Place the microtome in the cryostat without the tissue holder, and allow at least 45 minutes for it to come to equilibrium with the chamber. Fit the blade of the microtome with a plate of glass to keep the sections from curling as they are cut. This plate is held at a distance of 50 μ from the knife by two strips of cellophane tape and is kept in place by a metal clamp. Construct the clamp such that the glass can be easily removed and the sections taken from the blade. Position the glass such that the sections slide under it as they are cut. A brush may also be used in place of the glass to keep the sections flat, but this requires more skill.

3. Freeze the tissue rapidly, using isopentane cooled by liquid nitrogen. Next, affix the frozen tissue to the tissue holder by freezing the end of it to the holder with water, moist filter paper, salt solutions, or a brei made from the same tissue. The important point is that the temperature

of the tissue should never be allowed to rise above −20°C. In general, it is preferable to work in a cold room during these manipulations.

4. After the tissue has reached the temperature of the cryostat, it can be sectioned. Discard the first one or two sections, and maintain an even cutting speed to obtain uniform sections.

5. After removing the microtome from the chamber, either place it in a large desiccator with sulfuric acid or wrap it in plastic until it has reached room temperature. If this is not done the excessive condensation that will form on the microtome will cause rusting.

6. Unfortunately, heavy gloves must be worn when using the microtome in the cryostat, which increases the difficulty in using the apparatus.

7. This apparatus has been described because it may be easily constructed from readily available materials. For routine work, however, the commercial refrigerated models would probably be superior.

B. COMMERCIAL REFRIGERATED COLD MICROTOMES

1. As noted earlier (page 132) three commercial models are available. Each appears to have advantages and disadvantages, but since none of them has been used extensively with plant tissue, no specific recommendation can be made at the present time.

2. In general the techniques used in operating the commercial models are similar to those listed above, although two of the microtomes have controls which are external to the refrigerated unit.

3. Regardless of which apparatus is used, the handling of frozen sections is identical.

VII. Preparation of Plant Tissue for Sectioning on a Cold Microtome (Alternate Methods to the Quick Freezing of Plant Tissue Described in Procedure VI A, Step 3)

A. FREEZING IN GELATIN (FRIED AND FRANKLIN, 1961)

1. Place the tissue in water held between 0° and 5°C for 1 minute.
2. Make a paper embedding boat, and chill it by placing it on dry ice.
3. Spoon into the embedding boat a gelatin mixture made as follows: mix 50 ml of melted 10% gelatin mounting medium (Harelco), 7 ml of glycerine-jelly mounting medium (Brandt), and 50 ml of water.
4. Push the tissue into this mixture, orient the tissue, and freeze it by placing boat and tissue in isopentane cooled with liquid nitrogen for at least 1 minute.

5. Bring the tissue to the temperature of the cold microtome, and section it.

B. FREEZING AFTER POLYVINYL ALCOHOL TREATMENT
(CHAYEN, CUNNINGHAM, GAHAN, AND SILCOX, 1960)

1. Place the tissue for 2 hours in a 5% aqueous solution of polyvinyl alcohol.

2. Freeze the tissue by placing it in vials (2 × 1 in.) which have been left standing, capped, overnight in dry ice. Freeze the tissue for about 5 to 10 seconds between −40° and −70°C.

3. Frozen tissue may either be stored at −40°C or be sectioned between −20° and −25°C.

VIII. Handling Frozen Sections

A. FIXATION OF FROZEN SECTIONS (ADAMSTONE AND TAYLOR, 1948; FRIED AND FRANKLIN, 1961; PEARSE, 1960)

1. Mount the sections on a slide or cover slip either by using a brush or by gently pressing the sections on to a slide or cover slip while the sections are still adhering to the blade (Pearse, 1960).

2. Then place the mounted sections in one of the standard fixatives (formalin is recommended), and allow them to thaw (Adamstone and Taylor, 1948).

3. Alternatively, the mounted sections may be thawed, dried, and then fixed with a standard fixative (Pearse, 1960).

4. Another alternative is to float the tissue on the slide with 4% formalin and then allow them to dry at room temperature (Fried and Franklin, 1961).

B. FREEZE-DRYING OF FROZEN SECTIONS (CHAYEN, CUNNINGHAM, GAHAN, AND SILCOX, 1960)

1. Mount the frozen sections on slides.

2. Place the mounted sections in a vacuum desiccator containing phosphorus pentoxide below −20°C. Drying should take less than 24 hours.

C. FREEZE-SUBSTITUTION OF FROZEN SECTIONS (CHANG AND HORI, 1961)

1. Place unmounted sections in vials of absolute acetone embedded in dry ice.

2. After 24 hours replace with fresh absolute acetone, and mount the sections on slides or cover slips.

3. Air-dry the sections. The preparation is now ready for use.

LITERATURE CITED

Abbe, L. B., 1946. A rapid histological technic for staining latex in roots of *Taraxacum kok-saghyz*. *Stain Technol.*, **21**:19–22.

Adamstone, F. B. and A. B. Taylor, 1948. The rapid preparation of frozen tissue sections. *Stain Technol.*, **23**: 109–116.

Baker, J. R., 1950. *Cytological Technique*. 3rd ed. Meuthen, London.

Chang, J. P. and S. H. Hori, 1961. The section freeze-substitution technique. I. Method. *J. Histochem. and Cytochem.*, **9**:292–300.

Chang, J. P., W. O. Russel, and E. B. Moore, 1961. An improved open-top cryostat. *J. Histochem. and Cytochem.*, **9**:208.

Chang, J. P., W. O. Russel, E. B. Moore, and W. K. Sinclair, 1961. A new cryostat for frozen section technic. *Am. J. Clin. Pathol.*, **35**:14–19.

Chayen, J., G. J. Cunningham, P. B. Gahan, and A. A. Silcox, 1960. Life-like preservation of cytoplasmic detail in plant cells. *Nature*, **186**:1068–1069.

Coons, A. H., E. H. Leduc, and M. H. Kaplan, 1951. Localization of antigen in tissue cells. VI. The fate of injected foreign proteins in the mouse. *J. Exptl. Med.*, **93**:173–188.

Fried, M. and A. H. Franklin, 1961. Rapid preparation of fresh frozen sections of barley roots. *Nature*, **189**: 414–415.

Glick, D., R. Swigart, S. T. Nayyar, and H. Stecklein, 1955. Studies in Histochemistry. XXXII. Flame photometric determination of potassium in microgram quantities of tissue and the distribution of potassium and lipid in the adrenal of the monkey and guinea pig. *J. Histochem. and Cytochem.*, **3**:6–15.

Jensen, W. A., 1955. A morphological and biochemical analysis of the early phases of cellular growth in the root tip of *Vicia faba*. *Exptl. Cell Research*, **8**:506–522.

Johansen, D. A., 1940. *Plant Microtechnique*. McGraw-Hill, New York.

Linderstrøm-Lang, K., 1952. *Micromethods in Biological Research*. Lane Medical Lecture. Stanford Univ. Press, Stanford.

Linderstrøm-Lang, K. and K. R. Mogensen, 1938. Studies on enzymatic histochemistry. XXXI. Histological control of histochemical investigations. *Compt. rend. trav. lab. Carlsberg Sér. Chim.*, **23**:27–35.

Lowry, O. H., 1953. The quantitative histochemistry of the brain—Histological sampling. *J. Histochem. and Cytochem.*, **1**:420–428.

McLane, S. R., 1951. Higher polyethylene glycols as water soluble matrix for sectioning fresh or fixed plant tissue. *Stain Technol.*, **26**:63–64.

Pearse, A. G. E., 1960. *Histochemistry, Theoretical and Applied*. 2nd ed. Little, Brown, Boston.

Richards, O. W., 1959. *The Effective Use and Proper Care of the Microtome*. American Optical Co., Buffalo.

Sunderland, N. and R. Brown, 1956. Distribution of growth in the apical region of the shoot of *Lupinus albus*. *J. Exptl. Botany*, **7**:127–145.

Thornburg, W. and P. E. Mengers,

1957. An analysis of frozen section techniques. I. Staining of fresh-frozen tissue. *J. Histochem. and Cytochem.*, **5**:47–52.

Van Fleet, D. S., 1954. Cell and tissue differentiation in relation to growth (plants). In *Dynamics of Growth Processes*. E. J. Boell (Editor). Princeton Univ. Press, Princeton.

Wanner, H. and U. Leupold, 1947. Über die longitudinale Verteilung der Saccharaseaktivität in der Wurzelspitze. *Berichte Schweizerischen Botan. Ges.*, **57**:156–163.

PART III

Tissue and Cell Analysis

CHAPTER 7

Tissue Sampling and Analysis for Quantitative Histochemistry

Introduction

Barley is an important component in the production of beer, thus it is not surprising that men associated with a brewery, however indirectly, should be interested in barley seeds and roots. This explains in part the early interest in the histochemistry of barley seeds and roots shown by Linderstrøm-Lang, Holter, and their associates at the Carlsberg Laboratory, Copenhagen, Denmark (Linderstrøm-Lang, 1952)—a laboratory founded on the profits of the Carlsberg brewery.

One of the first pieces of work in modern quantitative histochemistry was the investigation by Linderstrøm-Lang and Engel (1938) of amylase activity in the tissues of barley seeds. The seeds were first soaked and frozen; then a 2-mm cylinder of tissue was punched from the seed. Next, with the aid of a cold microtome, $25\text{-}\mu$ sections were cut parallel to the surface of the seed. The sections were photographed, and the areas of aleurone cells and endosperm cells were measured with a planimeter. Extracts of the sections were obtained, and determinations of amylase content (total and active) were made. The results of these determinations were expressed in milligrams of maltose per cubic millimeter of tissue per hour. The method of sampling and the results of the analyses are shown in Fig. 7-1. The graph indicates not only the amylase concentration but also the percent of aleuron cells per section. From

145

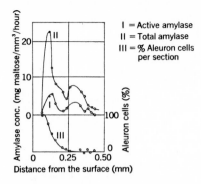

I = Active amylase
II = Total amylase
III = % Aleuron cells
      per section

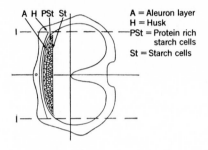

A = Aleuron layer
H = Husk
PSt = Protein rich
       starch cells
St = Starch cells

Figure 7-1
Correlation of amylase activity with cell type in barley seed.

their analyses Linderstrøm-Lang and Engel (1938) concluded that a high content of amylase could be ascribed to the protein-rich starch cells.

This work is an example of the type of approach made famous by the Carlsberg group—an approach that is still widely employed in quantitative histochemistry. Serial sections form the basis of the sampling procedure. A single section may be used for both the morphological and the histochemical analysis. In other determinations one section may be used for the morphological analysis and the next for the histochemical analysis (Fig. 7-2). This method, known as the alternate-section procedure, has been used more frequently with animal than with plant material (Linderstrøm-Lang, 1952). An example in which this method was employed to study plant material is found in another piece of early quantitative histochemical work from the Carlsberg group. In this study barley roots were used (Linderstrøm-Lang and Holter, 1932; Bottelier, Holter, and Linderstrøm-Lang, 1943). Living roots were embedded in low-melting-point paraffin and were cut into 100-μ sections. Alternate sections were analyzed for dipeptidase activity and for reduced weight or total nitrogen. The results were expressed as dipeptidase per reduced weight, dipeptidase per total nitrogen, and total nitrogen per reduced weight and were plotted against the distance from the tip of the section analyzed. All curves showed a peak at about 0.5 mm from the tip. Further morphological analysis of the roots indicated that (1) these peaks corresponded to the region in which the root cells contained dense cytoplasm; and (2) that the decrease in dipeptidase activity was correlated with cell elongation and vacuolization.

The data for both seeds and roots were expressed in terms of the sections used and were correlated with the cellular composition of the tissue. Frequently, however, it is desirable to express the data directly in terms of the cell, placing the data on a per cell basis. For example, with respect to the root analyses by Bottelier, Holter, and Linderstrøm-Lang

(1943) the question arises as to the reality of the decrease in dipeptidase activity per cell, particularly where the cells are undergoing rapid elongation. As the cells become longer, fewer are contained in a 100-μ section, hence the drop which is found when the data are expressed per section may not be found if the data are expressed per cell. To facilitate the solution of this type of problem, as well as others of a similar nature, various methods have been developed to determine the number of cells per section.

The most commonly used and easiest of these methods is that developed by Brown and Rickless (1949) for histochemical work on roots. In this procedure (given later in this chapter) the cells are separated by maceration of the tissue with chromic acid or pectinase. The cells are shaken into a suspension; a sample is pipetted onto the grid of a haemocytometer; and the sample is counted. The number of cells in the original tissue is then calculated. This method yields accurate cell numbers in a short time without a great amount of work. It is particularly useful on irregularly shaped organs or tissue masses such as plant embryos (Pollock and Olney, 1959; Olney and Pollock, 1960), with which other techniques are impossible to use. The average cell volume can be obtained

Figure 7-2. *Alternate sectioning method of Linderstrøm-Lang and Holter.*

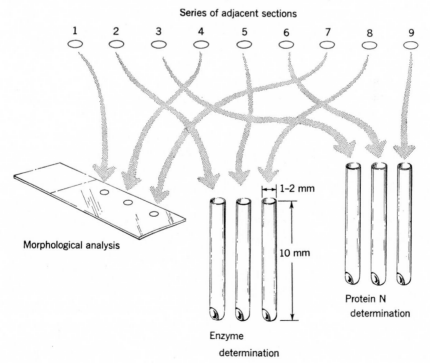

Series of adjacent sections

Morphological analysis

1–2 mm

10 mm

Enzyme determination

Protein N determination

by measuring the volume of the organ or tissue mass and determining the cell number (Brown and Broadbent, 1950). The principal difficulty with this procedure is that the organ or tissue mass must be treated as if it were uniform throughout. There is no way to determine the number of cells in the different types of tissues or cells present in the material. This may or may not be important, depending on the objective of the research. A second procedure, developed by Sunderland and Brown (1956), is useful primarily with leaves and with such tissue as shoot apices, which do not macerate satisfactorily. In this procedure the material is softened, stained, and carefully squashed. The cells are then counted under a microscope with the aid of an ocular grid.

When it is necessary to analyze the material in terms of cell types and tissues, maceration techniques are not adequate. To date, however, cellular analyses which permit the recognition of the heterogeneity of the material are possible only with organs showing great regularity and relative simplicity. Examples of this type of analysis are found in the work of Jensen (1955a) and Jensen and Kavaljian (1958) on root tips. A section 10 μ in thickness, which represents the midpoint of the segment of interest (100–200 μ in length) was selected from sectioned, stained roots. The section is drawn or photographed, and the area of the various tissues or tissue systems, such as the epidermis, cortex, and stele, is measured with a planimeter. Tissue volumes are obtained by multiplying the area of each tissue by the length of the segment of interest. The cross-sectional area per cell is found by counting the number of cells visible in a particular tissue and dividing this number into the tissue area. The cell length is then determined from longitudinal sections. To obtain the cell volume the cell cross-sectional area is multiplied by the cell length. The cell number per tissue is found by dividing the tissue volume by the cell volume. Similar procedures are followed for each tissue in a given segment; the total cell number per segment can be found by adding the cell numbers of the individual tissues.

Such an analysis requires considerable time and labor but yields a vast amount of data. The analysis can, of course, be made more elaborate, depending on the tissue and on the manner in which the material is divided into units for analysis. For some materials, such as coleoptiles, a slightly simpler analysis is possible (Avery and Engel, 1954).

The advantage of this type of analysis can be illustrated by the work of Jensen (1955b), in which peroxidase activity was induced in roots by treating them with indoleacetic acid. Peroxidase activity was determined in 200-μ segments of treated roots. The data were graphed by plotting activity per cell against distance from the tip of the section analyzed.

The curve obtained showed a general correlation with the development of the vascular tissue. Microscopic histochemical studies further indicated that peroxidase activity was extremely high in certain tissues of the root, namely the provascular, the protophloem, the protoxylem, and the epidermis. When the quantitative histochemical data were expressed in terms of the active cells, which was possible only because of the nature of the cellular analysis, the relation of the enzyme activity to the development of the various vascular tissues became much clearer. The application of a similar type of analysis to cell wall materials permitted conclusions to be drawn regarding the wall composition of the individual tissues (Jensen and Ashton, 1960; Jensen, 1960).

Although it permits the recognition of tissue heterogeneity, this method, as does the maceration method, presents an essentially static picture of cell growth. Methods have been developed by Erickson and co-workers (Erickson and Goddard, 1951; Erickson and Sax, 1956a,b) and by Goodwin and Avers (1956) which allow for a consideration of the time element. In these methods the growth of the root is followed by recording the pattern of movement of marks on the root with time or by analyzing photographic records of the growth of the epidermal cells. The rate of extension and the cell number of separate root segments are determined. Root growth can then be mathematically analyzed in terms of cell division and cell elongation. This type of analysis permits calculation of the rate of increase of cellular materials and permits the observation of changes of rate in various parts of the root (Erickson and Goddard, 1951). The principal difficulty with this method lies in the necessity of treating each segment as if it were uniform. At present this method is being used more by physiologists than by histochemists, but it offers such important advantages that it should see greater use in the future.

Although cellular analyses and the expression of data on a per cell basis have been stressed in the discussion, the data from histochemical analyses can be expressed in a variety of ways. In their work on barley seeds Linderstrøm-Lang and Engel (1938) used tissue volume. The early enzyme work of Linderstrøm-Lang and Holter (1932) was expressed per section and in terms of protein nitrogen per section, whereas the later work (Bottelier, Holter, and Linderstrøm-Lang, 1943) was expressed in terms of reduced weight and total nitrogen per section. In his work on root tips, of *Vicia faba*, Jensen (1955a) also used reduced weight and protein nitrogen as a means of expressing the data. Brown used cell number, dry weight, protein nitrogen, and cell volume in the analysis of his data from root tips (Brown and Broadbent, 1950; Brown,

Reith, and Robinson, 1952). In their embryo work Pollock and Olney (1959) used dry weight, total nitrogen, and cell number to express the data they obtained. They felt that none of these was an adequate way in which to express the data but that the cell number was least objectionable. For his work on *Avena* coleoptiles, Avery used reduced weight, protein nitrogen, cell number, and cell volume in presenting the data obtained from the histochemical analysis of sections (Avery and Linderström-Lang, 1940; Avery and Engel, 1954).

Histochemical procedures frequently permit the utilization of biological systems for particular problems, systems which could not be used with conventional chemical methods. This point is illustrated beautifully by the work of Stern and his group on the biochemistry of cell division (Stern, 1958, 1960; Foster and Stern, 1959). They have based their work on the careful morphological study of anther development made by Erickson (1948), in which he was able to correlate the bud length of lily flowers with the stage of development of the microspores.

An example of the type of research possible with such a system is the work of Nasatir and Stern (1959) on changes in the activity of aldolase and D-glyceraldehyde-3-phosphate dehydrogenase during the mitotic cycle in the microspores. The microspores from four anthers were separated from the wall and adjacent tissues by cutting the anthers open and into pieces, stirring them with 0.5 M sucrose, and filtering out the wall and adjacent material. The resulting suspension of microspores was analyzed for aldolase and D-glyceraldehyde-3-phosphate dehydrogenase, and the results were expressed as shown in Fig. 7–3. From this graph it is clear that both enzymes show minimal activity during mitosis and that increased glycolytic capacity is not necessarily related to mitosis.

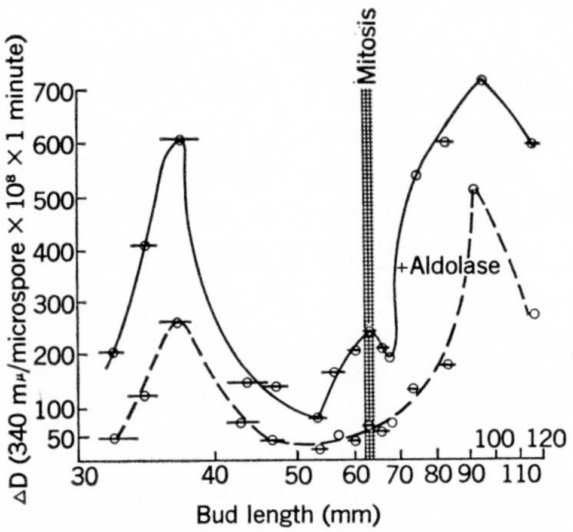

Figure 7-3

Variations in aldolase and d-glyceraldehyde phosphate dehydrogenase activities during microspore development. The dotted line represents the activity of the enzyme system catalyzing the reduction of DPN by hexose diphosphate. The solid line represents the activities measured in the presence of an excess of crystalline aldolase. [Redrawn from Nasatir and Stern, J. Biophys. Biochem. Cytol. 6, 1959.]

Another example of this type of research is the work of Hotta and Stern (1961) on the deamination of deoxycytidine and 5-methyldeoxy-cytidine to deoxyuridine and thymidine respectively. They used intact anthers with one end cut off, homogenates of whole anthers, and microspore suspensions. The microspore suspensions were obtained by cutting off both ends of the anthers and pushing out the microspores with a glass rod slightly smaller in diameter than the anther locule. In younger anthers the microspores and associated material came out as a paste-like cylinder. In older anthers it was necessary to scoop out the microspores with a 1- to 2-mm glass disk at the end of a fine glass rod. In both, 80–90% of the spores were removed without injury. Six anthers from one bud were sufficient for an experiment.

The data obtained from whole anthers, either intact or homogenized, indicated a positive correlation between mitosis and the production of deoxyuridine and thymidine through the deamination of their precursors. This appeared, however, to have little if any direct bearing on DNA synthesis in developing microspores. The problem of distinguishing the events which occur in any developing tissue is difficult, and is stressed by Hotta and Stern (1961) in their work on anthers; "Anther development, like all organ development, is a morphogenetic process in which non-sporogenous and sporogenous tissues are participants. Although there may be concurrence of cyclical metabolic patterns in the anther with the mitotic cycle in the microspores, one must nevertheless distinguish between supporting and morphogenetic metabolic processes. The former extend over a relatively broad interval of time and presumably support general growth requirements. The latter are brief in duration and are immediately associated with distinctive biosynthetic events occurring sequentially in the life history of a cell."

The key point to always keep in mind in tissue sampling and analysis for quantitative histochemistry is that histochemical methods permit the recognition of tissue diversity if the investigator will use them constructively and with imagination.

Procedures

1. Maceration-haemocytometer Method (BROWN AND BROADBENT, 1950)

A. Use either fresh or fixed tissue.

B. Place the tissue in a known volume of 5% chromic acid, and allow it to remain there until the cells have separated. Occasionally shake the tissue while in the chromic acid; when the tissue has begun to separate, force the cell aggregates through a pipette to facilitate separation (Fig. 7-4). The time required for satisfactory separation depends on the tissue, and may range from 4 to 24 hours. Usually, complete separation is not obtained, but enough separation is usually obtained to render the technique valid. Some tissues will not macerate but, instead, may dissolve.

C. Count the suspended cells in a haemocytometer with a Fuchs-Rosenthal grid and a 0.2 mm depth (volume 3.2 mm³). This type of haemocytometer gives more consistent results than the usual type, although the latter may be used. With either, it is important that enough counts be made.

D. The number of cells can be calculated by the usual method: average number of cells in unit volume of the haemocytometer × total volume of the sample = total number of cells.

E. A 5% pectinase solution at 37°C may be used in place of chromic acid. The tissue may be either fresh or formalin-fixed.

II. Maceration-squash Method (SUNDERLAND AND BROWN, 1956)

A. CELL NUMBER

1. Place the fresh tissue in a depression slide which is balanced on a watch glass in a Petri dish. Cover the bottom of the Petri dish with the same solution that is placed on the tissue to prevent excessive evaporation during the process.

2. Treat the tissue with a solution of 1 part acetic acid and 3 parts

Figure 7-4. *Maceration-haemocytometer method of cell-number determination.*

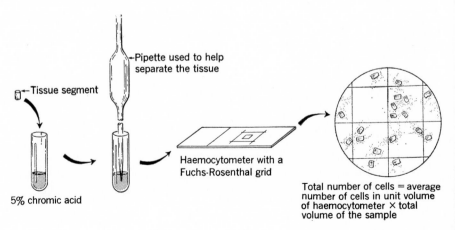

ethyl alcohol for 10 minutes, and then with 1 N HCl for 8 minutes at 60°C.

3. Replace the acid with 1% methyl green at a basic pH, which may be obtained by adding sodium bicarbonate. Leave the tissue in the stain overnight.

4. Place the tissue in a drop of 50% glycerol on the flat portion of the slide, and cover it with a plastic cover slip. While observing it under a dissecting microscope, flatten the cell mass by pressing on the cover slip with a rounded glass rod.

5. Count the cells under high dry magnification with the aid of an ocular grid.

(a) If the microscope has a mechanical stage, count the number of cells present in bands across the cell mass at specific intervals; determine the average number of cells per band; and then multiply this average by the number of bands constituting the cell mass. It is important that the cell mass be in as uniform a configuration as possible and that it be unicellular in depth.

(b) Count the number of cells in grids placed at random, and determine the average. Draw the outline of the cell mass with a camera lucida, and determine the total area. First, divide this area by the area of the grid, and then multiply it by the number of cells in the grid to obtain the total cell number.

B. TISSUE AND CELL VOLUME

1. Treat the tissue as above.

2. Place the tissue fragment in a drop of paraffin oil on a glass plate the same size as a microscope slide. Place a second glass plate on top of the first, and press it down. Use pieces of cellophane to adjust the distance between the two plates to about 25 μ. Clamp the plates at the ends.

3. Spread the cells and the expressed cell sap from the cells. The cell sap will remain closely associated with the flattened tissue.

4. Use a planimeter to determine the areas of the cell sap and of the tissue from a camera lucida drawing of the flattened mass.

5. Find the exact distance between the two plates by compressing a drop of mercury of known weight and finding its area. From the weight and density of the mercury, calculate the volume of the drop; use this volume and the area of the compressed drop to calculate the distance between the two plates.

6. Calculate the total volume of the tissue from the area of the tissue and cell sap and the distance between the two plates. Use the tissue volume and the number of cells to calculate the cell volume.

The above procedures have been used with shoot apex material. The following is a variation for use with leaf material (Beatty, 1946).

1. Cut a 1-mm disc from the leaf, and fix it in a solution of acetic acid and alcohol.

2. Place the tissue in a solution of HCl and alcohol until clear (approximately 5 minutes), and return it to the fixative for 2 minutes.

3. Stain the tissue in acetocarmine for 1 hour; mount the tissue in a drop of acetocarmine under a cover slip; and gently smear the mounted tissue. Heat may be necessary.

4. Use the counting methods described above.

III. Section Analysis

A. CELL NUMBER—CELL LENGTH FOR MATERIAL SHOWING GREAT REGULARITY (AVERY AND ENGLE, 1954)

1. Fix, dehydrate, section, and stain the segment of tissue. Make both longitudinal sections and cross sections.

2. Determine the average cell length from measurements with an ocular micrometer or with a camera lucida (see below).

3. Count the number of cell files in the cross section.

4. Calculate the cell number as follows:

$$\frac{\text{segment length}}{\text{cell length}} \times \text{number of files} = \text{cell number}$$

B. COMPLETE ANALYSIS (JENSEN, 1955a; JENSEN AND KAVALJIAN, 1958)

1. This method is useful for the analysis of material showing great regularity and relative simplicity, in which the tissues can be treated as simple cylinders. The basis of the method is the analysis of a thin section (10μ) which represents the midpoint of the segment of interest (100–200 μ long).

2. Fix, dehydrate, section at 10 μ, and stain the material following the standard procedures. Make cross and longitudinal sections of similar material.

3. Study the cross sections carefully; analyze the histology of the material; and determine the area of interest. Determine the area of the tissues, tissue systems, or cell types by making camera lucida drawings to outline the tissue, and measure this area with a planimeter. Enlarged photomicrographs may be used instead of drawings.

4. Calculate the tissue volume from the tissue area and the length of the segment of interest, say 100 μ.

5. Determine the cell cross-sectional area by one of the following means:

(a) Measuring camera lucida drawings with a planimeter and obtaining an average;

(b) Measuring camera lucida drawings of the outline of a group of cells and dividing this area by the number of cells in the group, thereby obtaining an average figure;

(c) Using the photomicrographs made for the tissue area, counting all the cells visible, and dividing this number into the tissue area, thus obtaining an average per cell area.

6. Examine the longitudinal sections, and determine the region which corresponds to the cross section used above. Identify the individual tissues or cell types and measure the length of the cells. An ocular micrometer may be used, although a more accurate procedure consists in using a camera lucida to draw an outline of the end walls of the cell and then measuring the distance between them with an accurate millimeter rule.

7. To obtain the cell volume multiply the cross-sectional area and the length of the cell. Calculate the cell number per tissue by dividing cell volume into tissue volume. To find the number of cells in the 100 μ-segment add the number of cells in each tissue.

8. In measuring the areas remember to divide the planimeter readings by the square of the magnification.

LITERATURE CITED

Avery, G. S., Jr. and F. Engel, 1954. Total nitrogen in relation to age and position of cells in *Avena* coleoptiles. *Am. J. Botany*, **41**:310–315.

Avery, G. S., Jr. and K. Linderstrøm-Lang, 1940. Peptidase activity in the *Avena* coleoptile phytohormone test object. *Compt. rend. trav. lab. Carlsberg, Sér. chim.*, **23**:219–234.

Beatty, A. V., 1946. Respiration and cell division in plants. I. Oxygen consumption and cell division in the leaves of *Ligustrum lucidum* and *Hedera helix. Am. J. Botany*, **33**:145–148.

Bottelier, H. P., H. Holter, and K. Linderstrøm-Lang, 1943. Studies on enzymatic histochemistry. XXXVI. Determination of peptidase activity, nitrogen content, and reduced weight in roots of barley, *Hordeum vulgare.* *Compt. rend. trav. lab. Carlsberg, Sér. chim.*, **24**:289–313.

Brown, R. and D. Broadbent, 1950. The development of cells in the growing zones of the root. *J. Exptl. Botany,* **1**:249–263.

Brown, R., W. S. Reith, and E. Robinson, 1952. The mechanism of plant growth. *Symposium Soc. Exptl. Biol.,* No. VI:329–347.

Brown, R. and P. Rickless, 1949. A new method for the study of cell division and cell extension with some preliminary observations on the effect of temperature and nutrients. *Proc. Roy. Soc. B.,* **136**:110–125.

Erickson, R. O., 1948. Cytological and growth correlations in the flower bud of *Lilium longiflorum. Am. J. Botany,* **35**:729–739.

Erickson, R. O. and D. R. Goddard, 1951. An analysis of root growth in cellular and biochemical terms. Tenth Symposium on Development and Growth, *Growth,* **15**:89–116.

Erickson, R. O. and K. B. Sax, 1956a. Elemental growth rate of the primary root of *Zea mays. Am. Philos. Soc.,* **100**:487–498.

———, 1956b. Rates of cell division and cell elongation in the growth of the primary root of *Zea mays. Am. Philos. Soc.,* **100**:499–514.

Foster, T. and H. Stern, 1959. The accumulation of soluble deoxyribosidic compounds in relation to nuclear division in anthers of *Lilium longiflorum. J. Biochem. Biophys. Cytol.,* **5**:187–192.

Goodwin, R. H. and C. Avers, 1956. Studies on roots. III. Analysis of root growth in *Phleum pratense* using photomicrographic records. *Am. J. Botany,* **42**:479–487.

Hotta, Y. and H. Stern, 1961. Deamination of deoxycytidine and 5-methyl-deoxycytidine in developing anthers

of *Lilium longiflorum* (var. Croft). *J. Biochem. Biophys. Cytol.,* **9**:279–284.

Jensen, W. A., 1955a. A morphological and biochemical analysis of the early phases of cellular growth in the root tip of *Vicia faba. Exptl. Cell Research,* **8**:506–522.

———, 1955b. The histochemical localization of peroxidase in roots and its induction by indoleacetic acid. *Plant Physiol.,* **30**:426–432.

———, 1960. The composition of the developing primary wall in onion root tip. II. Cytochemical localization. *Am. J. Botany,* **47**:287–295.

Jensen, W. A. and M. Ashton, 1960. The composition of the developing primary wall in onion root tip cells. I. Quantitative analyses. *Plant Physiol.,* **35**:313–323.

Jensen, W. A. and L. G. Kavaljian, 1958. Analysis of cell morphology and the periodicity of division in the root tip of *Allium cepa. Am. J. Botany,* **45**:365–372.

Linderstrøm-Lang, K., 1952. *Micromethods in Biological Research.* Lane Medical Lecture. Stanford University Press, Stanford.

Linderstrøm-Lang, K. and C. Engel, 1938. Uber die Verteilung der Amylase in den aussern Schicten des Gerstenkornes. *Compt. rend. trav. lab. Carlsberg, Sér. chim.,* **21**:243–258.

Linderstrøm-Lang, K. and H. Holter, 1932. Contributions to the histochemistry of enzymes. II. The distribution of peptidase in the roots and sprouts of malt. *Compt. rend. trav. lab. Carlsberg, Sér. chim.,* **19**:1–39. *Z. Physiol. Chem.,* **204**:15–33.

Nasatir, M. and H. Stern, 1959. Changes in the activities of aldolase and D-glyceraldehyde-3-phosphate dehydrogenase during the mitotic cycle in microspores of *Lilium longiflorum. J.*

Biophys. Biochem. Cytol., **6**:189–192.

Olney, H. O. and B. M. Pollock, 1960. Studies of the rest period. II. Nitrogen and phosphorous changes in embryonic organs of after-ripening cherry seed. *Plant Physiol.*, **35**:970–975.

Pollock, B. M. and H. O. Olney, 1959. Studies of the rest period. I. Growth, translocation, and respiratory changes in the embryonic organs of the after-ripening cherry seed. *Plant Physiol.*, **34**:131–142.

Stern, H., 1958. Variations in sulphydryl concentration during microsporocyte meiosis in anthers of *Lilium and Trillium. J. Biophys. Biochem. Cytol.*, **4**:157–161.

———, 1960. Biochemical sequences in mitosis, pp. 135–166. In *Developing Cell Systems and their Control*. 18th Symposium on Development and Growth. D. Rudnick (Editor). Ronald, New York.

———, 1961. Periodic induction of deoxyribonuclease activity in relation to the mitotic cycle. *J. Biophys. Biochem. Cytol.*, **9**:271–277.

Sunderland, N. and R. Brown, 1956. Distribution of growth in the apical region of the shoot of *Lupinus albus. J. Exptl. Botany*, **7**:127–145.

CHAPTER 8

Microscopic
Histochemistry
and Cell
Morphology

Introduction

The plant cell is a wonderfully complex structure both morphologically and biochemically. The complex morphology of the plant cell was
not fully appreciated before the work of the electron microscopists
(Porter and Machado, 1960; Setterfield, Stern, and Johnston, 1959;
Whaley, Mollenhauer, and Kephart, 1959) revealed the existence of
previously unknown cell parts (Fig. 8-1). Among the discoveries of the
electron microscopist are the endoplasmic reticulum and ribosomes; other
parts whose existence was questioned by light microscopists, such as the
Golgi apparatus, were found in considerable numbers in electron microscope preparations. Moreover, mitochondria, proplastids, and several
unnamed particles were found to have roughly the same size and shape,
making their identification by light microscopy difficult if not impossible.

When the morphological complexity of the cell is considered in the
light of the biochemical composition and activity of the cell, the problems facing the botanical histochemist are formidable indeed. The
basic question to which the botanical histochemist frequently seeks
an answer is, Where in the cell are substances and activities localized?
To answer this question he must know the effect of the procedure he
has employed on the morphology of the cell, and he must be able to
identify the site at which the substance or activity is localized.

158

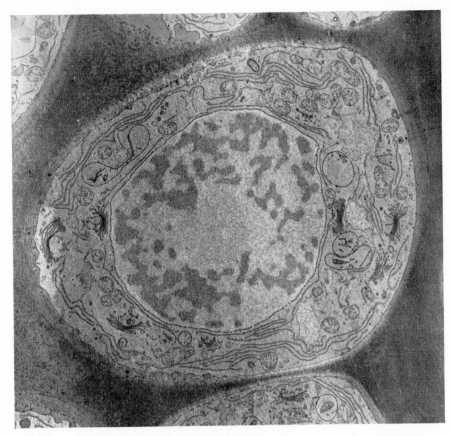

Figure 8-1. *Transverse section of a cell in a corn root tip, 75 μ from the tip. 10,425×. [Courtesy of Dr. G. Whaley.]*

The first point is a very important one, particularly when the cells used in the procedure are not living, but have been fixed in some manner. The importance of establishing the existence of all possible sites of the substance or activity before and during the localization procedure cannot be overemphasized. Simple morphological controls, which involve either staining the sections at various stages of the procedure or examining them with a phase microscope, are frequently of great help. As a routine part of all histochemical procedures, at least one morphological control should be run. Such controls should be used with fresh sections or living cells, as well as with fixed preparations.

The second point is also a very important one. The aim of many histochemical procedures is the localization of a substance or activity. The identity of the site therefore becomes the focal point of the procedure.

If the site is large, such as a nucleus or chloroplast, or if it is adequate to know that the localization is nuclear or cytoplasmic in broad terms, there is little difficulty, provided the morphological control shows that all sites existed during localization.

Problems arise when the nature of a cytoplasmic localization is investigated in terms of plastids, proplastids, mitochondria, microsomes, spherosomes, and other bodies both beyond and within the resolving power of the light microscope. For example, that the actual site of an enzyme may be submicroscopic does not exclude the possibility that the end product of the reaction used to demonstrate the enzyme may have accumulated to such an extent that the site is, in effect, magnified many times (Fig. 8-2).

In some cases the identity of the particle is inherent in the technique. Thus, cytoplasmic bodies which stain with Janus green in aerobic conditions and lose this color in anaerobic conditions are by definition mitochondria. Such criteria have been used successfully by Sorokin (Sorokin, 1955; Sorokin and Sorokin, 1956). For many problems, however, such procedures are ruled out by the nature of either the material or the histochemical technique.

Sometimes the biological material may be open to special methods which help resolve the nature of the site. An example is the work of Zalokar (1960) on *Neurospora* hyphae. Zalokar found that by centrifuging the hyphae the various cell parts could be stratified and identified. Then before remixing could occur he freeze-substituted the cells and carried out the necessary histochemical procedures. By this method he was able to separate the cell into layers of glycogen, ergastoplasm, mitochondria, nuclei and nucleoli, enchylema (supernatant), vacuoles, and fat.

Figure 8-2. *Acid phosphatase localization after 1 hour (A) and after 12 hours (B) in the same substrate medium. The 12-hour preparation has also been stained with crystal violet (1000×).*

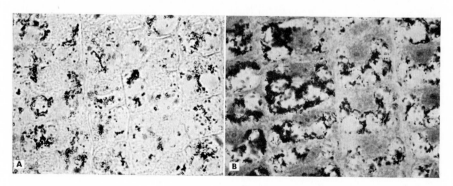

Another approach consists in using the chemical composition of the cell parts to distinguish the various possible sites. Thus, starting with freeze-dried material, one section is stained as a morphological control; another is run through the localization procedure without any pretreatment; a third is first extracted with an organic solvent to remove the mitochondria; and a fourth is treated with ribonuclease to remove the ribosomes (Jensen, 1956; Jensen and Kavaljian, 1956). A comparison of the final localization patterns can be used to help draw general conclusions as to the nature of the site.

The enzymology of the particles may possibly be used to distinguish the cell organelles or to distinguish differences which may exist among a given organelle, such as mitochondria. This may be done by counting the number of reacting cell parts after various histochemical procedures. This approach was developed by Avers (1961), who used living root epidermal cells and made careful counts on the number of reactive sites after a variety of enzyme procedures. Her data indicate a certain regularity in the number of particles that react in different tests. Such counts may serve as a basis for distinguishing cell parts or differences in the same type of cell organelle.

All the methods discussed so far have been based on the concept of studying the cell parts while they are still in the cell. A spectacularly different approach developed by Bensley and Hoerr (1934) is to isolate the cell parts first and then analyze them. The procedure involves homogenating a mass of cells and isolating the various parts present in the homogenate by differential centrifugation. Separation of the parts is accomplished by utilizing their differences in mass, which influence their rate of sedimentation in a centrifugal field. The isolated parts are analyzed by standard chemical and biochemical techniques. The data obtained refer to the cell parts obtained in the homogenization of a large mass of cells and not to the localization of a particular substance in a known cell type. Consequently, these procedures are not a regular part of microscopic histochemistry, although they have an important role in the interpretation of data obtained by microscopic histochemical methods.

The general procedures used in the separation of cell parts by homogenization and differential centrifugation are not particularly difficult. The material is homogenized either in a mortar and pestle with sand, in a homogenator, or by being pressed between rollers. The homogenate is strained to remove the coarse pieces of tissue remaining, and the filtrate is placed in centrifuge tubes. At first the homogenate is spun at slow speeds to bring down unbroken cells and large starch grains. Repeated centrifugations are then carried out at increasingly higher speeds and for longer periods of time. The heavier cell parts, such as the nuclei and chloroplasts come down first, then the lighter parts, such as mitochondria and proplastids, and finally the lightest parts, such as the ribosomes. The fraction which always remains is usually called the soluble portion. To retain the biochemical activity of the cell parts during the isolation, it is important to carry out all operations in the cold. A selection of homogenization and differential centrifugation methods for various cell parts (mitochondria, chloroplasts, nuclei, and ribosomes) is given in the section on Procedures in this chapter. Every material requires its own special set of conditions, however, and the schedules must be adjusted accordingly.

In theory the method of differential centrifugation for the separation of the various cell parts is simple and easy. In practice the method has a number of difficulties which limit the scope of its application and the meaning of the data obtained.

One of the most serious of these difficulties is the problem of the purity of the fractions. This problem has two aspects. One part of the problem is concerned with the initial phase of the procedure, namely the disruption of the cells. Here the aim is to disrupt the cell without disrupting any of the cell parts, with the exception, of course, of the cell wall and cytoplasmic membrane. If the parts are disrupted to any considerable extent, the data obtained from the analysis of the remaining intact parts becomes essentially meaningless. When the initial disruption of the cell is faulty, compounds which are usually confined to one fraction containing the nuclei, such as DNA, will show up in all fractions. The various means of disrupting cells have, however, been examined in some detail, and acceptable methods have been found (Anderson, 1956; Alfrey, 1959) which cause the least damage to the isolated cell parts. Examples of these methods are given in the Procedures section of this chapter.

The second part of the problem concerning the purity of the fractions involves the next step in the procedure, namely the centrifugation of the suspension of cell parts. In theory the cell parts differ sufficiently from one another such that in a centrifuge they sediment at different rates. Therefore, fractions composed of only one type of cell part can be collected. In practice, however, a number of difficulties can easily arise. One is that the heavier cell parts, which come down first, carry the lighter parts with them, with the result that when nuclei are isolated they may be found to be mixed with mitochondria or ribosomes. Cleaning such contaminated fractions is frequently difficult if not impossible, thus the reliability of data obtained by the analysis of such fractions is questionable. An example of the type of difficulty which may arise from the possibility of contamination is that of the RNA content of mitochondria. Most analyses of isolated mitochondria show some RNA present, usually 3–15%. The question is whether this RNA is part of the mitochondria or the result of contaminating ribosomes (Kmetec and Newcomb, 1956). The answer is not simple, and has not been made to the satisfaction of all cytologists (Brachet, 1957). Another difficulty is that two cell parts may not differ sufficiently such that they can be separated by the usual centrifugation schedules. This has been shown to be the case for mitochondria and lysosomes in animal tissue (De Duve, 1957, 1959), and is probably true for plant tissues as well.

There are several ways of testing the purity of the fractions. These involve chemical and various kinds of microscopic analyses of the sedimented fractions. Chemical markers can be used, such as DNA for nuclei, succinoxidase for mitochondria, and RNA for ribosomes (Potter, Recknagel, and Hurlbert, 1951). Hence, if large amounts of DNA appear in the fraction believed to be only mitochondria, additional precautions must be taken. Another way to establish the purity of the fractions is to examine the sediment with a phase microscope. In preparations where the contaminating part may be either submicroscopic, as are ribosomes, or identical in shape to the primary fraction, as are mitochondria and lysosomes, phase microscopy will not be adequate, and observations with the electron microscope will be necessary. The sediment is collected from the bottom of the centrifuge tube, fixed, embedded in plastic, sectioned, and observed under the electron microscope. The purity of the fraction is determined by direct observation. Although this method is the most involved, it is highly recommended.

Another difficulty with the isolation of cell parts by homogenization and differential centrifugation lies in the change which occurs in the parts as a result of the isolation procedure. For example, when the tissue is homogenized in aqueous media, and the parts separated while suspended in aqueous solutions, water soluble materials, including many proteins, will be lost. If, however, the tissue is freeze-dried, ground, suspended in nonaqueous media, and centrifuged in organic solvents, the water soluble substances will remain, but many lipids and substances soluble in organic solvents will be lost. The chloroplasts shown in Fig. 8-3 were first isolated in both aqueous and nonaqueous media, then fixed, embedded, and sectioned, and, finally, photographed through an electron microscope. The chloroplasts isolated in aqueous media are lighter in contrast, indicating the loss of protein from the stroma regions. The

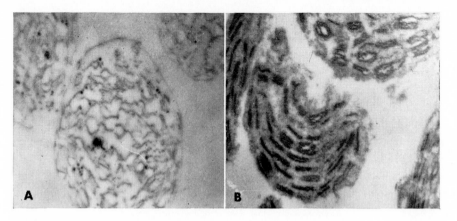

Figure 8-3. *Chloroplasts isolated (A) in aqueous medium and (B) in nonaqueous medium (20,000×). [Courtesy of Dr. R. Park.]*

membrane delimiting the chloroplast is present. The chloroplasts isolated in nonaqueous media are more dense, indicating the presence of water-soluble protein, but the outer limiting membrane is absent. There are advantages and disadvantages to both methods, and, consequently, both must frequently be used in any given problem. Both methods are given in the Procedures section of this chapter.

To the histochemist the most serious disadvantage of this procedure is that large masses of tissue must be used, with the result that all differences between cell types are lost. Frequently, pea seedlings or spinach leaves are used as the source of cells. Differences in enzyme distribution of the type found by Van Fleet (1950) and Avers (1958) in various types of root cells would go completely unnoticed if whole roots were ground and analyzed. By averaging data from different cell types, only a generalized picture of cell composition and function can be obtained.

The importance of this generalized picture to the field of cytology, however, has been tremendous (for example, see Millerd and Bonner, 1953; Hackett, 1955; and Crane, 1961). Knowledge gained through these methods, particularly of mitochondria, chloroplasts, and nuclei, has given us a dynamic view of the cell—a view which could not be obtained in such detail by any other method. Moreover, this generalized knowledge of the cell can be used as a basis on which to build microscopic histochemical methods which can be used to analyze differences in cell types and tissues. As important as the data obtained from homogenization and differential centrifugation are, such data should not be looked upon as the final arbitrator of microscopic histochemical data.

The problems remain, however, of the precise localization of substances and activities within the cell and the identification of the site. The solution of this problem rests, at least in part, on the adaptation of microscopic histochemical methods to the electron microscope. Rapid progress is being made in this area by investigators using animal material, and a beginning has been made by botanists (for example, see Albersheim, Mühlethater, and Frey-Wyssling, 1960). However, until more techniques have been developed, and until electron microscopes become more widely used by botanists, the assignment of an enzyme or a substance to a cell particle on the basis of the morphology of the site as studied by light microscopy should be done with considerable caution.

Despite these difficulties the procedures of microscopic histochemistry have a definite and real place in the study of the plant cell and have an even more important role in the study of plant tissues. They, and for many problems, they alone, offer the possibility of treating the plant as it really is, a complex morphological and biochemical system.

Procedures

1. Isolation of Mitochondria in Aqueous Media (MILLERD, BONNER, AXELROD, AND BANDURSKI, 1951; AXELROD, 1955)

A. Carry out all operations in the cold (0–4°C).

B. Use 3- to 4-day-old mung bean seedlings.

C. Remove the cotyledons, and grind 30 g of the plants for 2 minutes in a mortar with 10 g of sand and 40 ml of 0.01 M phosphate buffer (pH 7.1) in 0.4 M sucrose.

D. Strain the brei through muslin or a double layer of cheese cloth, and centrifuge at 500 g for 5 minutes.

E. Then centrifuge the supernatant for 15 minutes at 10,000 g.

F. Resuspend the sedimented material in 20 ml of fresh sucrose buffer.

G. Centrifuge again at 10,000 g for 15 minutes.

H. Resuspend the sediment in 3.5 ml of 0.5 M sucrose in 0.02 M phosphate buffer, pH 7.2. The mitochondria are now ready for analysis.

See Kmetec and Newcomb (1956) for a method for isolating mitochondria and ribosomes from peanut cotyledons. This procedure includes a density barrier for purifying the fractions. Axelrod (1955) gives a method for the isolation of mitochondria from avocados; Laites (1953), a method for extracting mitochondria from cauliflower heads; and Stafford (1951), a method for extracting mitochondria from pea seedlings.

II. Isolation of Fungal Mitochondria in Aqueous Media
(BONNER AND MACHLIS, 1957)

A. Grow *Allomyces macrogynus*, a filamentous watermold, in liquid, agitated culture in 125-ml Erlenmeyer flasks containing 50 ml of growth medium (Machlis, 1953).

B. Remove the plants from 40 flasks, and wash them on a nylon cloth over a Büchner funnel with approximately 500 ml of cold 0.4 M potassium phosphate buffer at pH 7.0 or 7.4.

C. Press excess buffer from the plants, and grind in a cold room with 50–60 g of ground glass and a final total volume of 150–180 ml of a solution containing 0.5 M sucrose, 0.1 M potassium phosphate, and 0.001 M potassium ethylenediamine tetraacetate (EDTA) at pH 7.0 or 7.4.

D. Grind plants, glass, and one third of the buffer in a cold mortar on ice for 6–8 minutes until a smooth paste is formed. Add more buffer, mix with the paste, and strain through a nylon net on a funnel into test tubes immersed in ice.

E. Return paste remaining on the nylon net to the mortar, add remaining buffer, regrind paste for 2–3 minutes, filter through the nylon net again, and squeeze the liquid out.

F. Centrifuge the crude, filtered homogenate for 10 minutes at 500 g in a refrigerated centrifuge.

G. Decant the supernatant into 50 ml tubes, and centrifuge for 15 minutes at 10,000 g.

H. Resuspend the sediment in 10 ml of sucrose buffer solution used in C, to which 0.1 M phosphate buffer has been added. Use a plastic pestle and a small tissue homogenizer operated by hand to resuspend the sediment.

I. Consolidate the suspension into two tubes, and centrifuge at 10,000 g for 15 minutes.

J. Suspend the sediment, which consists of the mitochondria in 5–10 ml of a solution of 0.5 M sucrose, 0.001 M potassium EDTA, and 0.001 M potassium phosphate buffer at pH 7.0 or 7.4. The mitochondria are now ready for analysis.

III. Isolation of Chloroplasts in Saline Solution
(ARNON, ALLEN, AND WHATLEY, 1956)

A. Carry out all operations in the cold to prevent loss of activity of the choloroplasts.

B. Wash spinach leaves with distilled water, shake to remove excess water, place in a plastic bag, and store in a refrigerator to maintain turgidity.

C. Remove the midribs of the turgid leaves, and weigh the leaf blades.

D. Quickly cut the blades into pieces roughly 0.5 cm² to facilitate grinding. Grind in a large ice-cold mortar 100–200 g of sliced leaf blades. Use 100–250 ml of cold 0.35 *M* NaCl and cold sand to assist in the grinding.

E. Squeeze the resulting brei through a double layer of cheese cloth, and centrifuge the liquid which passes through the cloth in the cold at 200 g for 1 minute to remove the sand, leaf debris, and whole cells.

F. Carefully decant the supernatant fluid, and centrifuge in the cold for 7 minutes at 1000 g. The whole chloroplasts will be sedimented at this speed; broken chloroplasts and smaller cell parts will remain in the solution.

G. Suspend the sedimented whole chloroplasts in 25 ml of 0.35 *M* NaCl solution. The chloroplasts are now ready for use.

IV. Isolation of Chloroplasts in Nonaqueous Media
(HEBER, 1957; STOCKING, 1959)

A. Wash spinach leaves with distilled water, remove midribs, and blot off excess water.

B. Freeze by plunging into liquid nitrogen, and, while frozen, break into relatively small pieces.

C. Freeze-dry or lyophilize tissue at −10°C or less.

D. When dry, place 5 g of leaves in a Waring blendor with 250 ml of petroleum ether, and run the blendor at full speed for 3 minutes.

E. Strain homogenate through 8 layers of cheese cloth and glass wool.

F. Centrifuge supernatant very slowly (less than 10 g) for 5 minutes.

G. Discard residue, and centrifuge supernatant at 2000 g for 10 minutes.

H. Discard supernatant, and resuspend sediment in 50 ml of petroleum ether.

I. Centrifuge for 3 minutes at 800 g, and discard the supernatant. The sediment contains the crude chloroplasts.

J. Repeat steps H and I three times, using the sediment obtained in step I.

K. Resuspend the sediment in carbon tetrachloride and petroleum ether at a specific gravity of 1.34 (80 ml of carbon tetrachloride to 20 ml of petroleum ether), and centrifuge at 12,000 g for 15 minutes.

L. Discard the sediment which contains cell debris. Adjust the supernatant to a specific gravity of 1.00 by adding petroleum ether (equal volumes of petroleum ether and carbon tetrachloride have a specific gravity of approximately 1.00).

M. Centrifuge supernatant at 1000 g for 3 minutes. Sediment consists of purified chloroplasts.

V. Isolation of Ribosomes from Pea Seedlings
(T'SO, BONNER, AND VINOGRAD, 1956)

A. Use seedlings of *Pisum sativum* grown for 7 days in the dark at 25 °C on vermiculite.

B. Collect the first 2.5–4 cm of the stem, and grind in a mortar at 2–4°C with washed sand and 0.4 M sucrose solution. Use 0.5 ml of sucrose solution per g of tissue.

C. Filter the homogenate through cheese cloth, and centrifuge at 40,000 g for 10 minutes.

D. Resuspend the sediment, and centrifuge at 110,000 g for 60 minutes.

E. Resuspend the pellet obtained from 11 ml of the crude extract at the end of step D in 2–4 ml of distilled water. Stir gently but constantly for 1 hour.

F. Centrifuge this solution at 18,000 g for 10 minutes, and then resuspend the sediment, and centrifuge at 110,000 g for 60 minutes.

G. Finally, resuspend the pellet resulting from this last centrifugation, and centrifuge at 40,000 g for 5–8 minutes.

H. The pellet, which is now composed primarily of ribosomes, is ready for analysis.

VI. Isolation of Ribosomes from Onion Roots (SZARKOWSKI,
BUTTROSE, MÜHLETHALER, AND FREY-WYSSLING, 1960)

A. Cut roots from fourteen-day-old onion bulbs grown in tap water in the dark into 1-cm segments.

B. Place segments in a refrigerator at 2°C for 30 minutes, and then homogenate in either 0.25 M sucrose solution or 0.25 M sucrose with 0.01 M Versene (0.5 g of tissue/ml of solution) in a Bühler homogenizer at 75% maximum voltage for three periods of 30 seconds separated by 30-second intervals. Neutralize the sucrose-Versene solution to pH 7.0 with KOH.

C. Strain the homogenate through muslin or a double layer of cheese cloth.

D. Remove debris and nuclei by centrifuging at 2400 g for 20 minutes in a refrigerated centrifuge.

E. Remove the supernatant, and centrifuge at 20,000 g for 30 minutes. This step removes the mitochondria and plastids.

F. Centrifuge the remaining supernatant (which is light yellow) at 50,000 g for 20 minutes and finally at 105,000 g for 60 minutes.

G. The pellet obtained at the end of the final centrifugation—the ribosomal fraction—is ready for analysis.

VII. Isolation of Nuclei, Nucleoli, Chromatin, Nuclear Ribosomes, and Nuclear Sap from Pea Seedlings —Aqueous Method (BIRNSTIEL, RHO, AND CHIPCHASE, 1961; RHO AND BONNER, 1961)

A. NUCLEI

1. Grow pea seedlings (*Pisum sativum*) in vermiculite in the dark for 4 days at 25 °C. Cut the apical tips into 1- to 2-cm lengths, and wash in 0.5% Clorox for 3 minutes.

2. Chop the segments into 1-mm sections, and pass them through a set of counterrotating rollers on a nylon mesh with the simultaneous addition of a sucrose-$CaCl_2$ medium (0.6 M sucrose, 0.004 M $CaCl_2$, 0.005 M tris buffer, at pH 7.0).

3. Centrifuge the juice obtained at 350 g for 10 minutes. The pellet consists of a dense starch layer at the bottom covered by a nuclear layer.

4. Carefully remove the nuclear layer with a syringe, and resuspend in the original medium. To this suspension, add enough supersaturated sucrose (245 g of sucrose in 100 ml of H_2O) to bring the density to 1.316 g/cm³.

5. Place the nuclear suspension in a nitrocellulose centrifuge tube, underlayer it with supersaturated sucrose, centrifuge at 12,100 g for 10 minutes to allow settling of the sucrose layers. Then centrifuge for 45 minutes at 72,000 g for the actual separation.

6. After centrifugation the nuclei will be found banded above the supersaturated sucrose, the starch will be at the bottom of the tube, and broken nuclei and other contaminants will be floating at the top of the tube. Remove the nuclei by cutting the centrifuge tube a few mm above the nuclear band, and carefully pour off the supernatant. Then cut the tube further, and ease out the purified nuclear suspension with a spatula. Adjust the density to 1.310 g/cm³ by adding water. The volume yielded is roughly 15 ml (from 3 tubes) and contains 75% of the intact nuclei.

B. NUCLEOLI, CHROMATIN, NUCLEAR RIBOSOMES AND NUCLEAR SAP

1. Grind the nuclear suspension in a Serval Omnimix at 40 v for 1–4 minutes in the presence of sodium citrate (0.5 to 1 mM, pH 7.2) until

most of the nuclei disintegrate. The citrate is used to remove the calcium present by the formation of a calcium-citrate complex.

2. Dilute the suspension with water to bring the density to 1.260 g/cm^3.

3. Centrifuge for 20 minutes at 1935 g. Remove the supernatant, and discard the sediment.

4. Centrifuge the supernatant for 20 minutes at 4340 g; again, save the supernatant, and discard the sediment, which consists primarily of unbroken nuclei.

5. Centrifuge the supernatant for 20 minutes at 14,500 g. The sediment consists of nucleoli.

6. Recentrifuge the supernatant for 20 minutes at 30,900 g. The sediment consists primarily of nucleoli.

7. Save the supernatant, and centrifuge for 20 minutes at 48,200 g. The sediment consists of some nucleoli and smaller, DNA-rich bodies termed chromatin.

8. Centrifuge the supernatant again for 2 hours at 72,000 g. The sediment, rich in DNA, is termed chromatin I.

9. Dilute the supernatant 5 fold with a solution of 0.01 M KCl, 0.0005 M $CaCl_2$, and 0.002 M tris (pH 7.2), and centrifuge for 25 minutes at 34,850 g. This sediment, also rich in DNA, is termed chromatin II.

10. Finally, centrifuge the supernatant for 6 hours at 78,400 g. The sediment is considered to be composed of nuclear ribosomes; the supernatant, of nuclear sap.

VIII. Isolation of Nuclei from Wheat Germ—Nonaqueous Method (ALFREY, STERN, MIRSKY, AND SAETREN, 1959; STERN AND MIRSKY, 1952)

A. Thoroughly extract fresh wheat germ with petrol ether. If tissue other than wheat germ is used it must first be freeze-dried.

B. Suspend about 60 g of the extracted tissue in 300 ml of petrol ether, and grind in a ball mill for 48 hours.

C. Collect the tissue by passing the ground suspension through a single layer of cheese cloth, and centrifuge the filtered suspension at 900 g for 20 minutes.

D. Resuspend the sediment in about 500 ml of a cyclohexane-CCl_4 mixture adjusted to a specific gravity of 1.395, and recentrifuge.

E. Resuspend the sediment in a cyclohexane-CCl_4 mixture adjusted to a specific gravity of 1.400, and centrifuge again at 6000 g.

F. Repeat step E, gradually adjusting the specific gravity of the

cyclohexane-CCl₄ mixture toward 1.420. Between specific gravities of
1.416 and 1.420 the sediment consists predominately of clear nuclei.

LITERATURE CITED

Albersheim, P., K. Mühlethaler, and A.
Frey-Wyssling, 1960. Stained pectin
as seen in the electron microscope.
J. Biophys. and Biochem. Cytol., **8**:
501–516.

Alfrey, V., 1959. The isolation of sub-
cellular components. In *The Cell*,
J. Brachet and A. Mirsky (Editors).
Academic, New York.

Alfrey, V., H. Stern, A. E. Mirsky, and
H. Saetren, 1952. The isolation of
cell nuclei in non-aqueous media. *J.
Gen. Physiol.*, **35**:529–554.

Anderson, N. G., 1956. Techniques for
the mass isolation of cellular com-
ponents. In *Physical Techniques in
Biological Research*. G. Oster and
A. W. Pollister (Editors). Academic,
New York.

Arnon, D. I., M. B. Allen, and F. R.
Whatley, 1956. Photosynthesis by
isolated chloroplasts. IV. General
concept and comparison of three
photochemical reactions. *Biophys. et
Biochim. Acta.*, **20**:449–461.

Avers, C. J., 1958. Histochemical localization of enzyme activity in the root
epidermis of *Phleum pratense*. *Am.
J. Botany*, **45**:609–613.

———, 1961. Histochemical localization
of enzyme activities in root meristem
cells. *Am. J. Botany*, **48**:137–142.

Axelrod, B., 1955. Preparation of mito-
chondria from plants, pp. 19–22. In
Methods of Enzymology. Vol. 1.
Colowick, S. P. and N. O. Kaplan
(Editors). Academic, New York.

Bensley, R. R. and N. L. Hoerr, 1934.

Studies on cell structure by the freezing-drying method. The preparation
and properties of mitochondria. *Anat.
Record*, **60**:449–455.

Birnstiel, M. L., J. H. Rho, and M. I.
H. Chipchase, 1961. Fractionation of
isolated pea nuclei. *Biophys. Biochim.
Acta.* In press.

Bonner, B. A. and L. Machlis, 1957. Respiration of the mycelia and mitochondria of the filamentous water
mold *Allomyces macrogynus*. *Plant
Physiol.*, **32**:291–301.

Brachet, J., 1957. *Biochemical Cytology.*
Academic, New York.

Crane, F. L., 1961. Structure and function of mitochondria. *Ann. Rev.
Plant Physiol.*, **12**:13–34.

DeDuve, C., 1957. The enzymatic
heterogeneity of cell fractions isolated by differential centrifugation.
Symposia, Soc. Exptl. Biol., **10**:50–61.

———, 1959. Lysosomes, a new group
of cytoplasmic particles. In *Subcellu-
lar Particles*. Hiyaski, T. (Editor).
Am. Physiol. Soc., Washington, D.C.

Hackett, D. P., 1955. Recent studies on
plant mitochondria. *Intern. Rev. Cytol.*, **4**:143–196.

Heber, U., 1957. Zur Frage der Lokali-
sation von löslichen Zuckern in der
Pflanzenelle. *Ber. Dtsch. Botan. Ges.*,
70:371–382.

Jensen, W. A., 1956. The cytochemical
localization of acid phosphatase in
root tip cells. *Am. J. Botany*, **43**:50–
54.

Jensen, W. A., and L. G. Kavaljian,

1956. The cytochemical localization of ascorbic acid in root tip cells. *J. Biophys. Biochem. Cytol.*, **2**:87–92.

Kmetec, E. and E. H. Newcomb, 1956. Properties of particulate fractions isolated from homogenates of peanut cotyledons. *Am. J. Botany*, **43**:333–342.

Laites, G. G., 1953. The dual role of adenylate in the mitochondrial oxidations of a higher plant. *Physiol. Plantarium*, **6**:199–211.

Machlis, L., 1953. Growth and nutrition of water molds in the subgenus *Euaelomyces*. II. Optimal composition of the minimal medium. *Am. J. Botany*, **40**:450–460.

Millerd, A. and J. Bonner, 1953. The biology of plant mitochondria. *J. Histochem. and Cytochem.*, **1**:254–275.

Millerd, A., J. Bonner, B. Axelrod, and R. S. Bandurski, 1951. Oxidative and phosphorylative activity of plant mitochondria. *Proc. Nat. Acad. Sci.* (US), **37**:855–862.

Porter, K. R. and R. D. Machado, 1960. Studies on the endoplasmic reticulum. IV. Its form and distribution during mitosis in cells of onion root tip. *J. Biophys. Biochem. Cytol.*, **7**: 167–180.

Potter, V. R., R. O. Recknagel, and R. B. Hurlbert, 1951. Intracellular enzyme distribution; interpretations and significance. *Federation Proc.*, **10**:646–653.

Rho, J. H. and J. Bonner, 1961. The site of ribonucleic acid synthesis in the isolated nucleus. *Proc. Natl. Acad. Sci.* (US), **47**:1611–1619.

Setterfield, G., H. Stern, and F. B. Johnston, 1959. Fine structure in cells

of pea and wheat embryos. *Can. Jour. Botany*, **37**:65–72.

Sorokin, H. P., 1955. Mitochondria and spherosomes in the living epidermal cell. *Am. J. Botany*, **42**:225–231.

Sorokin, H. P. and S. Sorokin, 1956. Staining of mitochondria with neo-tetrazolium chloride. *Am. J. Botany*, **43**:183–190.

Stafford, H. A., 1951. Intracellular localization of enzymes in pea seedlings. *Physiol. Plantarium*, **4**:696–741.

Stern, H. and A. E. Mirsky, 1952. The isolation of wheat germ nuclei and some aspects of their glycolytic metabolism. *J. Gen. Physiol.*, **36**:181–200.

Stocking, C. R., 1959. Chloroplast isolation in nonaqueous media. *Plant Physiol.*, **34**:56–61.

Szarkowski, J. W., M. S. Buttrose, K. Mühlethaler, and A. Frey-Wyssling, 1960. Studies on the microsomal fraction of onion roots. *J. Ultrastructure Research*, **4**:222–230.

T'so, Paul, O. P., J. Bonner, and J. Vinograd, 1956. Microsomal nucleoprotein particles from pea seedlings. *J. Biophys. Biochem. Cytol.*, **2**:451–466.

Van Fleet, D. S., 1950. A comparison of histochemical and anatomical characteristics of the hypodermis with the endodermis in vascular plants. *Am. J. Botany*, **37**:721–725.

Whaley, W. G., H. H. Mollenhauer, and J. E. Kephart, 1959. The endoplasmic reticulum and the golgi structures in maize root cells. *J. Biophys. Biochem. Cytol.*, **5**:501–506.

Zalokar, M., 1960. Cytochemistry of centrifuged hyphae of *Neurospora*. *Exptl. Cell Research*, **19**:114–132.

PART IV

Histochemical Techniques

CHAPTER 9

Carbohydrates
and Cell Wall
Constituents

Quantitative Histochemistry

The carbohydrates have a prominent place in the biochemistry, physiology, and morphology of the cell. Because of their importance one would expect that a large number of quantitative histochemical procedures would have been developed for carbohydrates, but this is decidedly not the case. Little quantitative histochemistry has been done on carbohydrates with either vascular or nonvascular plants. This is all the more surprising in view of the importance of carbohydrates in the wall and in view of the amount of study given to the wall by physiologists, biochemists, and cytologists.

The principal difficulties in dealing with carbohydrates in plants are that they are numerous, show considerable chemical similarity, and rarely, if ever, occur singly. The large numbers of complex polysaccharides, particularly in the cell wall, present further difficulties. The sum of these complications is that any carbohydrate procedure must be highly specific and, if it is to be used as a histochemical method, highly sensitive.

The methods available for the analysis of carbohydrates are based either on colorimetry or paper chromatography. The colorimetric methods are highly sensitive but, in general, are not specific for a given sugar. Paper chromatographic procedures, on the other hand, are highly specific but require more material. The problems so far attacked through quantitative histochemical techniques have demanded the maximum sensitivity without requiring complete specificity (see, for example, the cell wall analyses of Jensen and Ashton, 1960). For this reason, colorimetric methods have been the more intensely developed. All the procedures given in the quantitative part of this chapter are color methods. There is no reason why suitable chromatographic procedures for carbohydrates should not be developed, beginning for example, with the work of Partridge (1946); Jermyn and Isherwood (1949, 1956); and Hough, Jones, and Wadman (1950).

The methods for sugars given in this chapter are based on the formation of a reaction product formed when the sugar is heated in the presence of a strong acid. The reaction product, usually a furfural, combines with a compound such as cysteine, orcinol, or indole to form a colored end product (Ashwell, 1957; Dische, 1955). The conditions of furfural formation differ for the various classes of sugars. These differences, combined with differences in the reaction of the furfurals with the final color-producing compound, form the basis of the specificity of the reactions (Dische, 1955). The limits of the reactions and some of the difficulties involved in their use will be apparent in the procedures presented later in this chapter.

The orcinol procedure for total hexoses and pentoses (Procedure I) provides an example of the effect of the duration of heating on the reactants. In this procedure the sugar is heated with sulfuric acid in the presence of orcinol. Under the conditions given in the procedure (60% H_2SO_4, 80°C, 30 minutes incubation) hexoses and pentoses, with the exception of xylose, react equally well. Xylose produces roughly 30% more color than do the other sugars. Under these conditions hexuronic acids produce few furfural derivatives and yield only one-tenth the color of the other sugars. If the incubation time is extended to 1 hour, however, the hexuronic acids yield one-half the color of the pentoses and hexoses other than xylose (Wilson, 1961). A further increase in incubation time results in a decrease in color in the hexoses and pentoses as the color complex is destroyed.

The orcinol method does not distinguish between hexoses and pentoses in mixtures of the two groups. The amount of hexoses and pentoses can be measured, however, in the presence of hexuronic acids if the shorter incubation time is used. If a measure of total hexoses, pentoses, and hexuronic acids is desired, the longer incubation time should be used. An example of a problem in which this type of measurement was used is the cell-wall analysis of Wilson (1961), in which the development of a single growth ring in *Abies concolor* was studied. Wilson analyzed 20-μ sections at 100-μ intervals from the phloem through the cambium and new xylem to the xylem produced the previous year. Trees were analyzed at different times of the year. The sections were extracted for the various wall components (pectic substances, hemicellulose, non-cellulosic polysaccharides, and cellulose), and the combined amount of hexoses, pentoses, and hexuronic acids was measured by the orcinol method, using the longer incubation period. By these analyses, Wilson was able to demonstrate the differences in wall composition during the development of the cambial derivatives. An example of the type of data Wilson collected is shown in Fig. 9-1.

The indole procedure for total hexoses and pentoses is similar to the orcinol method in principle of operation, but the color intensity produced by different sugars varies considerably. Hexuronic acids react

Figure 9-1. *The cell wall composition of the cambium, xylem, and phloem of* Abies concolor *expressed as glucose equivalents per cell. The analyses were based on 100-μ sections [Redrawn from Wilson, Ph. D. thesis, Univ. of Calif., Berkeley, 1961.]*

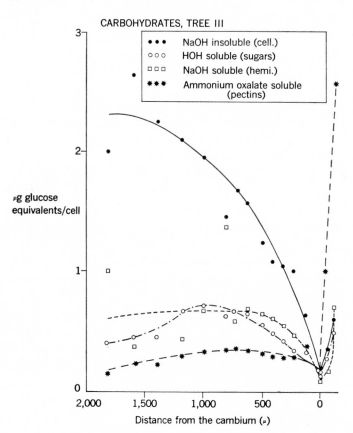

very strongly, and conditions cannot be arranged to eliminate them. Ascorbic acid also reacts in this test. Therefore, only if the hexoses and pentoses are known to be free of ascorbic and hexuronic acids can the indole method be used to measure them.

The cysteine reactions for hexoses and pentoses have been largely developed by Dische (1955). These excellent procedures can be used to measure hexoses and pentoses separately in samples in which both groups are present. In the cysteine procedure given for hexoses the conditions (85% H_2SO_4, 100°C, 3 minutes incubation) are arranged such that only the hexoses form stable reaction products. The reaction products formed by hexuronic acids and pentoses are unstable under these conditions (Dische, 1955) and do not enter into the reaction enough to interfere significantly. The cysteine procedure given for pentoses is a modification of Dische's generalized cysteine reaction for carbohydrates (Ashwell, 1957). In this procedure the only heat involved is that generated by the addition of concentrated H_2SO_4 to water. The heat and concentrated acid are sufficient to produce furfurals from all the sugars present. These furfurals, once formed, are stable, and the solution is kept at room temperature for 2 hours to prevent the excessive formation of bubbles when the cysteine is added. The colored product resulting from the combination of the pentose reaction product and the cysteine is measured in a spectrophotometer at two wave lengths; the difference in absorption indicates the amount of pentose present.

The use of absorption measurements at two wave lengths is important in both of the cysteine procedures because it permits the elimination of substances that would interfere with the analyses (Dische, 1955). One measurement is made at the maximum absorption of the sugar of interest, for example, in the pentose tests, at 390 mμ. This measurement represents the amount of color resulting from the pentoses plus the absorption of light by hexoses and other carbohydrates present. A second measurement is made at a wave length at which the absorption resulting from the presence of the hexoses and other carbohydrates is the same as it was at 390 mμ but at which the amount of absorption due to the pentoses is less. In the pentose test this is 426 mμ. By subtracting the two amounts the absorption of the hexoses and other carbohydrates is eliminated and a measure of the pentoses obtained.

The method for hexuronic acids is similar to the other procedures discussed so far but employs a different color-producing agent, carbazole. The reaction product, which is formed in the presence of H_2SO_4 and heat, reacts with carbazole to produce a brown-red color. This method, also utilized by Dische (1955), was first applied to plant tissues by

Stark (1950) and was further developed by McCready and McComb (1952). [See also McComb and McCready (1952).] The procedure given in this chapter is Jensen and Ashton's adaptation of Dische's method for use with plant tissues. This method for hexuronic acids is simple, is highly sensitive, and gives almost identical values for both glucuronic and galacturonic acids.

The procedure given for the measurement of starch is based on the reaction of the furfural produced from glucose in the presence of H_2SO_4 and heat with anthrone (Ashwell, 1957). The anthrone reaction is highly sensitive but is not specific, since color is produced with all classes of sugars, hence the necessity of washing the tissue free of soluble sugars and then extracting the starch with perchloric acid.

Many carbohydrate procedures are available in addition to those given in this chapter. For a source of additional procedures and excellent discussions of carbohydrate procedures in general, see Ashwell (1957) and Dische (1955).

When making any of the above carbohydrate determinations it is necessary to take certain preliminary steps and precautions. Absorption curves must be made for the tissue and for the various sugars believed to be present. Only on the basis of these absorption curves is it possible to determine the wave lengths to use in the actual measurement. It is necessary to run not only a control containing the acid and color-producing agent without tissue but also one containing the acid and tissue without the color-producing agent. When making determinations of the polysaccaride components in tissue sections, it is necessary that the polysaccharides be hydrolyzed completely by the acid. This may be facilitated by using thin sections (10 μ) and by stirring them in the acid. The problem of complete hydrolysis arises particularly in those determinations in which the only source of heat is that generated by the addition of sulfuric acid to the aqueous tissue or sample. Finally, it is always necessary to consider the problem of interference from noncarbohydrate compounds, which may eliminate the possibility of using crude preparations.

The problem of dust and lint must also be stressed in carbohydrate measurements. Lint is particularly troublesome and is almost universally present in reaction vessels unless extreme care is taken. Tubes should be cleaned carefully in cleaning solution, rinsed repeatedly, and dried upside down. The openings of the tubes must be covered at all times. Aluminum foil makes an effective cover.

Histochemical procedures for carbohydrates can be used to advantage in the study of cell wall development. Standard extraction procedures such as those used by Bishop, Bayley, and Setterfield (1958), Boroughs and Bonner (1953), and Jermyn and Isherwood (1956) can be adapted to histochemical work. The Boroughs and Bonner extraction schedule was adapted by Jensen and Ashton (1960) for use with 100-μ segments of onion roots and by Wilson (1961), as noted earlier, for use with 20-μ sections of the wood of *Abies concolor*. By using a narrow-tipped, stationary pipette and small tubes mounted on a movable platform by means of which the tubes can be positioned beneath the pipette, successive extractions can be made without loss of tissue (see p. 22). Difficulty may be encountered in the extraction of alkali-soluble material in lignified tissue (Wilson, 1961), but this is a result of the characteristics of the material rather than of the technique.

On a macro scale gravimetric and chromatographic methods are used in the analyses of the extracted wall substances. For most histochemical work these methods are not applicable, thus the materials must be measured by the colorimetric methods discussed in the foregoing. The major difficulty encountered in the application of these procedures to extracted wall substances is that alkali-extracted materials will not react in the tests. Therefore, the amount of hemicellulose and noncellulosic polysaccharides present must be found by measuring the difference in the amount of these materials contained in extracted and nonextracted tissue.

Another difficulty lies in the measurement of lignin. The method most widely used in the determination of lignin involves weighing the walls before and after extraction of the lignin. The means available for weighing small amounts of material were discussed in Chapter 2. The combination of such techniques with extraction procedures should make this type of lignin analysis applicable to many histochemical problems. For this reason one method of lignin extraction (Jermyn and Isherwood, 1956) is included in this chapter, although it has not been used in quantitative histochemistry. This method is based on the breakdown and removal of lignin from cell walls by chlorine water.

Also included in the procedures is a method developed by Stafford (1960) for the extraction and measurement of lignin from young herbaceous tissue. In this method the lignin is extracted with 0.5 N NaOH, which is not possible with mature woody tissue (Bondi and Meyer, 1956). The extracted, soluble lignin is measured by ultraviolet absorption and by the phenol content. This procedure is a highly attractive one and should prove useful in developmental studies.

More detailed analyses of the development of cell walls are needed. Few such analyses exist in the literature (see Setterfield and Bayley,

1961). An analysis of developing walls in *Avena* coleoptiles, so widely used by physiologists, should prove interesting in the light of the current controversy concerning the composition of this wall (Setterfield and Bayley, 1961). The careful morphological and protein analysis of Avery and Engel (1954) of the cells of the *Avena* coleoptile provides an excellent starting point for such an analysis.

A carbohydrate derivative which requires special consideration is ascorbic acid. This acid is a very strong reducing agent and is highly soluble in aqueous solutions. It can be quantitatively extracted from tissue by 0.5% oxalic acid, 5% metaphosphoric acid, and 10% acetic acid. The measurement of ascorbic acid is complicated by the ease with which it is oxidized to dehydroascorbic acid and by the conversion of this to diketogulonic acid. Care must be taken to prevent this oxidation if the true ascorbic acid content of the tissue is to be measured.

The reducing capacity of ascorbic acid is the basis for the technique described in Procedure IX (Glick, Alpert, and Stecklein, 1953). The ascorbic acid reacts with the dye, 2,6-dichlorophenol indophenol, and is oxidized to dehydroascorbic acid; the dye is reduced to a colorless form. The ascorbic acid content of the sample is obtained by measuring the amount of color loss or the amount of residual dye. In the procedure given, the residual dye is extracted from the aqueous medium containing the ascorbic acid with amyl alcohol, a water-immiscible solvent for the dye. The amount of residual dye, which is proportional to the amount of ascorbic acid, is then measured in a colorimeter.

Frequently, not only the amount of ascorbic acid present but also the amount of dehydroascorbic acid and diketogulonic acid is of interest. In the procedure just discussed, the ascorbic acid is completely converted to dehydroascorbic acid, thus the solution contains the original dehydroascorbic and diketogulonic acids plus the dehydroascorbic acid from the ascorbic acid in the tissue. A second reagent, 2,4-dinitrophenylhydrazine, is used to measure the amount of dehydroascorbic acid plus diketogulonic acid. The amount of dehydroascorbic acid plus diketogulonic acid present in the tissue can be measured by subtracting the amount of ascorbic acid found in the first part of the procedure from the amount of dehydroascorbic acid plus diketogulonic acid measured in the second part of the procedure.

The second method is based on the ultraviolet absorption of ascorbic acid, which results from the presence of the double bond in the reduced form (Chayen, 1953). To distinguish between the ultraviolet absorption resulting from the ascorbic acid and that from other ultraviolet-absorbing compounds, such as nucleic acids, copper sulfate is added to the extract and the ultraviolet absorption measured again. The copper sulfate oxidizes the ascorbic acid, decreasing its ultraviolet absorption but not affecting the absorption of the other compounds. The difference between the two readings is proportional to the amount of ascorbic acid present. Chayen (1953) gives a good review of the methods available for the analysis of ascorbic acid.

There has been relatively little work done on the quantitative histochemistry of ascorbic acid in plant tissue. One of the problems which has been attacked is the site of ascorbic acid synthesis in the germinating barley seed. This work, carried out at the Carlsberg Laboratory, was done by Glick (1938), now famous for his work with animal tissue. Barley seeds were first germinated for 10 days, after which parts of the seedling were analyzed for their ascorbic acid content. The data obtained were expressed in mg of ascorbic acid/g of fresh weight of the tissue.

One of the finest pieces of research on the relation of ascorbic acid to cell development is the work of Reid (1941b). Working with cowpeas, Reid first undertook a detailed morphological analysis which included the measurement of cell number and cell surface area (Reid, 1941a). At the same time, determinations of the nitrogen and phosphorus content were made; the analysis was based on five consecutive segments of the root, 1 mm, 2 mm, 2mm, 5 mm, and 10 mm in length. Similar sections were analyzed for ascorbic acid content (Reid, 1941b). From this analysis Reid was able to demonstrate a positive correlation between ascorbic acid content and increase in cell size resulting from elongation. However, all chemical measurements were made using standard macro chemical methods; in addition, large numbers of root segments were required to make the analyses, and considerable time (5–6 hours) was required to collect the sample. Whereas Reid required 145–390 segments for a measurement, current quantitative histochemical methods require only one.

Procedures

I. Total Hexoses and Pentoses—Orcinol Method (JENSEN, 1955)

A. Use either fresh, freeze-substituted, or freeze-dried tissue.

B. Place tissue in reaction vessels.

C. If the tissue is paraffin infiltrated, remove the paraffin with toluene, and rinse the tissue with absolute alcohol.

D. Add to each tube 0.3 ml of 2% orcinol in 20% H_2SO_4 and 2.5 ml of 60% H_2SO_4. (Make up a supply of 20% H_2SO_4, and add the orcinol the day of use. The 2% orcinol in 20% H_2SO_4 is not fully effective after a couple of days.)

E. Heat in a water bath at 80°C for 30 minutes. Cool in cold water.

F. Read in a spectrophotometer or colorimeter at 425 mμ.

G. To obtain a standard curve make a glucose solution (0.1 mg/ml), place 0.01 ml (1 μg), 0.02 ml (2 μg), and 0.03 ml (3 μg) and 0.05 ml (5 μg) in a series of tubes, and use the same procedure as for D, E, and F. This procedure for a standard curve is useful only when the difference in volumes (0.01 ml and 0.05 ml) of the standard solution is minor in relation to the total volume of the reaction mixture (2.8 ml). The results, expressed on the basis of a glucose standard curve, are termed "glucose equivalents."

All hexoses and pentoses, with the exception of xylose, give the same absorption value per gram. Xylose gives a value 30–50% higher. The hexuronic acids, give absorption values that are one-tenth the value of the hexoses and pentoses, whereas ascorbic acid does not react.

The color should be read against a blank of the reaction mixture that has been treated in the same way as the tissue and the standard. A control containing tissue and H_2SO_4 but lacking orcinol is necessary, particularly when working with new materials for the first time.

II. Total Hexoses and Pentoses—Indole Reaction
(JENSEN AND ASHTON, 1960)

A. Use fresh, freeze-substituted, or freeze-dried tissue.

B. Place the tissue in a reaction vessel.

C. Deparaffinize if the tissue is paraffin infiltrated.

D. To the sample add 50 μl of water, 500 μl of 75% H_2SO_4, and 20 μl of 1% alcoholic (95% ethyl alcohol) indole solution.

E. Heat for 10 minutes in boiling water.

F. Cool.

G. Measure the absorption at 470 mμ in a spectrophotometer.

The range of this procedure is 0.5–5 μg $\pm$ 0.1 μg for hexose and pentose. All hexoses and pentoses have equal absorption with the exception of xylose, which is $1\frac{1}{2}$ times higher. The hexuronic acids react very intensely, whereas ascorbic acid gives a much less intense, although still appreciable, amount of color. The indole test can therefore be used only when the hexoses and pentoses are free of hexuronic acids and ascorbic acid.

III. Total Hexoses—Cysteine Reaction
(JENSEN AND ASHTON, 1960)

A. Use fresh, freeze-substituted, or freeze-dried tissue. If the tissue is fresh it may have to be homogenized; if it is paraffin infiltrated, 10-μ sections should be used.

B. Place the tissue in a reaction vessel.

C. Deparaffinize the tissue.

D. Add 50 μl of water to the sample, and place it in an ice water bath.

E. Now add 500 μl of a solution containing 6 parts concentrated H_2SO_4 and 1 part water.

F. After 5 minutes remove the tubes from the ice water, allow them to warm to room temperature, and then heat in boiling water for 3 minutes.

G. Cool in a water bath at room temperature.

H. Add 100 μl of 3% aqueous cysteine solution. At this point add a "flea," and stir thoroughly.

I. Measure the absorption at 415 mμ and at 380 mμ in a spectrophotometer. The difference in the absorption readings equals the amount of hexose present. The range of the procedure is 0.5–5.0 μg $\pm$ 0.1 μg. Glucose, fructose, galactose, and mannose give almost identical absorption values. There is no interference from pentoses, hexuronic acids, or ascorbic acid.

This is a good procedure but not an easy one. Care must be taken to insure complete hydrolysis of tissue when tissue is used. Extracts are generally easier to handle. The color must be measured against a blank treated in exactly the same way as the samples but lacking the sample. For a new tissue, absorption curves should be plotted to determine the peaks accurately.

IV. Total Pentose—Cysteine Reaction
(JENSEN AND ASHTON, 1960)

A. Use fresh, freeze-substituted, or freeze-dried tissue. Fresh tissue should be homogenized or cut into very small fragments. Section paraffin-infiltrated tissue at 10 μ.

B. Place the tissue in a reaction vessel.

C. Deparaffinize the tissue.

D. Cool the tubes containing tissue in a cold aluminum block, and add 50 μl of cold water and 200 μl of cold concentrated H_2SO_4.

E. After shaking, remove the tubes from the block, add a "flea," and allow the tubes to come to room temperature.

F. Keep the solutions at room temperature for 2 hours, and stir at regular intervals, using a small hand magnet to move the flea. The solution is too viscous to permit the use of an electric magnet equipped with a breaker.

G. Now add 5 μl of freshly prepared 3% aqueous cysteine, and stir.

H. After 15 minutes measure the absorption at 390 mμ and at 425 mμ in a spectrophotometer. The difference in absorption readings equals the amount of pentose present. The range of this procedure is 0.5 − 5 μg ± 0.1 μg. There is no reaction with hexoses, hexuronic acids, or ascorbic acid. The greatest difficulty with this procedure is that xylose gives 4.5 times the color per microgram as do the other pentoses.

This test, like the cysteine hexose reaction given above, is a good one but is not easy. All operations must be carried out in precise order. Stirring during the 2 hours at room temperature is very important and must be performed at regular intervals if the tissue is to be completely digested. Again, a blank consisting of everything but the tissue must be used, and complete absorption curves must be made when working with a new tissue. The use of extracts minimizes many of these difficulties. Additional pentose procedures are given in the chapter on nucleic acids.

V. Hexuronic Acids—Carbazole Reaction
(JENSEN AND ASHTON, 1960)

A. Use fresh, freeze-substituted, or freeze-dried tissue.

B. Place the tissue in a reaction vessel.

C. Deparaffinize the tissue.

D. Add 50 μl of water and 300 μl of concentrated H_2SO_4.

E. Heat the tubes in an aluminum block at 100°C for 20 minutes.

F. Cool the tubes in a cold aluminum block for 5 minutes.

G. Then add 10 μl of a freshly prepared solution of 0.1% carbazole in 95% ethyl alcohol. Add a "flea," and stir.

H. Measure the absorption at 535 mμ in a spectrophotometer.

This procedure has a range of 0.5–5 μg ± 0.1 μg. Glucuronic and galacturonic acids give identical values. Pentoses and ascorbic acid do not react, and there is negligible interference from hexoses.

This is an easy, dependable procedure which should have wide use in cell wall studies.

VI. Starch—Anthrone Reaction (MCCREADY, GUGGOLZ, SILVIERA, AND OWENS, 1950)

A. Wash the tissue repeatedly, whether fresh, dried, freeze-dried, or freeze-substituted, with 80% ethyl alcohol to remove all trace of soluble sugars. The last wash should be tested with the anthrone reagent given in steps G–I. If a positive reaction is obtained, continue the washing.

B. Wash the tissue in water, and then place it in a solution composed of 5 ml of water and 6.5 ml of 52% perchloric acid.

C. Extract the starch with perchloric acid at 0°C for 20 minutes.

D. Remove and save this extract.

E. After 30 minutes repeat step C, using fresh perchloric acid.

F. Remove this extract, and add it to the extract obtained in step C. Dilute the combined extracts with water to 100 ml, filter this, and then dilute 5–10 ml of the combined extract to 500 ml.

G. Prepare anthrone-sulfuric acid reagent by dissolving 0.2 g of anthrone reagent in 100 ml of cold 95% H_2SO_4. Store the reagent at approximately 0°C for not more than 2 days.

H. Add 10 ml of cold anthrone-sulfuric acid reagent to 5 ml of starch extract in an ice bath.

I. Heat for 7.5 minutes at 100°C, and cool rapidly to 25°C.

J. Measure the absorption at 6300 Å in a spectrophotometer. In the Klett-Summerson colorimeter, use a K-64 filter.

K. Glucose is used as a standard. Calculate the starch content by multiplying the equivalents by 0.90.

VII. Lignin—Extraction Method
(JERMYN AND ISHERWOOD, 1956)

A. Dry and weigh the tissue carefully.

B. Place the tissue in a flask or reaction vessel, and add water, acetic acid, and sodium chlorite. (In the method given by Jermyn and Isherwood, a 250-ml Erlenmeyer flask, 5 g of tissue, 160 ml of water, 10 drops of acetic acid, and 1.5 g of sodium chlorite were used.)

C. Close the flask with a loose-fitting glass bubble or marble.

D. At hourly intervals add more acetic acid and sodium chlorite in the same amounts as originally used. Complete extraction takes 4 hours.

E. Place the tissue on a small sintered-glass funnel, and wash it repeatedly with ice water.

F. Next wash the tissue with acetone and air-dry.

G. Weigh the tissue in the same manner as in step A. The difference in weight represents the lignin content of the tissue.

VIII. Lignin—Spectrophotometric Procedure for Lignin from Young Herbaceous Tissue (STAFFORD, 1960)

A. EXTRACTION OF LIGNIN

1. Place the tissue in reaction vessels.

2. If present, extract the chlorophyll from the tissue with ether.

3. Thoroughly extract the tissue with distilled water.

4. To extract the lignin use 0.5 *N* NaOH at 70°C for 16 hours.

5. Remove the NaOH from the tissue, and wash the tissue twice with fresh 0.5 *N* NaOH.

6. Combine the extract and the washes, and adjust the *p*H to 8.5–9.

7. Within 3 hours analyze the extract for ultraviolet absorption and phenolic content.

B. MEASUREMENT OF LIGNIN

1. Ultraviolet absorption spectra

(a) Dilute one aliquot of the extract from the extraction procedure given above with 0.005 *N* NaOH.

(b) Dilute a second aliquot with 0.05 *M* phosphate buffer at *p*H 7.

(c) Make optical density readings of 230–450 mμ in a spectrophotometer at intervals of 5–10 mμ for each aliquot.

(d) Obtain a difference spectrum by subtracting the absorption values obtained from the two aliquots.

2. Phenol analysis

(a) Add suitable aliquots (containing 1–3 μg phenol) of the extract in 0.55 ml of distilled water to 0.4 ml of 0.5 *M* tris (hydroxymethyl) aminomethane buffer at *p*H 9.0. Then add 0.05 ml of a freshly prepared alcoholic solution containing 25 μg of 2,6-dichloro-quinonechlorimide.

(b) Incubate the mixture at room temperature for 1 hour.

(c) Measure the optical density at 610 mμ with a spectrophotometer, using guaiacol as a standard.

IX. Ascorbic Acid, Dehydroascorbic Acid, and Diketogulonic Acid—Colorimetric Method
(GLICK, ALPERT, AND STECKLEIN, 1953)

A. ASCORBIC ACID

1. To a glass-stoppered reaction vessel with a 0.25 ml capacity, add 20 μl of 0.5% oxalic acid or 5% metaphosphoric acid. Add the tissue sample to this, using a glass needle.

2. Allow to stand at room temperature for 30 minutes without stirring.

3. Add 50 μl of *n*-amyl alcohol to form a layer over the solution.

4. To the extract below the amyl alcohol layer, add 32 μl of 5 mg% 2,6-dichlorophenol indophenol. Add the dye rapidly, and bubble air into the vessel to stir the mixture. Then quickly remove the pipette, stopper

the tube, and shake it vigorously by hand for 15 seconds to extract the residual dye.

5. Centrifuge the stoppered tube for 30 seconds to separate the liquid layers.

6. Transfer a portion of the clear amyl alcohol layer to a cuvette, and measure the optical density at 546 mμ.

7. Prepare a blank by repeating the entire procedure but replacing the dye solution with water.

8. Measure the optical density of the sample at 546 mμ, using the blank n-amyl alcohol extract for the control. For a standard curve use ascorbic acid of known concentration, prepared in the same manner as the control.

B. TOTAL OF ASCORBIC ACID, DEHYDROASCORBIC ACID, AND DIKETOGULONIC ACID

1. Using a narrow, fine-tipped pipette, draw off the remaining amyl alcohol layer from the aqueous phase remaining from 6, above.

2. Mix the solution in the reaction vessel by holding the vessel against a flattened nail turning in the chuck of a power drill, and then centrifuge for several minutes. When the solution is clear, transfer a 16 μl aliquot to each of 2 reaction vessels.

3. To one vessel add 7.2 μl of 2% 2,4-dinitrophenylhydrazine (Eastman Kodak) in 9 N H_2SO_4. Use the solution in the other vessel as a blank.

4. Stopper both vessels, and let them stand for 6 hours at 37°C.

5. Place the vessels in an ice bath, and, when cold, add 7.2 μl of the 2% dinitrophenylhydrazine in 9 N H_2SO_4 to the blank, place a stopper in the vessel, and return it to the ice bath.

6. Very slowly add 27 μl of 85% H_2SO_4 to each vessel, stopper them, and return them to the ice bath.

7. Measure the optical density at 519 mμ, using the blank to balance the spectrophotometer. Compare with standards prepared by oxidizing solutions of ascorbic acid of known concentrations with dichlorophenol indophenol according to the procedure for the determination of ascorbic acid.

X. Ascorbic Acid—Ultraviolet Absorption Method (CHAYEN, 1953)

A. Use only fresh tissue. Handle the tissue carefully to prevent oxidation of the ascorbic acid.

B. Extract the tissue with 100 μl of 10% acetic acid for 30 minutes. Keep the tissue and the solution cold.

C. Using a Beckman spectrophotometer model DU with an ultra-violet adaptor and microcuvettes, measure the absorption of the extract at 248 mμ.

D. Add one drop of 1% copper sulfate, and leave the mixture exposed to the atmosphere for 2 hours.

E. Again measure the absorption at 248 mμ. The difference from the first reading is the measure of the ascorbic acid present.

F. Obtain a standard curve by preparing a series of samples of high purity L-ascorbic acid, treating them as above and plotting the difference in absorption against amount.

Microscopic Histochemistry

The usual question asked by the botanical microscopic histochemist of his material is, What is the distribution of specific saccharides or polysaccharides within the tissue? However, there are surprisingly few valid methods available in comparison with the wide range of carbohydrate materials found in the plant cell. For example, there are no procedures for the localization of soluble sugars. For the insoluble polysaccharides found in the cell and in the cell wall, there is only one method available which localizes all of them, and there are only a few which localize specific ones.

The method available for the localization of the total polysaccharide complement of the cell is an excellent histochemical procedure (Hotchkiss, 1948). The basis of the reaction is the production of aldehydes by the action of an oxidative agent on the polysaccharide. The aldehydes then react with leucofuchsin, producing highly colored complexes.

The most commonly used oxidant is periodic acid (HIO$_4$). The reaction is as follows:

For this reaction to occur the hydroxyl groups of the sugar must be free (Hale, 1957). In general, if they are substituted or involved in a linkage, they will not react. This appears to be the case for deoxyribose nucleic acid and ribose nucleic acid. Some substitutions still permit the reaction to occur. If one of the hydroxyls is substituted with an amino group, an alkyl amino group, or a carbonyl group, the reaction will occur (Hale, 1957). This means that chitin will give a positive reaction.

Color is developed by the reaction of the aldehydes with the dye fuchsin. In acid solution, with excess SO_2, fuchsin is transformed into colorless N-sulfinic acid (also called leucofuchsin), which forms highly colored addition complexes with aldehydes. This reagent is commonly called Schiff's reagent, after the German chemist who developed it for work with aldehydes. Thus, this carbohydrate test is often called the periodic acid-Schiff's (PAS) reaction.

The periodic acid-Schiff's reaction is highly suitable from a histochemical point of view, since (1) it does not cause the polysaccharide chains to be broken down, resulting in diffusion; (2) it is specific, and the basis for the reaction is understood, (3) it offers little or no possibility of interference or of false localization, and (4) it gives a color which is both intense and stable (Gomori, 1952; Hale, 1957). The reactions of polysaccharides and other saccharide complexes containing hexoses, pentoses, and hexuronic acids seem equally intense. Differences between various polysaccharides, notably a decreased staining of cellulose, have been reported, but the author has not observed such differences in a wide range of plant materials. One complicating factor, however, is that lignin reacts directly with Schiff's reagent without oxidation.

As all of the carbohydrate components of the cell wall react equally well in the periodic acid-Schiff's reaction, the reaction alone cannot be used as a differential cell wall stain. By combining this procedure with differential extraction of the various cell wall constituents, it is possible to study the distribution of the various wall materials indirectly. One possible extraction procedure is based on mounting sections of one root on 4 slides (Fig. 9-2). This permits differential extraction of adjacent sections of the same piece of tissue. One of the 4 slides is set aside as the control. The other 3 are extracted with warm ammonium oxalate to remove both the water-soluble and the pectic substances. One of these is set aside, and the tissue on the remaining 2 slides is next extracted with 4% NaOH. This treatment removes the hemicellulose from the wall. One slide is set aside and represents tissue with walls that are minus pectin and hemicellulose. The tissue on the remaining slide is extracted with 17.5% NaOH. The walls of the cells on this final slide consist only of cellulose; the pectic substances, hemicellulose, and the noncellulosic polysaccharides having been removed by the previous extractions. Finally, all the tissue is stained by the periodic acid-Schiff's reaction.

Comparison of the intensity of color in the cell walls after the various extractions gives an indication of the amount and localization of the cell wall components (Fig. 9-3). This procedure is not as ideal as one consisting of a set of reactions which would be specific for each component of the wall. On the other hand, it is better than the older staining meth-

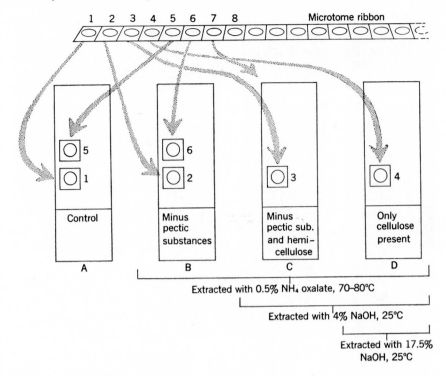

Figure 9-2. *Extraction procedure for the microscopic histochemical localization of cell wall carbohydrate constituents.*

ods because the chemical basis of the reaction is understood, the extraction procedure is based on established biochemical knowledge of the solubilities of the wall constituents, and the final preparations are stable. Moreover, this is the only method that allows, even indirectly, the localization of the noncellulosic polysaccharides and the hemicelluloses.

The method has been used successfully with onion roots (Jensen, 1960), developing fruit (Flemion, 1961), various bryophytes (Doyle, 1960; Scott, personal communication), and algae. It has not yet been used on older tissues, thus some difficulty may be encountered in using this procedure with lignified tissue. As noted earlier, Schiff's reagent reacts directly with lignin without prior oxidation, and will therefore give a positive reaction in the control, in which the tissue without treatment with periodic acid is placed in Schiff's reagent. This means, however, that the PAS will color all wall constituents, a point which may extend its usefulness. Lignin is usually found in close association with the noncellulosic polysaccharides and cellulose portions of the wall. Wilson (1961) found it impossible to extract the noncellulosic polysac-

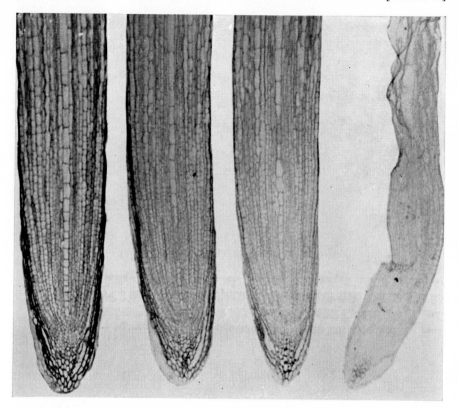

Figure 9-3. *Onion root tip sections extracted as indicated in Fig. 9-2 and stained with periodic acid-Shiff's reaction. All sections are from the same root (800×).*

charides in the wall with 17.5% NaOH after lignification had taken place. This close association of lignin with these wall components may influence the extent of their color development.

The one available specific histochemical test for a polysaccharide is the very old and very effective potassium iodide-iodine (IKI) reaction for starch. This reaction was first used by Coventow in 1825. The basis of this reaction appears to be the accumulation of iodine in the center of the helical starch molecule. The length of the starch molecule apparently determines the final color of the reaction—the shorter the molecule, the more red the color; the longer the molecule, the more blue the color. Consequently, starch in the process of formation often appears red to violet as a result of the short molecules. Amylopectin also appears red to violet because of the branched-chain configuration of the molecule.

In the literature various reactions are described as useful in localizing various polysaccharide components of the cell wall. Most of these techniques are based on nonspecific or unknown reactions, cause dissolution of the polysaccharides, or are interfered with by other components present. Unfortunately, biochemical techniques based on furfural formation are not applicable to localization procedures, since they result in dissolution of the polysaccharide, have end products that are not distinct enough in color, and may give false results with other cellular constituents.

The two "classic" cellulose tests, zinc-chlor-iodide and IKI-H_2SO_4, are based on essentially the same principle as the IKI procedure for starch. The iodine is believed to accumulate within the cellulose molecule, but this is not possible as long as the native structure of the molecule remains intact. For this reason, an acid or strong ionic salt solution is introduced to disrupt the hydrogen bonds that are essential for the maintenance of the molecular structure. The result is the separation of the glucose strands, the accumulation of iodine in the enlarged space, and the appearance of a blue color. The color will not develop in the presence of lignin; hemicellulose not only interferes but may also appear blue (Whaley, Mericle, and Heimsch, 1952). The acid causes a complete hydrolysis in a short time, resulting in a dissolution of the cellulose. Both of these procedures offer only an approximation of cellulose localization. Much better techniques are urgently needed for the localization of polysaccharides, particularly those containing pentoses and uronic acid.

The pectic substances are some of the more important chemical constituents of the cell wall, yet few good procedures exist for their localization. The standard procedure consists in staining them with ruthenium red. This method results in staining the pectic substances red if they are present in fairly high concentrations and if various ill-defined interfering substances are not present. Failure to stain does not confirm the absence of pectin. Since the basis of the reaction is not known, it must be considered only partially specific. Reeve (1959a) has devised a new, highly specific pectin localization procedure. This method is based on the reaction of alkaline hydroxylamine hydrochloride with methyl esters of pectins to produce pectin hydroxamic acid, which in turn produces red complexes with ferric ions. The method can be used for the quantitative estimation of the degree of pectin esterification with the aid of photometric techniques (Gee, Reeve, and McCready, 1959; Reeve, 1959c). The amount of color in the untreated tissue depends on the amount of esterified pectins and on the degree of esterification. The tissue can then be completely esterified and the total amount of esterification of the pectin measured. The procedure given here is a qualitative one, however, and Gee, Reeve, and McCready (1959) should be consulted for the quantitative version. For an example of the application of these methods see Reeve's (1959c) study on wall changes accompanying fruit development.

The pectin method developed by Reeve (1959a) and by Gee, Reeve, and McCready (1959) has been used by Albersheim, Mühlethaler, and Frey-Wyssling (1960) as a localization procedure for electron microscopy. Utilizing the electron density of iron, they were able to localize the site of the pectin-bound iron in the cell wall. This work is a fine example of the direction which localization studies of wall constituents must take in the future.

One additional carbohydrate cell wall constituent that must be discussed is callose. Although callose has been most widely studied in phloem, recent work by Currier (1957) makes it apparent that callose is more widely distributed in plant tissues. The chemical nature of callose is not understood, although there is some recent evidence that it is essentially a glucose noncellulosic polysaccharide, differing from cellulose in the type of linkage involved between the glucose residues. Callose can be localized and studied because of its specific affinity for certain dyes. Thus, the definition of what callose is and how it is localized are so intimately linked that a substance in a cell that gives the proper reaction is termed callose (Currier, 1957). This approach has thus far proved reasonable and has uncovered some very interesting data. But until the chemical basis of the localization procedure is understood, there is always the possibility that a variety of substances could give the same reaction and receive the same name.

The most widely used test for callose is aniline blue (Johansen, 1940), which stains the callose a clear blue. This procedure was first used in 1880 and has been used repeatedly since then. A recent adaptation of this classical procedure is the coupling of aniline blue staining with ultraviolet microscopy (Currier, 1957). The use of the fluorescence of the dye rather than its color in visible light results in a far more sensitive method (Fig. 9-4). The additional advantage of the fluorescence method is that, since the aniline blue can be used at such low concentrations at reasonably physiological pH's, it can be used as a vital stain.

Chitin, a substance which occurs in the walls of many fungi, is a carbohydrate derivative. As already noted, it reacts in the periodic acid-Schiff's test. There is another test that, with the proper controls, is quite specific for chitin (Roelofsen and Hoette, 1951). In this procedure the chitin is converted to chitosan by autoclaving the walls in 23 M KOH. The chitosan is then stained with IKI in 1% H_2SO_4. A violet color is assumed to indicate the presence of chitin; a brown color is assumed to indicate a negative reaction. To prove that the violet color is in fact due to chitosan, walls that have been autoclaved in KOH are treated in 2% acetic acid, in which the chitosan, but not the cellulose, is soluble. Staining with a mixture of IKI and 1% H_2SO_4 after the acetic acid treatment should give negative results if chitin was originally present. Cellulose can be removed with Schweitzer's reagent, which is a strong copper hydroxide solution in ammonium hydroxide.

A fine example of the use of microscopic histochemical methods in the study of fungal cell walls is the work of Fuller (1960) with the fungus *Rhizidimyces*. Earlier evidence from X-ray diffraction studies (Fuller and Barshad, 1960) indicated the existence

Figure 9-4

Localization of callose using the aniline blue-phosphorescent method (130×). [From Currier, Am. J. Botany. 44, 1957.]

of both cellulose and chitin in the wall. Histochemical localization procedures were used to confirm this conclusion, to indicate the site of the cellulose and chitin, and to resolve the chemical nature of pegs of wall material which extended into the cell. The methods used in this study and the results obtained are shown in Fig. 9-5. This study emphasizes that any one test is not adequate and that several must be used in order that a valid conclusion can be drawn from the data.

Ascorbic acid localization presents difficulties which are instructive in that they illuminate the problems of working with soluble compounds (Chayen, 1953; Jensen and Kavaljian, 1956). The localization procedure is based on the high reducing capacity of ascorbic acid in acid medium. The tissue is placed in an acidified silver nitrate solution in the dark; the black deposits of metallic silver which form are taken as the site of ascorbic acid localization. No other substance normally found in the cell can cause the reduction of silver nitrate to silver under these conditions. The reaction is therefore quite specific under these conditions and results in clear localization (Chayen, 1953).

The problems of ascorbic acid localization arise not from the final reaction but from the solubility of the ascorbic acid in aqueous solution.

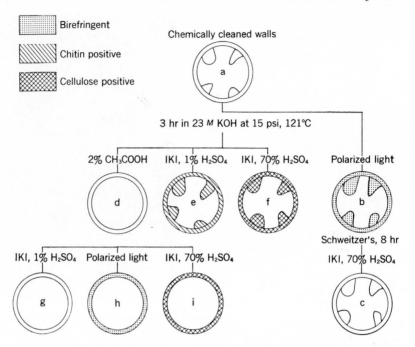

Figure 9-5. *Summary of the results obtained with the microchemical and birefringence studies of* Rhizidiomyces *cell walls. a. Chemically cleaned cell walls. b. Birefringence of chemically cleaned cell walls. c. Negative cellulose reaction of the chemically cleaned cell walls after extraction for 8 hours with Schweitzer's reagent. d. Solution of pegs in 2% acetic acid after conversion of chitin to chitosan. e. Positive chitosan reaction of the sporangium wall and pegs on its inner side. f. Positive test for cellulose in the sporangium wall, and negative test for cellulose in the pegs on its inner wall surface. g. Negative test for chitosan after it was dissolved with acetic acid. h. Birefringence of the sporangium wall after removal of the chitosan. i. Positive test for cellulose in the cell wall after removal of the chitosan. [Redrawn from Fuller, Am. J. Botany. 47, 1960.]*

This means that only freeze-dried tissue may be used and that great care must be taken to prevent the tissue from coming into contact with aqueous solutions prior to localization (Jensen and Kavaljian, 1956). This is accomplished by pressing the sections to the slide with the finger and not removing the paraffin from the sections until after the localization procedure. Paraffin is usually removed from the sections before localization, since it is assumed that the paraffin will interfere with the diffusion of the reagents or otherwise impede the reaction. Although it is true that the presence of the paraffin increases the time necessary for the reagents to penetrate and that there is a tendency to lose tissue as a result of sections floating off the slides, these difficulties are more than balanced by the increased certainty of localization and the reduction of artifact formation. By leaving the paraffin in the tissue until localization is complete, the tissue does not come in contact with organic solvents until the effect of such contact is minimal. The greatest danger in subjecting the tissue to either organic or aqueous solvents lies in the possibility of damaging or destroying various cell organelles, resulting in the diffusion of chemical constituents throughout the cell. It must always be kept in mind that in microscopic histochemistry it is not only necessary to visualize the substance of interest on a site but also to demonstrate that no possible sites have been destroyed in the localization procedure.

Many of the procedures that have just been discussed are for carbohydrate components of the cell wall. One major component of the wall—one that is not at all related to the carbohydrates—is lignin. Lignin is a complex substance the chemistry of which is but partially understood. The basic units of organization are complicated, ill-defined chemicals composed of aromatic nuclei (Siegel, 1953). Their structure includes many double bonds. The presence of double bonds means that the substance will absorb ultraviolet light. Since no other wall component possesses this characteristic, it can be used for the localization of lignin (Wardrop and Bland, 1959). The method is an excellent one but requires a complete ultraviolet microscope that is costly and difficult to use (see Chapter 3).

For reasons that are not clearly understood, lignin reacts with various dyes to give characteristic colors. One of these is Azure B, which is discussed more fully in Chapter 11. With Azure B at *p*H 4, lignin stains a clear blue-green, whereas the other components of the wall do not react. This stain has been little used by botanists but shows great promise both as a stain for the nucleic acids and for lignin.

Lignin reacts directly with Schiff's reagent, indicating the presence of natural aldehydes. This reaction has been proposed as a test for lignin (McLean and Cook, 1941) and should be useful with some materials. More work, however, is needed on the basis of the reaction with lignin, as is more knowledge of interfering substances.

A standard technique that is often used for lignin localization is the phloroglucinol reaction (Johansen, 1940). In this procedure lignin is stained in the presence of hydrochloric acid with phloroglucinol. Lignin develops a red-violet color that is reasonably specific but not too sensitive. A test that is reported as more sensitive than the phloroglucinol test (Siegel, 1953) is based on the chlorination of the lignin and on the subsequent development of a red color with sodium sulfite.

The tests for lignin involve the same difficulties as do the other wall methods. A negative reaction does not necessarily mean that lignin is absent. Further, the bases for most of the reactions are not completely understood. For these reasons, care must be taken in utilizing the lignin procedures, as much as with the pectin and cellulose methods. When used with care they can be meaningful; when used indiscriminately they can lead to incorrect conclusions.

A group of compounds which may be vaguely related to lignin are the tannins. Although they are not carbohydrates and are not usually considered as wall constituents, they are similar to lignin in that they contain polyhydroxy aromatic nuclei. The tannins are a diverse group of substances found in a wide range of plants and plant tissues (Nierenstein, 1935). The tannins are, in general, amorphous, astringent substances which combine with ferric salts to produce colors, precipitate gelatin from solution, dissolve in hot water, and contain polyhydroxyphenols or derivatives of polyhydroxyphenols (Gortner, 1949).

The traditional test for tannins is the ferric sulfate reaction, in which a blue color is assumed to indicate the presence of tannins. Ferric sulfate solutions may be applied to fresh sections or may be added to 10% formalin and used as a fixative (Reeve, 1951). This test is not particularly selective, since other plant constituents may yield a positive reaction (Reeve, 1951).

Another reaction for tannins is the nitroso reaction (Reeve, 1951). This test is based on the reaction of the phenols present with nitrous acid and on the production of a cherry-red color in the presence of a base. The color is fairly stable; Reeve (1959b) believes it to indicate the presence of catechol tannins.

This reaction was used by Reeve (1959d) as the basis for a careful quantitative study of tannin development in ripening peaches. To follow the changes in tannin content of the cells Reeve (1959a) developed a microphotometer for reflected rather than transmitted light. This careful work is another example of the interesting data which can be obtained by combining morphological and histochemical techniques in the investigation of cell development in plants.

Procedures

*1. Total Carbohydrates of Insoluble Polysaccharides
—Periodic Acid-Schiff's (PAS) Reaction*
(HOTCHKISS, 1948; MCMANUS, 1948)

A. Use chemically fixed, freeze-substituted, or freeze-dried tissue. Section at $10–20\mu$, and mount on slides with any standard adhesive (page 89).

B. Remove the paraffin, and bring the slides through a graded alcohol series to water.

C. Place the slides in an 0.5% periodic acid solution in distilled water at room temperature for 5–30 minutes. In using a new tissue, test for the optimum time in the periodic acid. For root tips, 15 minutes works well.

D. Wash in running water for 10 minutes.

E. Stain in Schiff's reagent for 10–15 minutes. Standard Schiff's reagent can be made as follows (Longley, 1952): dissolve 0.5 g of basic fuchsin (C.I. No. 677 is generally preferred) and 0.5 g of potassium or sodium metabisulfite in 100 ml of 0.15 N HCl; shake the mixture at intervals of 2–3 hours or until dye is converted to fuchsin-sulfurous acid; add 300 mg of fresh decolorizing charcoal, and shake for at least 5 minutes; filter through hard filter paper. The filtrate should be clear and colorless; if not, repeat the last two steps. Schiff's reagent should be stored in the refrigerator. It may keep for several weeks to a year, but the only way to know whether it is good or not is to try it. There is no gross indication of spoilage.

F. Rinse the sections in water, and place them in 2% sodium bisulfite for 1–2 minutes.

G. Wash in running tap water for 5–10 minutes.

H. Counterstain if desired, dehydrate, and mount.

The polysaccharides will stain an intense purplish red. The cytoplasm will remain colorless, but the nuclei may stain very lightly. The structure of the wall will be shown with remarkable clarity. Because of the use of aqueous solutions, and the washings that are required, the water soluble saccharides and polysaccharides do not become localized. However, starch reacts very strongly.

II. Extraction Procedure of Cell Wall Components for Use with the Periodic Acid-Schiff's Reaction (JENSEN, 1960)

A. Section freeze-substituted or freeze-dried tissue at 10 μ, and mount on four slides as shown in Fig. 9-2. A gelatin adhesive, made by dissolving 5 g of gelatin in 1000 ml of warm distilled water and then adding 0.5 g of chromium potassium sulfate, is recommended. Dip the clean slides into the adhesive, and allow to dry in a vertical position in order that most of the adhesive will drain off. Spread the sections on small drops of water, and then evaporate the water by placing the slides on a slide warmer. Use a minimum amount of water.

B. Remove the paraffin with xylene, and then coat the sections with celloidin by dipping the slides in an 0.5% celloidin solution in ether-alcohol. Drain the excess celloidin from the slide, and harden the celloidin by placing the slides in 95% alcohol. Finally, air dry the slides.

C. Place one slide aside. This slide will represent total cell wall constituents.

D. Place the other three slides in 0.5% ammonium oxalate in Coplin jars, and place in an oven or in a water bath at 90°C for 12 hours.

E. Carefully and gently rinse in distilled water, and air dry.

F. Place one slide aside. This slide will represent the cell wall constituents minus the pectic substances.

G. Place the remaining two slides on thin glass rods on the bottom of a large Petri dish. Carefully add 4% NaOH until the sections are covered. Extract the sections for 12 hours at 20–25°C. At the end of the extraction period remove the NaOH with a narrow necked pipette and very gentle suction. An alternate method for removing the NaOH consists in using a wick made of glass cloth (Flemion, personal communication). Since the NaOH removes both the celloidin coating and the adhesive, great care must be taken to prevent loss of the sections. *Do not* wash the sections; allow them to air dry before moving them. Ignore for the moment any crystals of NaOH that form.

H. Place one slide aside. This slide represents the cell wall with the pectic substances and the hemicellulose removed.

I. Cover the last slide (still in the Petri dish) very gently with 17.5% NaOH, and extract the sections for 12 hours at 20–25°C. At the end of this time remove the NaOH as in step G, using, if anything, even greater caution. Allow the slide to air dry. Again, *do not* wash the slide. Ignore the massive NaOH crystals.

J. This final slide represents the cell wall with the pectic substances, hemicellulose, and the noncellulosic polysaccharides removed. The only wall component remaining is cellulose.

K. Pass all slides through an alcohol series: absolute, 95%, 70%, and 50%. In the 50% alcohol the NaOH crystals will dissolve from the last two slides. When the crystals are dissolved pass the slides up through the same series. Great care should be taken in these manipulations, since the sections can easily be lost.

L. Finally, coat the slides once again with celloidin, and carry all of them through the periodic acid-Schiff's reaction, taking care to treat all the sections identically.

M. Compare the intensity of the color in the walls after completing the various extractions to obtain an indication of the amount and localization of the wall components. The comparison of color intensities between sections on separate slides, or even on the same slide, is relatively difficult. The best procedure is to take photomicrographs of the sections under rigorously standardized conditions. The prints can then be compared with one another and checked against the original sections.

N. It is frequently difficult to keep the sections on the slide during the extraction procedure and during the subsequent handling, even with the precautions mentioned above. To reduce section loss add a few drops of alcohol to the solutions to reduce surface tension. For difficult material such as woody tissues the following procedure is recommended (Wilson, 1961).

1. Mount the tissue on a slide as in the procedure given above, and remove the paraffin.

2. Place a layer of glass wool about $\frac{1}{8}$ inch thick on top of the sections, and place a blank slide on top of that. Sandwich the glass wool and sections between the two slides, and bind the slides together as a unit with aluminum wire.

3. Extract the sections by placing this unit in the various solvents. The glass wool is porous enough to permit ready penetration of the solvents.

4. Perform all subsequent reactions with the unit intact. After the sections have been dehydrated and cleared in xylene unwind the wire, take off the top slide, and remove most of the glass wool. Leave just enough glass wool to hold the sections on the slide.

5. Mount the remaining glass wool and the sections beneath in piccolyte. The refractive index of the piccolyte and glass wool is so similar that the remaining glass wool does not interfere with observation or measurements.

III. Starch—IKI Reaction (JOHANSEN, 1940)

A. Use fresh, fixed, freeze-substituted or freeze-dried tissue.

B. Mount the sections in IKI solution. To make this solution dissolve 2 g of KI in 100 ml of water, and then dissolve 0.2 g of iodine in the KI solution.

The starch will appear blue to black in a few minutes. Newly formed starch may appear red to purple.

IV. Pectic Substances—Ruthenium Red Method (JOHANSEN, 1940)

A. Use fresh, FAA-fixed, freeze-dried, or freeze-substituted material.

B. Place the sections in aqueous ruthenium red (1:5000) until the walls are red.

C. Mount in water or gelatin. Pectic substances will appear pink to red.

V. Pectins—Hydroxylamine-ferric Chloride Reaction
(REEVE, 1959a)

A. Comparatively thick, fresh sections are better than sections of paraffin-embedded tissue. Allow the size of the cell to govern the thickness of the section. Cut the sections either by hand or with a sliding microtome.

B. Place the section on a slide in 5–10 drops of an alkaline hydroxylamine solution for 5 minutes or longer. Use fresh hydroxylamine reagent. Prepare this by mixing equal volumes of sodium hydroxide (14 g in 100 ml of 60% alcohol) and hydroxylamine hydrochloride (14 g in 100 ml of 60% alcohol).

C. Add to the slide an equal volume of a solution of 1 part concentrated hydrochloric acid and 2 parts 95% alcohol to acidify the reaction mixture.

D. Remove the excess solution from the section, and flood the section with 10% solution of ferric chloride in 60% alcohol containing 0.1 N hydrochloric acid.

Esterified pectins will appear red. Methylation of the sections will increase the intensity of the reaction. This can be accomplished by placing the sections in a hot solution of absolute methyl alcohol containing 0.5 N hydrochloric acid.

VI. Cellulose—Zinc-chlor-iodide Reaction
(RAWLINS AND TAKAHASHI, 1952)

A. Use fresh, FAA- or alcohol-fixed, freeze-substituted or freeze-dried tissue. Do not use tissue fixed in solutions containing chromium, such as Navashin's solution.

B. Mount the sections in several drops of zinc-chlor-iodide. To make this dissolve 50 g of zinc chloride and 16 g of KI in 17 ml of water. Add an excess of iodine, and allow to stand for several days. Pour the supernatant into brown dropping bottles.

C. Walls containing large amounts of cellulose will stain blue; walls containing large amounts of lignin, cutin, suberin, or chitin will appear yellow to orange. Only if these substances are removed will the cellulose stain. Some hemicellulose will stain blue. Thus, in this procedure a lack of color does not indicate the absence of cellulose; on the other hand the presence of color is not specific for cellulose alone.

VII. Cellulose—IKI-H₂SO₄ Method (JOHANSEN, 1940)

A. Place the fresh sections in IKI solution (see Procedure III) for 15 minutes or longer.

B. Mount the section in IKI under a cover glass, add a drop of 65% H_2SO_4 at the side of the cover glass, and allow it to diffuse under the glass.

Walls containing cellulose will stain dark blue; lignin will stain orange to yellow. As the H_2SO_4 reacts on the wall, the wall will swell, with the result that even in lignified walls the cellulose may be seen. In the middle lamella, where the cellulose and lignin are in very close relation, a green color may be evident. After a relatively short time the H_2SO_4 will dissolve the cellulose, and the tissue will fall to pieces. The method works well on wood.

VIII. Chitin (ROELOFSEN AND HOETTE, 1951)

A. Autoclave the cells or tissue at 15 psi and 121°C in 23 M KOH. The chitin will be converted to chitosan at this stage.

B. Wash the cells, and place them on a slide with a few drops of IKI in 1% H_2SO_4.

Chitosan, if present, will stain violet. Brown is considered a negative response. Treat a control with 2% acetic acid before applying the IKI-1% H_2SO_4. The chitosan is soluble in the acetic acid, whereas the cellulose, if present, is not. Cellulose can be dissolved in Schweitzer's reagent, which is made by dissolving as much copper hydroxide as possible in undiluted commercial ammonium hydroxide.

IX. Callose—Aniline Blue-Visible Light Method (JOHANSEN, 1940)

A. Place the fresh tissue in a 0.005% solution of aniline blue in 50% alcohol for 4–24 hours.

B. Rinse the sections in water, and mount in gelatin.

Callose should stain blue. Resorcin blue (lacmoid) may be used in place of aniline blue. Cotton blue may also be used.

X. Callose-Aniline Blue-Fluorescence Method (CURRIER, 1957; CURRIER AND STRUGGER, 1956)

A. Use fresh sections directly or store the sections in 0.1 M sucrose in 0.15 M phosphate buffer at pH 7 for short periods. Tissue may be fixed in FAA but must be washed thoroughly in tap water before staining.

B. Stain the sections for 10 minutes in a solution of 0.005% water-soluble aniline blue in 0.15 M K_2HPO_4 at pH 8.2. When this solution is first made up it will be colored, but after several hours it will become essentially colorless. Increasing the pH to 9 or 10 will increase the intensity of the stain, but will decrease its usefulness as a vital stain.

C. Mount the sections in buffered sucrose or in the staining solution.

D. Observe the preparations with a fluorescence microscope. Ultraviolet transmission filters UG_1 (2 mm) and UG_1 (4 mm), which have maximum transmissivity at 366 mμ, are recommended.

Under the fluorescence microscope callose will appear as a yellow fluorescence. Tissue that has not been stained must also be observed in the fluorescence microscope to determine the primary fluorescence of the tissue.

XI. Ascorbic Acid—Silver Method
(JENSEN AND KAVALJIAN, 1956)

A. Use only freeze-dried tissue.

B. Section at 10 μ, and mount the sections on slides coated lightly with Haupt's adhesive by pressing them onto the slide with a rolling motion of the finger. Before use, allow the slides to remain overnight on a warming table at 40°C.

C. Place the slides with the paraffin still in the tissue in an atmosphere of H_2S for 15 minutes. During handling of the tissue much of the ascorbic acid will be oxidized to dehydroascorbic acid, which will not react in this test. The H_2S will reduce the dehydroascorbic acid back to ascorbic acid.

D. Now pass high purity nitrogen over the tissue to remove the H_2S.

E. Place the tissue with the paraffin still in place in a 10% silver nitrate solution in 3% acetic acid for 4–24 hours. Then rapidly wash the sections in water, and dehydrate in 95% and absolute ethyl alcohol. Remove the paraffin, and mount. These steps, following the placing of the tissue in the silver nitrate, must be carried out in the dark with only a weak red safety light.

F. Stain the tissue by adding crystal violet in absolute alcohol to the xylene. In this way the paraffin is removed and the tissue is stained at the same time.

G. Three types of controls are necessary. One is placed in 3% acetic acid without the silver nitrate. The second is placed in a copper sulfate solution for a short time and is then localized. The copper sulfate acts as an oxidizing agent, converting all the ascorbic acid to dehydroascorbic acid. Any positive reactions in this control are not due to the presence of ascorbic acid. The third, a morphological control, is handled in the same manner as the other tissue but is stained with azure B or Heidenhain's haematoxylin. The morphological control is necessary to show the effect of the treatments on the morphology of the cells.

The essential point to keep in mind in working with ascorbic acid is that it is highly water soluble and may be easily moved from one site to another in the tissue or may be lost from the tissue altogether. This is why only freeze-dried tissue is used, and why the paraffin is kept in the tissue during the localization procedure.

XII. Lignin—Phloroglucinol Test
(JOHANSEN, 1940; SIEGEL, 1953)

A. Use fresh, fixed, freeze-substituted or freeze-dried tissue.

B. If the tissue is paraffin infiltrated, remove the paraffin, and bring to water.

C. Place on the slide a large drop of a saturated aqueous solution of phloroglucinol in 20% HCl.

D. Cover with a cover slip. The preparation is not permanent. Lignin will appear red-violet.

XIII. Lignin—Chlorine-sulfite Test (SIEGEL, 1953)

Steps A and B are the same as in the preceding procedure.

C. Place the slide in a fresh, saturated, acidified calcium hypochlorite (Clorox does well) solution for 5 minutes.

D. Then place in a fresh, cold 1% solution of sodium sulfite.

E. A bright red color will develop within a few minutes but will gradually fade to a brownish hue in 35–45 minutes.

XIV. Lignin—Schiff's Reaction (MCLEAN AND COOK, 1941)

A. Use fresh tissue or tissue fixed in fixatives which do not contain heavy metals.

B. Place the sections in Schiff's reagent (see p. 199) for 15 minutes to 4 hours.

Lignin will stain purplish-red. The only other wall substance which normally reacts under these conditions are waxes in cuticle. The test, however, is for aldehydes, and other methods must be used to confirm the presence of lignin.

XV. Tannins—Ferric Sulfate Reaction (REEVE, 1959b)

A. Cut fresh sections of the tissue, and place directly in a 0.5–1.0% solution of ferric sulfate or ferric chloride in 0.1 N HCl.

B. An alternate procedure is to fix the tissue in 10% formalin containing 2% ferric sulfate. Then dehydrate, paraffin infiltrate, and section the tissue.

In either procedure (A or B) a blue precipitate indicates the presence of tannins.

XVI. Tannins—Nitroso Reaction (REEVE, 1951)

A. To fresh sections add equal volumes of the following reagents in succession: (1) 10% sodium nitrite, (2) 20% urea, (3) 10% acetic acid.

B. Wait 3–4 minutes, and then add 2 volumes of 2 N sodium hydroxide.

A cherry-red color indicates the presence of catechol tannins. For controls add the sodium nitrate last or reverse the acid and base.

LITERATURE CITED

Albersheim, P., D. Mühlethaler, and A. Frey-Wyssling, 1960. Stained pectin as seen in the electron microscope. *J. Biophys. and Biochem. Cytol.*, **8**: 501–516.

Ashwell, G., 1957. Colorimetric analysis of sugars, pp. 74–105. In *Methods of Enzymology*, vol. 3. S. P. Colowick and N. O. Kaplan (Editors). Academic, New York.

Avery, G. S., Jr. and F. Engel, 1954. Total nitrogen in relation to age and position of cells in *Avena* coleoptiles. *Am. J. Botany*, **41**:310–315.

Bishop, C. T., S. T. Bayley and G. Setterfield, 1958. Chemical constitution of the primary cell walls of *Avena* coleoptiles. *Plant Physiol.*, **30**: 283–289.

Bondi, A., and H. Meyer, 1956. Lignins in young plants. *Biochem. J.*, **43**:769–778.

Boroughs, H. and J. Bonner, 1953. Effects of IAA on metabolic pathways. *Arch. Biochem. and Biophys.*, **46**: 279–290.

Chayen, J., 1953. Ascorbic acid and its intracellular localization, with special reference to plants. *Intern. Rev. Cytol.*, **2**:78–132.

Currier, H. B., 1957. Callose substance in plant cells. *Am. J. Botany*, **44**:478–488.

Currier, H. B. and S. Strugger, 1956. Aniline blue and fluorescence microscopy of callose in bulb scales of *Allium cepa* L. *Protoplasma*, **45**:552–559.

Dische, Z., 1955. New color reactions for the determination of sugars in polysaccharides. *Methods Biochem. Analysis*, **2**:313–358.

Doyle, W. L., 1960. The morphology and affinities of the Liverwort *Geothallus*. Thesis (PhD in Botany). Univ. of California, Berkeley.

Flemion, F., 1961. Cytochemical studies of the developing primary cell wall in the apical shoots of normal and physiologically dwarf peach seedlings. *Plant Physiol.*, **36**: supp. XXVII.

Fuller, M. S., 1960. Biochemical and microchemical study of the cell walls of *Rhizidiomyces* sp. *Am. J. Botany*, 47:838–842.

Fuller, M. S. and I. Barshad, 1960. Chitin and cellulose in the cell walls of *Rhizidiomyces* sp. *Am. J. Botany*, 47: 105–109.

Gee, M., R. M. Reeve, and R. M. McCready, 1959. Measurement of plant pectic substances. Reaction of hydroxylamine with pectinic acids. Chemical studies and histochemical estimation of degree of esterification of pectic substances in fruit. *Agr. and Food Chem.*, 7:34–38.

Glick, D., 1938. The quantitative distribution of ascorbic acid in the developing barley embryo. *Compt. rend. trav. lab. Carlsberg, Sér. chim.*, 21:203–210.

Glick, D., M. Alpert, and H. R. Stecklein, 1953. Studies in histochemistry. XXVII. The determination of L-ascorbic acid, and dehydro-L-ascorbic acid plus diketo-L-gulonic acid in microgram quantities of tissue. *J. Histochem. and Cytochem.*, 1:326–335.

Gomori, G., 1952. *Microscopic Histochemistry, Principles and Practice.* Univ. of Chicago Press, Chicago.

Gortner, R. A., 1949. *Outlines of Biochemistry.* 3rd Ed. Wiley, New York.

Hale, A. J., 1957. The histochemistry of polysaccharides. *Intern. Rev. Cytol.*, 6:193–263.

Hotchkiss, R. D., 1948. A microchemical reaction resulting in the staining of polysaccharide structures in fixed tissue preparations. *Arch. Biochem.*, 16:131–141.

Hough, L., J. K. N. Jones, and W. H. Wadman, 1950. Quantitative analysis of mixtures of sugars by the method of partition chromatography. V. Improved methods for the separation and detection of the sugars and their methylated derivatives on the paper chromatogram. *J. Chem. Soc.* (London), 1950 (7): 1702–1706.

Jensen, W. A., 1955. A morphological and biochemical analysis of the early phases of cellular growth in the root tip of *Vacia faba. Exptl. Cell Research*, 8:506–522.

———, 1960. The composition of the developing primary wall in onion root tip cells. II. Cytochemical localization. *Am. J. Botany*, 47:287–295.

Jensen, W. A. and M. Ashton, 1960. The composition of the developing primary wall in onion root tip cells. I. Quantitative analyses. *Plant Physiol.*, 35:313–323.

Jensen, W. A. and L. G. Kavaljian, 1956. The cytochemical localization of ascorbic acid in root tip cells. *J. Biophys. Biochem. Cytol.*, 2:87–92.

Jermyn, M. A. and F. A. Isherwood, 1949. Improved separation of sugars on the paper partition chromatogram. *Biochem. J.*, 44:402–407.

———, 1956. Changes in the cell wall of the pear during ripening. *Biochem. J.*, 64:123–132.

Johansen, D. A., 1940. *Plant Microtechnique.* McGraw-Hill, New York.

Longley, J. B., 1952. Effectiveness of Schiff variants in the periodic-Schiff and Feulgen nucleal technics. *Stain Technol.*, 27:161–169.

McComb, E. A. and R. M. McCready, 1952. Extraction and determination of total pectic materials in fruits. *Anal. Chem.*, 24:1986–1988.

McCready, R. M., J. Guggolz, V. Silviera, and H. S. Owens, 1950. Determination of starch and amylase in vegetables. *Anal. Chem.*, 22:1156–1158.

McCready, R. M. and E. A. McComb, 1952. Colorimetric determination of pectic substances, *Anal. Chem.*, 24: 1630–1632.

McLean, R. C. and W. R. I. Cook,

1941. *Plant Science Formulae.* Macmillan, London.

McManus, J. F. A., 1948. Histological and histochemical uses of periodic acid. *Stain Technol.,* 23:99–108.

Nierenstein, M., 1935. *The Natural Organic Tannins: History, Chemistry, Distribution.* Sherwood Press, Cleveland.

Partridge, S. M., 1946. Application of the paper partition chromatogram to the qualitative analysis of reducing sugars. *Nature,* 158:270–271.

Rawlins, T. E., and W. N. Takashi, 1952. *Techniques of Plant Histochemistry and Virology.* National Press, Millbrae, California.

Reeve, R. M., 1951. Histochemical tests for polyphenols in plant tissues. *Stain Technol.,* 26:91–96.

Reeve, R. M., 1959a. A specific hydroxylamine-ferric chloride reaction for histochemical localization of pectin. *Stain Technol.,* 34:209–211.

———, 1959b. Histological and histochemical changes in developing and ripening peaches. I. The catechol tannins. *Am. J. Botany,* 46:210–217.

———, 1959c. Histological and histochemical changes in developing and ripening peaches. II. The cell walls and pectins. *Am. J. Botany,* 46:241–247.

———, 1959d. Histological and histochemical changes in developing and ripening peaches. III. Catechol tannin content per cell. *Am. J. Botany,* 46:645–650.

Reid, M. E., 1941a. A study of physical and chemical changes in the growing region of primary roots of cowpea seedlings. *Am. J. Botany,* 28:45–51.

———, 1941b. Relation of vitamin C to cell size in the growing region of the primary root of cowpea seedlings. *Am. J. Botany,* 28:410–415.

Roelofsen, P. A. and I. Hoette, 1951. Chitin in the cell wall of yeasts. *Antonie van Leeuwenhoek,* 17:297–313.

Setterfield, G. and S. T. Bayley, 1961. Structure and physiology of cell walls. *Ann. Rev. Plant Physiol.,* 12:35–62.

Siegel, S. M., 1953. On the biosynthesis of lignin. *Physiol. Plantarium,* 6:134–139.

Stafford, H. A., 1960. Differences between lignin-like polymers formed by peroxidation of eugenol and ferulic acid in leaf sections of *Phleum. Plant Physiol.,* 35:108–114.

Stark, S. M., 1950. Determination of pectic substances in cotton. *Anal. Chem.,* 22:1158–1160.

Wardrop, A. B. and D. E. Bland, 1959. The process of lignification in woody plants. *4th Intern. Congress of Biochem.,* 2:92–116.

Whaley, W. G., L. W. Mericle, and C. Heimsch, 1952. The wall of the meristematic cell. *Am. J. Botany,* 39:20–26.

Wilson, B. F., 1961. Cell wall development of cambial derivatives in *Abies concolor.* Doctoral Thesis, Univ. of Calif., Berkeley.

CHAPTER 10

Proteins

Quantitative Histochemistry

More quantitative histochemical analyses of plant tissue have been made of protein than of any other cellular constituent. The reason for this is that protein content has repeatedly been used as an expression of the amount of protoplasm present in the cell, as a measure of cell growth, and as a basis for the expression of other cell constituents or activities. Protein determinations were used in this way in studies of cell development in *Avena* coleoptiles (Avery and Engel, 1954), cherry embryos (Olney and Pollock, 1960), shoot apex and leaf tissue (Sunderland, Heyes, and Brown, 1957), and roots (Brown and Broadbent, 1950; Erickson and Goddard, 1951; Jensen, 1955).

Most of the procedures for protein which have been used with plant tissue are based on the measurement of the nitrogen content of the protein. Nitrogen, however, is found in compounds other than proteins. The first problem in protein-nitrogen determinations, therefore, is the separation of the proteins from the rest of the nitrogen-containing compounds of the cell. The two major sources of nonprotein nitrogen in higher plants are the soluble amino acids and the nucleic acids. The usual procedure employed to separate the three groups consists in treating the cell with a chemical that denatures and precipitates the proteins while keeping the soluble nitrogen compounds in solution and causing the nucleic acids to become soluble. With the proteins insoluble and the rest of the nitrogen compounds soluble, it is an easy matter to remove the soluble nitrogen and measure the amount remaining as protein nitrogen. One of the most commonly used, and perhaps the best, protein precipitant available is trichloroacetic acid (TCA). In many tissues the amount of nitrogen present in the nucleic acids is so small in relation to the protein nitrogen and the soluble nitrogen that it can be disregarded. In fungi, the nitrogen present in the wall as part of the chitin may be significant in amount and may influence protein analyses in these plants.

There are a number of ways in which nitrogen can be measured histo-chemically. All, however, involve the digestion of either the protein extract or the tissue and the production of ammonia. This is accomplished by a digestion mixture of sulfuric acid and heavy-metal ions. The tissue is heated in the digestion mixture under conditions which result in the complete breakdown of the tissue but which do not cause the loss of nitrogen from the sample. These conditions have been carefully worked out in the procedures given in this chapter. A long, fairly narrow tube is usually used for the digestion. Only the bottom of the tube is heated, the upper parts of the tube remaining relatively cool. Thus, the acid vaporizes from the heat in the tube bottom, ascends as a vapor to the top portion of the tube, cools, condenses, and flows down the sides to the bottom of the tube. During digestion of the tissue the solution may turn a dark brown or black from the carbon present in the material. As this color interferes in various ways in many of the procedures for the determination of ammonia, the sample is decolorized by the addition of strong H_2O_2 and additional heat. At the end of the entire digestion process the nitrogen is present as ammonia, and is dissolved in the clear acid-digestion fluid. As an alternate to this type of digestion procedure, the sample may be digested in a sealed tube. For an example of this method see Chapter 13, Procedure I.

A number of ways exist by which the histochemist can measure the ammonia content of the digested sample, the choice depending on the amount of ammonia present and on the presence of other substances in the digest.

One of the easiest methods is that of Levy (1936). In this method the ammonia is left in the digest solution, which is diluted with water; Ness-ler's reagent is then added, forming a colored complex with ammonia. The absorption is measured in a colorimeter or spectrophotometer. This method, which is technically simple, is not as sensitive as some of the other procedures. A problem which arises in using this method with plant tissue is that silica, which is present in the walls of some algae, horsetails, and grasses, causes the color product to precipitate. For an example of the use of this procedure with plant tissue, see Jensen (1955).

The type of problem presented by the presence of silica or other inter-fering substances can be avoided by the use of techniques in which the ammonia is removed from the digestion mixture. This is accomplished by neutralizing the digestion mixture, thus releasing the ammonia, which diffuses to an acid solution the molarity of which is known. Part of the acid is neutralized by the ammonia; the remaining acid is titrated and the amount of ammonia present calculated. This is the famous Kjeldahl nitrogen procedure which has been adapted to the micro scale.

A large number of such nitrogen procedures are available. In general there is a direct correlation between the amount of nitrogen which can be measured and the difficulty of the technique: the more sensitive the method, the harder it is to perform.

One of the easiest, developed by Conway (1935), has the same range of ammonia determination as does the direct Nesslerization procedure discussed above. In this procedure the digestion is first carried out in a digestion tube. The digest is then transferred to a special diffusion cell. This cell consists of a squat dish with a center well. The digest is placed in the outer well, and a standard acid solution is placed in the center well. Base is added to the digest and the cell sealed. The ammonia then diffuses to the standard acid in the center well, which is then titrated after the addition of an indicator dye. This type of nitrogen analysis was used by Olney and Pollock (1960) in their work on cherry embryos. Little equipment is required for this type of analysis, and special cells, although helpful, are not necessary. Examples of nitrogen analyses that utilize this principle, and which require an absolute minimum of equipment, are found in the work of Boell (1945).

For extremely accurate nitrogen analyses there are the ultramicro versions of the diffusion-titration methods, some of which have an accuracy of 0.005 μg of nitrogen. These procedures, first developed by the Carlsberg group (Linderstrøm-Lang and Holter, 1933; Bottelier, Holter, and Linderstrøm-Lang, 1943; Bruel, Holter, Linderstrøm-Lang, and Rosits, 1947), have undergone many modifications as a result of attempts to simplify the technical manipulations yet maintain a high degree of accuracy and sensitivity. These attempts have not been fully successful, thus the quest continues. The procedure given in this chapter was developed by Doyle and Omoto (1950), and represents a compromise between sensitivity and technical difficulty. This is not to imply that the procedure is easy; on the contrary, it simply means that others are more difficult.

In the Doyle and Omoto method of nitrogen determination the digestion is performed in a fairly long, narrow tube. Since the next step, which involves the diffusion of the ammonia, is better performed in a shorter tube, the digest must be transferred. The rather elaborate procedure used in this transfer is designed to insure the complete removal of the digest from the original tube. To the digest, now at the bottom of a fresh tube (called the distillation tube), is added enough base to release all the ammonia in the digest. A seal consisting of a solution of known molarity, plus an indicator, is placed in the neck of the distillation tube. After the ammonia has diffused to this drop, a flea is added (see p. 24), and the titration is performed with a microburette.

In protein determinations, particularly when the nitrogen content is being measured, great care should be taken to avoid contaminating the samples or the tubes with tobacco or ashes of tobacco. Furthermore, as ammonia is present in tobacco smoke, and will be readily absorbed in the acid used in the procedure, it is advisable not to blow tobacco smoke over the tubes at any stage of the determination. With the ultramicro methods, smoking must not even be allowed in the same room. The various nitrogen methods given in this chapter form an important part of many quantitative histochemical investigations. The person entering histochemical research should seriously consider becoming familiar with all of them.

Protein measurement is also possible by methods which involve the direct combination of the protein molecule with a dye. These methods have not been used as widely as the nitrogen procedures for several reasons. The difficulty of extracting proteins from the tissue in a native state is one. Another is the possibility that interfering substances may be present in the cell, which may increase or decrease the color produced. Next, there is the difficulty of expressing the data. A standard must be used, but selection of the standard is difficult. Ideally, the standard would be a protein identical to the protein present in the tissue. Since such proteins are difficult or impossible to obtain, the measurements become arbitrary. Finally, the methods are not very sensitive. The sum of these complications is that protein measurement by color complexes is most useful where relative values are meaningful. The advantages of the methods are that they are simple, fast, and reasonably accurate for estimating protein content.

The most widely used of these protein methods is the biuret test. This colorimetric method is based on the formation, at basic pH's, of a purple complex between copper salts and compounds containing two or more peptide bonds. Racusen and Johnstone (1961) have examined the use of this method with a variety of plants and plant parts and have found that the cells must usually be extracted first with hot ethyl alcohol and perchloric acid before the method will work. They also found that the efficiency of the method differed with the material. For example, in bean leaves the estimation of protein by the biuret test and nitrogen analyses agreed within 5%, whereas in *Chlorella* the agreement was less than 15%. The biuret test is not very sensitive, and, in addition, the presence of ammonium salts interferes. For another similar procedure, which uses a slightly different reagent, the Folin phenol reagent, see Lowry, Rosebrough, Farr, and Randall, (1951).

The method of Nayyar and Glick (1954) is also based on the formation of a complex between a dye and the protein. In this procedure the dye is bromosulfalein. The protein and the dye form an insoluble complex that precipitates out of the solution. Starting with a known amount of dye in solution, the amount of dye remaining in solution is proportional to the amount of protein. This method has never been used on plant material, but appears to have potential application. The possible interference of cell wall materials will have to be considered in work with plant tissues.

Procedures

I. *Total Protein—Colorimetric Procedure* (JENSEN, 1955)

A. Use 100- to 200-μ sections of fresh, freeze-substituted or freeze-dried tissue. Place the tissue in 10 mm-tubes. If paraffin-infiltrated tissue is used remove the paraffin with toluene, and rinse the tissue with absolute alcohol.

B. Add to the tissue 0.3 ml of cold 10% trichloroacetic acid (TCA). Remove this, and add fresh, cold TCA. Let stand for 30 minutes in the cold (4°C), and then remove the TCA. Either discard the TCA or combine the two solutions, reduce the volume by heating in an oven, and measure the nitrogen content. This will give the value for the soluble nitrogen compounds present.

C. Add 30 μl of 50% H_2SO_4 to the tissue.

D. Place the tubes containing the tissue in the acid in aluminum blocks with shallow ($\frac{1}{4}$ inch deep) holes, and place on an electric hot plate with a continuous temperature range. Small "Tempco" hot plates work well.

E. Heat slowly until most of the water is driven off. Then raise the temperature to 250°C, and hold at that temperature for at least 1 hour. Great care must be taken to avoid overheating the tubes while a significant amount of water remains, or the contents will spurt from the tube and ruin the determination.

F. Cool the tubes and the aluminum block.

G. Add 20 μl of superoxal (30% H_2O_2) to each tube. Use great care in handling the superoxal. If it should contact the skin, *wash immediately*.

H. Replace the tubes and the block on the hot plate, and carefully heat as in step E to 250°C. Hold at that temperature for at least 1 hour. Care must be taken to heat the tubes long enough after the addition of the superoxal such that all the peroxide is removed. The solution in the tube should now be crystal clear. If it is not, repeat steps F, G, and H.

I. Cool the tubes, and then add 2 ml of distilled water.

J. Then, using a stream of air for mixing, add 0.5 ml of Nessler's color reagent. The color reagent can be easily obtained from a large number of chemical supply houses, it is ready to use after diluting 1:4 with 10% NaOH. The diluted solution will not keep.

K. After 15 minutes read the color at 425 mμ. The color should be read as soon as possible after the 15-minute development period, since it is stable only a short time.

L. Obtain a standard curve by placing 10 μl (1.0 μg), 20 μl (2 μg), and 30 μl (3 μg) of the standard stock solution of $(NH_4)_2SO_4$, which contains 0.1 mg of nitrogen/ml, in tubes and running the same procedure as for the tissue.

M. The range of this method is 0.5–10.0 μg $\pm$ 0.05 μg of nitrogen.

This procedure is a modification of Levy's (1936) method, which has been used with plant tissue by Jensen (1955).

II. Nitrogen Determination—Conway Diffusion Method
(CONWAY AND BYRNE, 1933; CONWAY, 1935; KIRK, 1950)

A. Prepare and digest the sample in essentially the same manner as in Procedure I.

B. At the end of the digestion period, cool the digest, and transfer the digest to a Conway diffusion cell. This is a dish with an inner well and a glass top. Place the digest in the outer ring of the cell.

C. Place a measured amount of 0.04 N H_2SO_4 containing neutral red in the center well, and add an amount of 18 N NaOH equal to the digest in the outer ring (solid pellets of NaOH may be added instead of liquid, Boell, 1945).

D. Immediately place the cover on the cell, using Vaseline to seal the edge.

E. After 2–4 hours open the vessel, and titrate the acid with 0.02 N NaOH, using a microburette.

III. Nitrogen Determination—Micro-Conway Diffusion
Method (OLNEY AND POLLOCK, 1960)

A. Place the tissue or extract in the bottom of straight-walled 10 × 75 mm Pyrex brand ignition tubes.

B. Use a constriction pipette to add 24 μl of a digestion mixture. To make the digestion mixture add to 100 ml of 50% H_2SO_4 1 g each of $CuSO_4$, K_2SO_4, and SeO_2.

C. Push the tubes into an electrically heated sand bath to a depth of about 2 cm. Support the tubes in place with a perforated asbestos plate. This plate will also insulate the upper part of the tube.

D. Heat the tissue and digestion mixture at 250°C for about 3 hours.

E. When the digest has cooled place 18-μl aliquots in paraffined vessels 13 mm in diameter by 13 mm deep. Add 18 μl of 8 N NaOH to the extract, and stir with a magnetic flea.

F. Cover the vessel with a glass plate. This plate has a depression in its center made with a dull No. 1 cork borer. Cover the plate with "Parafilm" and an 18-μl drop of 0.04 N H_2SO_4 containing bromocresol green indicator is placed in depression. Place the plate drop down over the vessel, and seal the edge with Vaseline.

G. Allow diffusion to continue for 70 minutes at room temperature.

H. Transfer the receiving acid on the glass plate to a small reaction vessel. Rinse the plate, and add the rinse to the vessel.

I. Titrate with 0.01 N NaOH, using a horizontal microburette, and mix with a magnetic flea.

This modification of the Conway method is sensitive to 0.05 μg nitrogen per diffusion vessel, and has been used on plant tissue. The digestion procedure used here is from Boell and Shen (1954).

IV. Total Protein—Titration Method
(DOYLE AND OMATO, 1950)

A. Use fresh, freeze-dried, or freeze-substituted tissue. Section the tissue, and place in 6×25 mm siliconed tubes. To silicone the tubes fill them with a 5% solution of G.E. Dri-film FC-87 in chloroform, pour out the solution, and place the tubes in a drying oven at 100°C for 2 hours to overnight.

B. Remove the paraffin with toluene, and rinse with toluene.

C. To each tube add 5 μl of a mixture made with 1 g of copper sulfate pentahydrate, 10 g of potassium sulfate, and 5 ml of concentrated sulfuric acid and 100 ml of water. Also add 10 μl of 50% sulfuric acid.

D. Place the tubes in an aluminum block drilled with holes 7 mm in diameter and 7–10 mm deep. Heat the block slowly from 90°C to 130°C and then to 170°C to remove most of the water. This should take about an hour.

E. When the tubes are free of condensed water transfer to a second aluminum block at 245 ± 5°C for 2 hours. Adjust the temperature such that a ring of condensed acid forms 5–10 mm above the surface of the block.

F. After 2 hours cool the tubes, and add 5 μl of superoxal (30% H_2O_2). Then repeat the two heatings, but for only 30 minutes at 245°C.

G. Cool the tubes, and add 10 μl of saturated potassium persulfate, and repeat the two heatings again for 30 minutes at 245°C. Finally, cool the tubes.

H. Discharge a 50-μl pipette of redistilled water onto a clean hydrophobic Teflon plate in three unequal drops. Insert the same pipette into the tube, and suck as much of the acid digest up as possible; then transfer to a fresh tube. Draw the smallest of the three drops up into the pipette, and discharge it onto the wall of the digestion tube to rinse it down. Now draw this drop up again, and transfer it to the acid digest in the second tube. Repeat the same process for the other two drops, using the smaller one first. *Do not* let the pipette touch the wall of the digestion tube except near the tip.

I. To the transferred digest add 20 μl of 13 N sodium hydroxide, and, immediately after, add a liquid seal of 100 μl of 0.05 M potassium dihydrogen phosphate containing 0.103 mg/ml of bromocresol green W.S. A seal is a drop large enough to completely fill the neck of the tube and is held in place by the surface tension of the sides of the tube (see Fig. 10-1). Mix the digest by rotating the tube, then close the tube with a cap made of a piece of rubber tubing and a glass rod.

J. Distil for 8–16 hours at 25°C. The distillation time may be decreased by half submerging the tubes in a 40°C water bath.

K. Drop a flea into the neck seal, and titrate the solution with 0.05 M hydrochloric acid containing 0.103 mg/ml of bromocresol green W.S. directly into the liquid seal to an end point at pH 4.5–4.6 (Fig. 10-2). Use a titration end-point standard (0.103 mg/ml of bromocresol green in 0.2 M acetate buffer, pH 4.5) to approximate the end point for the first blank. Then discard the acetate standard, and use the first blank as the matching standard for the series.

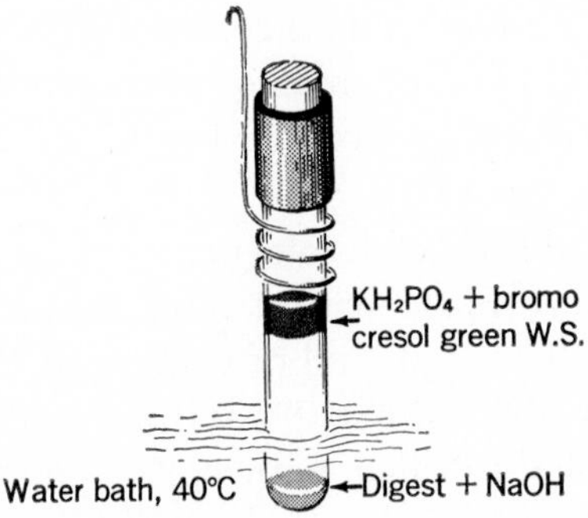

KH$_2$PO$_4$ + bromo cresol green W.S.

Water bath, 40°C — Digest + NaOH

Figure 10-1
Diffusion vessel in micronitrogen determination.

L. Run blanks and standards based on ammonium salt.

M. The range of this method is 0.1–10 μg $\pm$ 0.01 μg of nitrogen.

This procedure is a modification of the Carlsberg micro-Kjeldahl methods, which are more sensitive but also more difficult. For these elegant methods see Bottelier, Holter, and Linderstrøm-Lang (1943) and Bruel, Holter, Linderstrøm-Lang, and Rosits (1947).

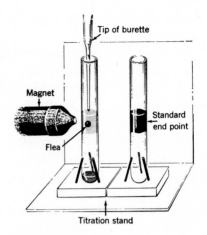

Figure 10-2
Titration in neck seal of diffusion vessel.

V. Total Protein—Biuret Method
(RACUSEN AND JOHNSTONE, 1961)

A. Most plant tissue must be pretreated before it can be used in the biuret test. To do this, first boil the tissue in 70–80% ethyl alcohol until the green color disappears in cells containing chlorophyll. Next, place the tissue in 10 volumes of 0.5 M perchloric acid, and incubate at 80°C for 90 minutes with occasional stirring. Finally, wash with water to remove reducing sugars.

B. Suspend the tissue in 10 volumes of water to which is added an equal volume of biuret reagent made as follows: dissolve 1.5 g copper sulfate ($CuSO_4 \cdot 5H_2O$) and 6.0 g. of sodium potassium tartrate ($NaKC_4H_4O_6 \cdot 4H_2O$) in 500 ml of water; then add with constant agitation 300 ml of 0.4 M NaOH; make up to 1000 ml with water; finally, before using, dilute 1:1 with water.

C. Incubate at room temperature for 1 hour with occasional stirring.

D. Centrifuge to remove any cell debris to obtain a clear solution.

E. Measure the absorption at 540 mμ in a colorimeter or spectrophotometer. If the absorption is not proportional at higher concentrations, dilute 1:1 with water, let stand 30 minutes, and measure the absorption.

F. Use a purified protein in making a standard curve.

VI. Protein—Bromosulfalein Method
(NAYYAR AND GLICK, 1954)

A. Place sections of fresh, freeze-substituted, or freeze-dried tissue in 1-ml centrifuge tubes. Remove any paraffin present. The sections should be less than 25-μ thick.

B. To the tissue add 18 μl of 1.0 N NaOH, and cap the vessel.

C. Stir the mixture by holding the vessel against a flattened nail held in the chuck of a high speed hand drill. This aids in the disintegration of the tissue.

D. Leave the tissue and NaOH at room temperature for 1 hour, and stir again by the same means.

E. Uncap the vessel, add 45 μl of the bromosulfalein reagent made as follows: to 1 ml of 5% bromosulfalein, add 100 ml of 1 N HCl, 50 ml of 1 M citric acid, and distilled water to make 250 ml.

F. Centrifuge the tubes until the supernatant is clear (1000 g for 5 minutes in a microcentrifuge.)

G. Transfer 55 μl of the supernatant to another tube, and add 1 ml of 0.1 N NaOH.

H. Measure the optical density at 580 mμ, using water as the blank.

I. Prepare a standard curve by determining the protein-nitrogen by Kjeldahl analysis on an aliquot of the particular kind of sample used. This need not be done on a micro scale. Dilute the sample serially, and subject the various dilutions to steps A–E, above. Plot the optical densities against the corresponding protein nitrogen values. According to Nayyar and Glick, a linear relationship exists over a wide range.

Microscopic Histochemistry

The importance of proteins to the functioning of the cell can hardly be overestimated. It is therefore surprising that so many of the techniques for the localization of proteins are of recent origin. Within the last 10 years there has been a great revival of interest in the localization of proteins, which has resulted not only in the development of new techniques but also in new concepts of working with proteins. These concepts include new ways of producing color, means of blocking specific reactive groups to test the validity of the reactions, and methods to identify particular reactive groups. As a result of these recent developments, greater interest in the distribution of proteins in cells and tissues has been shown, particularly by investigators using animal tissue. So far, botanists have made only minimal use of most of the newer methods.

Protein-localization procedures can be divided into two groups. The first group includes those techniques which visualize all the proteins in the cell. These techniques are analogous to the periodic acid-Schiff's reaction for carbohydrates. The second group includes those techniques which color specific amino acids and therefore localize proteins high in these amino acids. Interestingly, these procedures are, on the whole, older than those of the first group.

The problem of the effect of fixation on protein localization procedures has not been investigated in any comprehensive manner in plant tissues. Freeze-dried and freeze-substituted tissue will work in all the procedures given here, and is probably the material of choice. Fresh sections are also acceptable but usually do not permit precise localization because of the thickness of the sections obtained. With fresh sections, however, it can be assumed that free amino acids are present and that their localization, theoretically at least, is possible. When any sort of paraffin-embedded tissue other than freeze-dried material is used it must be assumed that the free amino acids have been lost. Thus, in those techniques that localize specific amino acids, it is the protein-bound amino acids that are being made visible in fixed material. The possibility exists that freeze-dried tissue with the paraffin in place could be used for the localization of free amino acids, but this has not been tried. Formalin is probably the best chemical fixative. Work on animal tissue (Barrnett and Roth, 1958) indicates, however, that there is no single proper protein fixative. A great deal depends on the protein technique to be used, particularly since many of the procedures require rather harsh treatment of the tissue. It is frequently necessary to precipitate the protein without inactivating the reactive groups. At present, the search for the best fixative or the best method for preparing plant tissue is a question of trial and error. When working with a new protein technique or with a new plant material, several methods of fixation and tissue preparation should be tried. A negative result may only mean that the wrong method was used in handling the tissue prior to the actual localization procedure. The careful work done by Barrnett and Roth (1958) regarding the effect of fixatives on protein localization is an example of the kind of work that is needed in plant histochemistry.

One of the techniques that belongs to the group which visualizes all types of proteins is a recent modification of an older method known as the ninhydrin reaction. In the older procedure the tissue was heated with ninhydrin (triketohydrindenehydrate), and a blue color appeared that was assumed to indicate the localization of amino acids. The color was diffuse and faded rapidly. The reaction was known to involve the production of an aldehyde which was found to be stable and nondiffusible (Yasuma and Ichikawa, 1953). This aldehyde can be used as the basis for a reaction with Schiff's reagent, yielding a precise method for the localization of α-amino acids. Actually the method requires the presence of both an α-amino and an α-carboxyl grouping to give a positive test. Besides ninhydrin, alloxan can be used for the production of the aldehyde. To show that the color is the result of an aldehyde produced by an α-amino, α-carboxyl amino acid, controls should be run in which the tissue has been treated with acetylating and deaminating reagents. This type of control helps eliminate the possibility that aldehydes will be formed from saccharides by the ninhydrin. In most tissue the possibility that this type of false reaction will occur is slight.

Aldehydes may also be produced from α-amino acids by chlorination. The chlorine may be obtained from either sodium hypochlorite or chloramine-T. The oxidative deamination of the amino acid is the same as with the ninhydrin, and the end result, after treatment with Schiff's reagent, is the same. Both the color and the localization should be the same for both procedures (Burstone, 1955). Deamination and acetylation should be used as controls.

Another approach to the localization of proteins is based on reactions in which the terminal amino groups combine with aldehydes to form addition products (Weiss, Tsow, and Seligman, 1954). This product is usually not colored enough to be visible, but is made so by the addition of a highly colored diazo dye. The aldehyde-containing compound most frequently used is 3-hydroxy-2-naphthaldehyde. The recommended diazo dyes are diazo blue B or diazo red RC. When the diazo blue B is used the end color ranges from red to blue. The reaction characteristics of the dye are such that red is assumed to indicate that there are relatively few free amino groups (noncoupling), whereas blue is assumed to indicate that the free amino groups are relatively abundant (dicoupling). When the diazo red RC is used only a bright red is obtained. This procedure cannot be run on formalin-fixed material, and formalin should be avoided in affixing the sections to the slide. Deamination should be used as a control.

A third approach to the localization of the bulk of the proteins present in the cell lies in the use of 2,4-dinitrofluorobenzene (DNFB) (Burstone, 1955). This compound reacts with α-amino groups, ε-amino groups of lysine, phenolic —OH groups of tyrosine, imidazole groups of histidine and sulfhydryl groups. The combination of the protein and the DNFB results in a yellow color that is not intense enough to be used. The protein-DNFB complex is therefore treated with a reducing agent that reduces the nitro groups of the DNFB to amino groups. The amino groups thus produced are diazotized with nitrous acid. The diazotized or protein-DNFB complex is finally reacted with 8-amino-1-naphthol-3,6-disulfonic acid (H acid). The end result is a deep reddish purple color.

All of the above methods have been developed for use on animal material (Burstone, 1955), but all have been applied successfully to plant tissue (Surrey, 1957, 1958). It must be emphasized, however, that this application to plant tissue has been of a limited nature and that caution should be used in any study resting heavily on these techniques until they are more fully understood.

A general protein method which is based on a specific group is the procedure of Barrnett and Seligman (1958), which localizes proteins containing α-acylamido carboxyl groups. In this procedure these groups are converted to methyl ketones by the action of acetic anhydride and absolute pyridine. The methyl ketones then react with 2-hydroxy-3-naphthoic acid, and a naphtholic group is linked to the protein. These naphtholic groups are then coupled with diazo blue B, and a red to blue color develops, depending on the number and spacing of the original α-acylamido carboxyl groups. The free δ- and ε-carboxyl groups of aspartic and glutamic acids do not react because they lack an acylamido group in the alpha position. The carbonyls associated with lipids are removed during the handling, particularly during the removal of the paraffin from the sections, thus there is little possibility of interference by them.

The second major group of techniques available for the localization of proteins include those based on particular amino acids. The oldest test for protein is one based on the amino acids tyrosine and tryptophan. This test was first described by Millon in 1849. The procedure depends on the formation of a complex between the amino acid, mercury, and nitrite, which is termed the Millon complex, or chromophore (Rasch and Swift, 1960). The presence of the phenol in the tyrosine and tryptophan is the important point; most phenolic compounds will react if not doubly substituted in the ortho- and meta-positions. The phenol apparently first forms an unstable complex with the mercury. This is then converted to a relatively stable complex by the addition of nitrite. The reaction is complicated and is not completely understood, although the careful work of Rasch and Swift (1960) has clarified many points. Their work also indicates that, with proper precautions, the reaction can serve as the basis of microspectrophotometric measurements. The procedure given is their modification of the method developed by Pollister and Ris (1947).

Another method for tyrosine-containing protein was proposed by Lillie in 1957. In this procedure, which appears quite specific, the protein is first treated with nitrous acid, which results in the nitrosation of the tyrosine and subsequent diazotization. No color is produced at this step. The color is developed by coupling in 1-amino-8-naphthol-4-sulfonic acid (S acid). This is done at an alkaline pH and in the presence of urea, which destroys the excess nitrous acid. The first part of this reaction is reported to be light-sensitive (Glenner and Lillie, 1959) and should be run either in the dark or in containers shielding the preparations from light.

A relatively old procedure is the Sakaguchi test for arginine, first reported in 1924. The reaction for arginine, or arginine-containing proteins, is based on the red or orange-red color produced by the combination of arginine with alpha-naphthol, 2-4-dichloro-α-naphthol, or 8-hydroxyquinoline and sodium hypochlorite in the presence of alkali. The actual mechanism of the reaction is not known. The reaction is, however, quite specific. The color is usually weak and fleeting, making it necessary to use thick sections. The strong alkali necessary to obtain the color is hard on the tissue. The work of McLeish and Sherrat (1958) indicates that under the proper conditions the method can be refined to the point at which microspectrophotometric measurements can be made. The procedure given here is their modification of the Sakaguchi test. They found after careful study (McLeish and Sherrat, 1958) that 2,4-dichloro-α-naphthol gave the best color. The procedure they recommend was developed using smears of isolated nuclei, but sections should also work well. Plant cells, as well as animal cells, were used in their experiments.

Until recently there were no good histochemical procedures for proteins that contain tryptophan. However, as a result of the work of Bruemmer, Carver, and Thomas (1957) and of Glenner and Lillie (1959) several excellent procedures now exist. These procedures are actually based on the presence of the indole group in the tryptophan, thus the tests are more for indole derivatives than tryptophan specifically. In actual practice, however, the tests are quite specific because most of the possible interfering substances are removed in the handling of the tissue. Indoleacetic acid gives a positive reaction in the Bruemmer procedure (Glenner and Lillie have not tested it in their procedures) and, although most of the IAA will probably be removed from the tissue during fixing, dehydration, and deparaffinizing of the sections, it represents a possible complication in plant material.

The procedure developed by Bruemmer, Carver, and Thomas (1957) is based on the treatment of the protein with nitrous acid. The result is probably a reaction between the tryptophan and the nitrous acid that produces an N-nitroso compound involving the nitrogen of the indole ring. A coupling then probably takes place, linking the nitrogen of the nitroso group to the nitrogen of the free amino group of the N-(1-naphthyl)-ethylendiamine.

Several other effective techniques for the localization of tryptophan have been devised. One is the post-coupled benzylidene reaction of Glenner and Lillie (1959); another is Fisher's rosindole reaction (Glenner, 1957). The first is based on a benzylidene condensation reaction with indole derivatives such as tryptophan. An azo coupling reaction is then applied to the benzylidene condensation product to intensify the initial color. In the second reaction a benzylidene condensation product of tryptophan is again formed, but in the presence of perchloric acid. Oxidation of this product results in the formation of a rosindole dye. This method, which is reported to give sharp localization and to be specific and sensitive, is given in the Procedures section of this chapter.

The procedure for histones, although not based on the reaction of a specific amino acid, comes roughly under this group of procedures because it is based on the fact that histones are high in basic amino acids (Alfert and Geschwind, 1953). Because histones are high in basic amino acids they have isoelectric points which are much more acid than other proteins. At the isoelectric point, dye binding by proteins is minimal. The general characteristics of proteins found in tissues are such that when the tissue is placed at pH 8.0, most of the proteins are above or near their isoelectric point. At pH 8.0, histones are still below their isoelectric point. This means that by placing tissue at pH 8.0 in an acid dye, such as Fast Green, the only proteins having groups available to bind the dye are the histones. The reaction is quite specific for histones. Nucleic acids must be removed from the cell before the reaction will work properly. When the conditions are standardized the color developed appears proportional to the amount of histone present and can be measured microspectrophotometrically.

Finally, there are those amino acids which can be localized because they contain sulfhydryl or disulfide groups—namely, cysteine, cystine, and methionine. Sulfhydryl groups are rather susceptible to oxidation to disulfides, hence care must be taken in the handling of the tissue or the disulfide groups may be reduced after the sections are cut. The tissue can be fixed in formalin, freeze-substituted, or freeze-dried. Tissue prepared by the latter method should work particularly well. The use of 1% trichloroacetic acid in 80% ethyl alcohol has been used, but it is not a good fixative and does not preserve the sulfhydryl better than formalin.

Three methods are available for the demonstration of sulfhydryls. They are (1) the dihydroxydinaphthyldisulfide (DDD) test, (2) the tetrazolium test, and (3) the mercaptide-formation test.

The DDD test (Barrnett and Seligman, 1952) is based on the reaction of the sulfhydryl groups with naphthols present in the 2,2'-dihydroxy-

6,6'-dinaphthyldisulfide (DDD). The product of this reaction is color-less, but it can be coupled with a diazo dye to give a visible color. The most commonly used diazo dye is diazo blue B, although diazo red RC is as good and in some instances better. This procedure can be refined to the point where it can be used as the basis of microspectrophotometric measurements (Teiger, Farah, and Di Stefano, 1957).

The application of the Barrnett-Seligman method to plant tissues has been carefully investigated by Hyde and Paliwal (1959). They tested fourteen different chemical fixatives and found that 10% TCA, alcohol-acetic acid (3:1), and alcohol-chloroform-acetic acid all work well. The 1% TCA in alcohol, which is recommended for animal tissue, did not give satisfactory results with plant cells. Their data raise some question as to the specificity and the mechanism of the reaction. This paper is an excellent example of the type of work needed in applying animal procedures to plant material.

The tetrazolium test is based on the reduction of tetrazolium salts at basic pH's by sulfhydryl groups. The most commonly used tetrazolium salt is neotetrazolium in a cyanide solution at pH 8.5–8.8 (Gomori, 1956). Triphenyltetrazolium has also been used in plant tissues at pH 7.2 (Roberts and Lucchese, 1955). The reduction of tetrazolium salts by sulfhydryl groups is influenced by such factors as pH, presence of other reducing substances, amount of dye, and the presence of oxygen. This means that the conditions most suitable for the tissue used must be worked out with some care. There is some evidence that the amount of tetrazolium reduced is not always proportional to the sulfhydryl groups present in plant tissue (Jambor, Devay, and Roberts, 1957).

The mercaptide formation test is based on the ability of sulfhydryl groups to react with mercuric compounds to form colored mercaptides. The best known of the mercury compounds is Bennett's reagent, 1-(4-chloromercuriphenylazo)-naphthol-2, or Mercury Orange (Bennett and Watts, 1958). The reaction is direct, simple, and specific. The color of the end product has a tendency to be weak, but it often results in a sharper localization than does the DDD test, which may give more color but is more diffuse. The reaction may also be used as the basis for a quantitative histochemical procedure for microspectrophotometric measurements (Bennett and Watts, 1958).

In all the above tests it is absolutely necessary to run controls in which the sulfhydryls are blocked. The two recommended blocking agents are N-ethyl maleimide and iodoacetate. The use of blocking agents as controls in sulfhydryl localizations cannot be stressed too highly. Both of these blocking agents can be reversed by placing the tissue in cyanide solutions at basic pH for 90 minutes or longer.

The field of protein histochemistry is developing so rapidly, particularly in research with animal tissue, that current issues of the *Journal of Histochemistry and Cytochemistry* and *Stain Technology* should be examined for recent developments. The increased use of protein stains in microspectrophotometry is also a recent development which, combined with the autoradiography of labeled amino acids, indicates that an exciting period of growth in the protein histochemistry of plants is in the offing.

Procedures

I. Total Protein—Ninhydrin-Alloxan-Schiff's Reaction
(YASUMA AND ICHIKAWA, 1953)

A. Use either freeze-dried, freeze-substituted, chemically fixed, or fresh tissue.

B. Section the paraffin-infiltrated tissue at 15–25 μ and affix to slides.

C. Deparaffinize the sections.

D. Place the sections in 0.5% ninhydrin or in 1.0% alloxan in absolute alcohol at 37°C for 20–24 hours.

E. Rinse in two changes of absolute alcohol and then in distilled water.

F. Place in Schiff's reagent for 10–30 minutes.

G. Rinse in water, and place in 2% sodium bisulfite for 1–2 minutes.

H. Wash in running tap water for 10–20 minutes.

I. Dehydrate, and mount.

J. Proteins will appear a reddish-purple color.

K. For controls run the following blocking procedures on alternate sections between steps C and D:

  1. Deamination: Place the tissue in a mixture made up of 20 ml of 60% sodium nitrite and 60 ml of 1% acetic acid at room temperature for 1–24 hours.

  2. Acetylation: Place the tissue in a 10% solution of acetic anhydride in pyridine at room temperature for 2–20 hours.

If color is obtained in either control the reaction is localizing some compound other than proteins having α-amino and α-carboxyl groups in the constituent amino acids.

II. Total Protein—Chloramine-T-Schiff's Reaction
(BURSTONE, 1955)

A. Use either freeze-dried, freeze-substituted, chemically fixed, or fresh tissue.

B. Section the paraffin-infiltrated tissue at 15–25 μ, and affix to slides.

C. Remove the paraffin, and bring sections to water.

D. Place sections in a 1% solution of chloramine-T in a 0.1 M phosphate buffer at pH 7.5 for 6 hours at 40°C.

E. Wash in water, and place in a dilute solution of sodium thiosulfate for 1 minute.

F. Place in Schiff's reagent for 10–30 minutes.

The results should be the same as for the above procedure.

III. Total Protein—3-hydroxy-2-naphthaldehyde-diazo Dye Method (WEISS, TSOW, AND SELIGMAN, 1954)

A. Use freeze-dried or freeze-substituted material. Do not use formalin-fixed tissue.

B. Section at 10–20 μ, and mount using a gelatin adhesive and water.

C. Remove the paraffin, and bring the tissue to water.

D. Place the tissue in a freshly prepared solution of 3-hydroxy-2-naphthaldehyde, made by dissolving 20 mg of the reagent in 20 ml of acetone and then adding 30 ml of an 0.1 M barbital buffer at pH 8.5. Leave the sections in this solution for 1 hour at room temperature.

E. Wash the sections in 3 changes of distilled water.

F. Place sections in 50 ml of 0.1 M barbital buffer at pH 7.4–7.5, and add 25 mg of either diazo blue B (Tetrazotized diorthoanisidine) or diazo red RC (diazotized P-chloro-o-anisidine). Stir the mixture gently, and allow the slides to remain in it until the color develops, usually 4–6 hours.

G. Wash briefly in tap water, dehydrate, and mount.

H. Use as controls the blocking procedures given in Procedure I, step K.

I. With the diazo blue B the color obtained may be red, blue, or some intermediate shade. If the color is red few free amino groups are indicated, if blue, many free amino groups may be present. With the diazo red RC only a red color is produced.

This test primarily involves the α-amino groups of terminal amino acids. The results obtained should be similar to the ninhydrin-Schiff's test.

IV. Total Protein—Dinitrofluorobenzene (DNFB) Test (BURSTONE, 1955)

A. Use either freeze-dried, freeze-substituted, chemically fixed, or fresh tissue.

B. Section at 10–20 μ, and mount as usual.

C. Remove the paraffin, and bring to water.

D. Place the slides in DNFB reagent, made by dissolving 0.5 g of 2,4-dinitrofluorobenzene in a mixture containing 5 ml of 0.2 N sodium hydroxide and 95 ml of 95% ethyl alcohol. Leave the slides in the DNFB reagent for 20–24 hours at room temperature. The sections should be yellow.

E. Wash the slides thoroughly in 95% ethyl alcohol by leaving them for 2–3 minutes each in 3 or 4 changes of alcohol. Rinse in distilled water.

F. Place the sections in a 5% solution of sodium hyposulfite for 40 minutes at 40–45°C. The sections should lose their yellow color or almost completely fade. If they do not, leave the slides in the hyposulfite until they do.

G. Rinse in distilled water.

H. Place the sections in freshly prepared nitrous acid at 4–5°C for 5 minutes. Prepare the nitrous acid by adding 2.5 ml of cold 4 N sulfuric acid to 50 ml of cold, freshly prepared 5% sodium nitrite. It is important that both solutions be cold before they are mixed and that the resulting nitrous acid also be kept cold.

I. Rinse slides in cold distilled water.

J. Place the slides in cold, saturated (about 2% solution) of H acid (1 amino-8-naphthol-3,6-disulfonic acid) in a barbital acetate buffer at pH 9.2 for 15 minutes.

K. Rinse the sections in distilled water, dehydrate, and mount.

L. Use as controls the blocking procedures given in Procedure I (step K) between steps C and D of this procedure.

The sites of proteins containing free α-amino groups, ε-amino groups of lysine, phenolic —OH groups of tyrosine, imidazole groups of histidine, and sulfhydryl groups will appear a deep reddish-purple. This method is highly sensitive.

V. Protein Bound α-acylamido Carboxyl Groups
(BARRNETT AND SELIGMAN, 1958)

A. Fix tissue in Carnoy's fixative (3 parts absolute alcohol, 3 parts chloroform, and 1 part glacial acetic acid), formalin, FAA, or other chemical fixative. Alcohol-fixed freeze-substituted tissue should also work well.

B. Mount the sections and remove the paraffin with xylene. Wash 3 times in absolute alcohol.

C. Incubate sections for 1 hour at 60°C in a 1:1 mixture of acetic anhydride and anhydrous pyridine. The pyridine must be anhydrous (redistill over barium oxide and store over commercial calcium carbonate—"drierite") for the reaction to proceed effectively.

D. Wash in absolute alcohol (all alcohol used should be aldehyde-free).

E. Incubate for 2 hours at room temperature in 0.1% 2-hydroxy-3-naphthoic acid hydrazide, prepared by dissolving 50 mg of the hydrazide in 2.5 ml of hot glacial acetic acid and adding 47.5 ml of 50% ethyl alcohol.

F. Wash in 3 or 4 changes of 50% ethyl alcohol, 10 minutes each.

G. Incubate for $\frac{1}{2}$ hour in 0.5 N hydrochloric acid at room temperature.

H. Rinse in distilled water.

I. Wash in several changes of 1% sodium carbonate.

J. Rinse in several changes of distilled water.

K. Place slides in a solution of 0.006 M phosphate buffer (pH 7.6), mixed with an equal volume of absolute alcohol, and stir in tetrazotized diorthoanisidine (1 mg/ml). Leave slides for 2–5 minutes.

L. Wash in several changes of distilled water.

M. Mount in glycerine jelly, or dehydrate and mount in Permount.

N. As a control treat the sections with 0.1 N hydrochloric acid in methyl alcohol for 24 hours at 60°C, and then perform the complete reaction. This procedure should esterify all of the carboxyl groups, and the reaction should be negative.

The sites of proteins containing α-acylamido carboxyl groups will appear red to blue. Red indicates few, or widely spaced, carboxyl groups, whereas blue indicates numerous, or closely spaced, α-acylamido carboxyl groups.

VI. Proteins Containing Tyrosine—Millons Reaction
(RASCH AND SWIFT, 1960)

A. Use either freeze-dried, freeze-substituted, formalin-fixed, acetic alcohol-fixed, or fresh tissue.

B. Section the paraffin-infiltrated tissue at 5–15 μ.

C. Remove the paraffin, and then coat the sections with celloidin.

D. Bring the sections to distilled water.

E. Place the slides in 5% mercuric acetate in 30% trichloroacetic acid for 10 minutes at 40°C.

F. Transfer immediately to another bath of the same solution, with 0.05% sodium nitrite added, for 1 hour at 30°C.

G. Put the slides directly into 70% ethyl alcohol for 10 minutes.

H. Make two additional changes of 70% ethyl alcohol, 10 minutes each.

I. Dehydrate the sections in 95% and absolute alcohol, 3–5 minutes each.

J. Clean in xylene, and mount in oil of proper refractive index.

VII. Proteins Containing Tyrosine—Diazotization-coupling Reaction (LILLIE, 1957; GLENNER AND LILLIE, 1959)

A. Use freeze-dried, freeze-substituted, or formalin-fixed tissue.

B. Remove the paraffin from the sections, and bring to water. (Place the slides in the dark or in Coplin jars wrapped in aluminum foil for steps C–E).

C. Nitrosate for 18 hours in the dark in a refrigerator (3°C) in 6.9 g of sodium nitrite, 5.8 ml of glacial acetic acid, and distilled water to make 100 ml.

D. Wash in 3 changes of ice cold distilled water, 5 seconds each.

E. Couple in a solution of 1 g 1-amino-8-naphthol-4-sulfonic acid (S acid), 1 g of potassium hydroxide, 2 g of urea, 100 ml of 70% alcohol for 1 hour at 3°C.

F. Wash in 3 changes of 0.1 N hydrochloric acid, 5 minutes each.

G. Wash in running water for 10 minutes, dehydrate, and mount.

VIII. Protein Containing Arginine—Sakaguchi Reaction (MCLEISH, 1959; MCLEISH AND SHERRAT, 1958)

A. Use freeze-dried, freeze-substituted, formalin-fixed, or fresh material. Smears fixed in equal volumes of 10% formalin and 1% chromic acid (Lewitsky's fixative) can also be used.

B. Section not thinner than 15 μ.

C. Deparaffinize and celloidin-coat the sections.

D. Mix rapidly 30 ml of 1% sodium hydroxide, 0.6 ml of 1% 2,4-dichloro-α-naphthol in 70% ethyl alcohol, and 1.2 ml of 1% sodium hypochlorite (use Clorox or other bleach, and dilute 1:10 with water).

E. Place slides in this mixture for 6 minutes.

F. Rinse rapidly in 5% urea, and then place in 1% sodium hydroxide.

G. Mount in a 9:1 mixture of glycerol and 10% sodium hydroxide.

Arginine-containing proteins will appear orange-red. The color is stable for only a few hours.

IX. Protein-containing Tryptophan—N-(1-naphthyl)-ethylenediamine Method (BRUEMMER, CARVER, AND THOMAS, 1957; BRUEMMER AND THOMAS, 1958)

A. Fix the tissue in 3 parts alcohol, 3 parts ether, and 1 part acetic acid (Carnoy's fixative) or FAA. Freeze-dried and freeze-substituted tissue should also work well.

B. Deparaffinize the sections with xylene, and pass through absolute, 95%, and 70% ethyl alcohol to 50% ethyl alcohol. The 50% alcohol should be placed in an ice water bath, as should all the other staining jars containing reagents through step F.

C. Place the slides for 15 minutes in nitrous acid (equal volumes of 8% sodium nitrite and 6 N hydrochloric acid).

D. Then make two changes of distilled water for 5 minutes each.

E. Place slides for 15 minutes in a solution prepared by mixing equal volumes of (1) a freshly prepared 2% solution of N-(1-naphthyl)-ethylenediamine dihydrochloride in 95% ethyl alcohol and (2) 1 N hydrochloric acid.

F. Place the tissue in one change of 70% tertiary butyl alcohol.

G. Then pass the tissue through two changes of absolute tertiary butyl alcohol at room temperature. To the TBA add a few drops of sulfuric acid.

H. Place the slides in two changes of xylene and glacial acetic acid (5:1), and mount.

Proteins containing tryptophan will appear purple. A control should be run to determine whether any part of the color in the tissue is the result of substances that might undergo diazotization rather than of the tryptophan. In the control, N-(1-naphthyl)-ethylenediamine is replaced by 1,6-dihydroxynaphthalene or 1-amino-8-hydroxynaphthalene-3,6-disulfonic acid. The color which develops with these reagents is not due to tryptophan.

X. Protein-containing Tryptophan—Rosindole Reaction (GLENNER, 1957)

A. Fix the tissue in 10% calcium acetate-formalin (10 ml of commercial formalin, 90 ml of water, 2 g of calcium acetate). Freeze-dried and freeze-substituted tissue can also probably be used.

B. Remove paraffin from the sections with xylene, and place in absolute ethyl alcohol.

C. Dry the slides for 30 seconds, and immerse for 30 minutes at 25°C in a solution made up of 1 g of p-dimethylaminobenzaldehyde in 5 ml of

60% perchloric acid, 1 ml of concentrated HCl, and 34 ml of glacial acetic acid.

D. Add a solution made up of 35 ml of glacial acetic acid and 5 ml of concentrated HCl to a Coplin jar previously layered with 500 mg of NaNO₂. Transfer the slides immediately to this solution, and let stand for 1 minute at 25°C.

E. Wash twice in glacial acetic acid, 1 minute each, and pass through glacial acetic acid-xylene (1:1), glacial acetic acid-xylene (1:5), and 3 changes of xylene. Mount.

The sites containing tryptophan and similar indole derivatives stain various intensities of blue.

XI. Proteins High in Basic Amino Acids (Histones)— Fast Green Test (ALFERT AND GESCHWIND, 1953)

A. Use freeze-dried, freeze-substituted, or FAA-fixed material.

B. Section at 10–20 μ, and mount.

C. Remove the paraffin, and bring to water.

D. Place for 15 minutes in 15% trichloroacetic acid in a boiling water bath, to extract the nucleic acids.

E. Place in 70% ethyl alcohol, and make three changes.

F. Stain for 30 minutes in a 0.1% aqueous solution of Fast Green FCF at pH 8.0–8.1. Do not use a buffer in making the stain solution; add a minimum of NaOH.

G. Wash the sections in distilled water for 5 minutes.

H. Place the slides directly in 95% ethyl alcohol, dehydrate, and mount.

The basic proteins, histones, will appear green. Inasmuch as histones are normally only found in the nuclei and chromosomes, these are the only cell parts that stain green in this test.

XII. Proteins Containing Sulfhydryl-disulfide: Cysteine, Cystine, and Methionine—DDD Test (BARRNETT AND SELIGMAN, 1952)

A. Use freeze-dried, freeze-substituted, formalin-fixed, or fresh material.

B. Section at 10–20 μ, and mount as usual.

C. Remove the paraffin, and celloidin-coat the sections.

D. In the paraffin-infiltrated tissue most of the sulfhydryl groups will be oxidized to disulfide groups that must be reduced by one of the following methods:

1. Place sections in a fresh aqueous 0.2–0.5 M solution of thio-

glycollic acid adjusted to pH 8.0 with 0.1 N NaOH for 1–2 hours at 50°C.

2. Place sections in a thioglycerol solution made by dissolving 3 ml of thioglycerol in 40 ml of water and adding 10 ml of 0.5 M borate buffer at pH 9.1–9.5. Leave the sections in this solution for 1–2 hours at 50°C or overnight at room temperature.

E. Wash in several changes of distilled water (*do not* use tap water).

F. Prepare a stock solution of DDD (2,2'-dihydroxy-6,6'-dinaphthyldisulfide) by dissolving 100 mg of DDD in 60 ml of absolute ethyl alcohol. Immediately before using, add 15 ml of the stock solution to 35 ml of barbital buffer at pH 8.5. Incubate the sections in this solution for 1 hour at 56°C, and then allow 10 minutes for them to come to room temperature.

G. Rinse the sections briefly in distilled water, and wash for 5 minutes each in two changes of distilled water adjusted to pH 4 with acetic acid.

H. Dehydrate in alcohols, wash in absolute ether for 5 minutes, and return through the alcohol series to water.

I. Place in a very fresh solution containing 50 mg of diazo blue B in 50 ml of phosphate buffer at pH 7.4 for 2 minutes at room temperature.

J. Wash in running tap water, dehydrate in acetone, and mount in clarite.

K. To show that the sulfhydryls are the reacting groups use one of the following blocking agents as a control.

1. N-ethyl maleimide. Place sections in an 0.1 M N-ethyl maleimide solution in a phosphate buffer at pH 7.4 for 4 hours at 37°C.

2. Iodoacetate. Place sections in an 0.1 M iodoacetate solution adjusted to pH 8.0 with NaOH for 20 hours at 37°C. This step should be placed between steps E and F in the above outline.

In this procedure the site of sulfhydryl groups will appear blue. Diazo red RC may be used to replace the diazo blue B. In this case the localization will appear red. This procedure appears highly specific and has been used on animal and plant tissue.

XIII. Sulfhydryl-disulfide-containing Proteins: Cysteine, Cystine, and Methionine—Tetrazolium Reduction Method (GOMORI, 1956)

Steps A–E are the same as in the Procedure XII.

F. Place the sections in a neotetrazolium reagent for 2–4 hours or until the sites of sulfhydryl groups are visible as a reddish-purple color.

Make the neotetrazolium reagent by dissolving 1 gm of sodium cyanide in 15 ml of distilled water, and then almost neutralize with 1 *M* acetic acid (12–15 ml are usually required, but test the *p*H on a *p*H meter or by using phenolphthalein as an indicator). Next, add 20 ml of an 0.5 *M* borate buffer at *p*H 8.5–8.8. Dissolve 25 mg of neotetrazolium chloride in 5 ml of ethyl alcohol, and add this to the buffered cyanide solution. The neotetrazolium reagent may be kept in a refrigerator for several weeks and can be used repeatedly if filtered between every use.

G. Wash briefly, and mount in glycerine.

An alternate method (Roberts and Lucchese, 1955) involves the use of a 1% aqueous solution of 2,3,5-triphenyltetrazolium chloride buffered at *p*H 7.2 in place of the neotetrazolium reagent. The results should be the same. In either, a sulfhydryl blocking agent must be used as a control.

XIV. Sulfhydryl-disulfide-containing Proteins: Cysteine, Cystine, and Methionine—Mercaptide Formation Method (BENNETT AND WATTS, 1958)

Steps A–E are the same as in Procedure VIII.

F. Place the sections in a toluene-saturated solution of 1-(4-chloro-mercuriphenylazo)-naphthol-2 (Mercury orange) for 30 minutes at room temperature.

G. Rinse in toluene, and mount in clarite.

The site of sulfhydryl groups will be visible as a red to pink color. This procedure is quite specific, but the color is usually less intense than that produced in the more commonly used DDD method.

LITERATURE CITED

Alfert, M. and I. I. Geschwind, 1953. A selective staining method for the basic proteins of cell nuclei. *Proc. Nat. Acad. Sci.* (US), **39**:991–999.

Avery, G. S., Jr. and F. Engel, 1954. Total nitrogen in relation to age and position of cells in *Avena* coleoptiles. *Am. J. Botany*, **41**:310–315.

Barrnett, R. J. and W. D. Roth, 1958. Effects of fixation on protein histochemistry. *J. Histochem. and Cytochem.*, **6**:406–415.

Barrnett, R. J. and A. M. Seligman, 1952. Histochemical demonstration of protein-bound sulphydryl groups. *Science*, **116**:323–327.

——, 1958. Histochemical demonstration of protein-bound alpha-acylamido carboxyl groups. *J. Biophys. Biochem. Cytol.*, **4**:169–176.

Bennett, H. S. and R. H. Watts, 1958. The cytochemical demonstration and measurement of sulphydryl groups by azo-aryl mercaptide coupling, with special reference to Mercury orange. *Gen. Cytochem. Methods*, 1:318–374.

Boell, E. J., 1945. Technique for the estimation of total nitrogen in tissues and tissue extracts. *Conn. Acad. Arts and Sci.*, 36:429–448.

Boell, E. J. and S. C. Shen, 1954. An improved ultramicro Kjeldahl technique. *Exptl. Cell Research*, 7:147–152.

Bottelier, H. P., H. Holter, and K. Linderstrøm-Lang, 1943. Studies on enzymatic histochemistry. XXXVI. Determination of peptidase activity, nitrogen content, and reduced weight in the roots of barley, *Hordeum vulgare. Compt. rend. trav. lab. Carlsberg, Sér. chim.*, 24:289–313.

Brown, R. and D. Broadbent, 1950. The development of cells in the growing zones of the root. *Exptl. Botany*, 1:249–263.

Bruel, D., H. Holter, K. Linderstrøm-Lang, and K. Rosits, 1946, 1947. A micro-method for the determination of total nitrogen (accuracy 0.005 μg N). *Compt. rend. trav. lab. Carlsberg, Sér. chim.*, 25:289–324; *Biochim. et Biophys. Acta*, 1:101–125.

Bruemmer, N. C., M. J. Carver, and L. E. Thomas, 1957. A tryptophan histochemical method. *J. Histochem. and Cytochem.*, 5:140–144.

Bruemmer, N. C. and L. E. Thomas, 1958. Tryptophan histochemical method. *J. Histochem. and Cytochem.*, 6:75.

Burstone, M. S., 1955. An evaluation of histochemical methods for protein groups. *J. Histochem. and Cytochem.*, 3:32–49.

Conway, E. J., 1935. Apparatus for the microdetermination of certain volatile substances. IV. The blood ammonia with observations on normal human blood. *J. Biochem.*, 29:419–429.

Conway, E. J. and A. Byrne, 1933. An absorption apparatus for the microdetermination of certain volatile substances. I. The microdetermination of ammonia. *J. Biochim.*, 27:419–420.

Doyle, W. L. and J. H. Omoto, 1950. Ultramicrodetermination of nitrogen. *Anal. Chem.*, 22:603–604.

Erickson, R. O. and D. R. Goddard, 1951. An analysis of root growth in cellular and biochemical terms. 10th Symp. Development and Growth. *Growth, Supplement*, 15:89–116.

Glenner, G. G., 1957. The histochemical demonstration of indole derivatives by the rosindole reaction of E. Fischer. *J. Histochem. and Cytochem.*, 5:297–304.

Glenner, G. G. and R. D. Lillie, 1959. Observations on the diazotization-coupling reaction for the histochemical demonstration of tyrosine: Metal chelation and formazan variants. *J. Histochem. and Cytochem.*, 7:416–424.

Gomori, G., 1956. Histochemical methods for protein-bound sulphydryl and and disulphide groups. *Quart. J. Microscop. Sci.*, 97:1–10.

Hyde, B. B. and R. Paliwal, 1959. The Barrnett-Seligman sulphydryl reaction for plant meristems. *Stain Technol.*, 34:175–186.

Jambor, B., M. Devay, and L. W. Roberts, 1957. A quantitative comparison of sulphydryl content and formazan in the tissues of the pea radicle. *Nature*, 180:997–998.

Jensen, W. A., 1955. A morphological and biochemical analysis of the early phases of cellular growth in the root tip of *Vicia faba. Exptl. Cell Research*, 8:506–522.

Kirk, P. L., 1950. *Quantitative Ultramicroanalysis*. Wiley, New York.

Levy, M., 1936. Studies on enzymatic histochemistry. XVII. A micro Kjeldahl estimation. *Compt. rend. trav. lab. Carlsberg, Sér. chim.*, 21:101–110. *Z. physiol. chem.*, 240:33–42.

Lillie, R. D., 1957. Adaptation of the Morel Sisley protein diazotization procedure to the histochemical demonstration of protein bound tyrosine. *J. Histochem. and Cytochem.*, 5:528–532.

Linderstrøm-Lang, K. and H. Holter, 1933. Studies on enzymatic histochemistry. V. A micro method for the estimation of sugars. *Compt. rend. trav. lab. Carlsberg, Sér. chim.*, 19:1–12.

Lowry, O. H., N. J. Rosebrough, A. L. Farr, and R. J. Randall, 1951. Protein measurement with the Folin phenol reagent. *J. Biol. Chem.*, 193:265–275.

McLeish, J., 1959. Comparative microphotometric studies of DNA and arginine in plant nuclei. *Chromosoma*, 10:686–710.

McLeish, J. and H. S. A. Sherrat, 1958. The use of the Sakaguchi reaction for the cytochemcial determination of combined arginine. *Exptl. Cell Research*, 14:625–629.

Nayyar, S. N. and D. Glick, 1954. Studies in histochemistry. XXXI. A method for the determination of protein in millimicrogram quantities. *J. Histochem. and Cytochem.*, 2:282–290.

Olney, H. O. and B. M. Pollock, 1960. Studies of rest period. II. Nitrogen and phosphorous changes in embryonic organs of after-ripening cherry seed. *Plant Physiol.*, 35:970–975.

Pollister, A. W. and H. Ris, 1947. Nucleoprotein determination in cytological preparations. *Cold Spr. Harb. Symp. Quant. Biol.*, 12:147–157.

Racusen, D. and D. B. Johnstone, 1961. Estimation of protein in cellular material. *Nature*, 191:492–493.

Rasch, E. and H. Swift, 1960. Microphotometric analysis of the cytochemical Millon reaction. *J. Histochem. and Cytochem.*, 8:4–17.

Roberts, L. W. and G. Lucchese, 1955. Sulphydryl localization and tetrazolium reduction. I. Reversible inhibition of its reduction by N-ethyl maleimide. *Stain Technol.*, 30:291–298.

Sunderland, N., J. K. Heyes, and R. Brown, 1957. Protein and respiration in the apical region of the shoot of *Lupinus albus*. *J. Exptl. Botany*, 8:55–70.

Surrey, K., 1957. Azo-coupling reactions of protein-bound amino groups in plant tissue by oxidative deamination method. *J. Histochem. and Cytochem.*, 5:606–610.

———, 1958. Detection of protein-bound amino groups in plant tissue by Schiff base formation and azo coupling. *Stain Technol.*, 33:109–114.

Teiger, D. G., A. Farah, and H. S. Di Stefano, 1957. Cytophotometric determination of protein-bound disulphide groups. *J. Histochem. and Cytochem.*, 5:403–407.

Weiss, L. P., K.-C. Tsow, and A. M. Seligman, 1954. Histochemical demonstration of protein-bound amino groups. *J. Histochem. and Cytochem.*, 2:29–49.

Yasuma, A. and T. Ichikawa, 1953. Ninhydrin-Schiff and alloxan-Schiff staining. A new histochemical staining method for proteins. *J. Lab. and Clin. Med.*, 41:296–299.

CHAPTER 11

Nucleic Acids

Quantitative Histochemistry

The nucleic acids, because of their role in chromosome structure and their function in protein synthesis, have assumed a place of eminence in the study of the cell. Indeed, they are currently the glamour chemicals of the cell. Both deoxyribonucleic acid (DNA) and ribonucleic acid (RNA) have been implicated in many important functions of the cell, giving an aura of urgency to their study in relation to cell development and function.

From the evidence already accumulated it would seem logical to investigate on a quantitative level changes in both DNA and RNA in plant tissue systems undergoing development. Interesting data on the processes of cell growth and differentiation would be expected from analyses of parts of developing plant embryos, flowers, stems, roots, and buds, using the methods of quantitative histochemistry. Yet, aside from limited investigations of roots (Holmes, Mee, Hornsey, and Gray, 1955; Jensen, 1958), virtually no quantitative histochemical analyses of plants or plant parts have been undertaken for the nucleic acids.

The quantitative histochemical analyses for DNA and RNA thus far completed have been on meristematic and young cells. In such material the nucleic acids are relatively easily extracted and measured, but this is not the case for all plants or plant tissues. Difficulties are encountered in both the extraction and the measurement of nucleic acids from mature tissues and nonvascular plants. As histochemical procedures are extended to these tissues and plants, methods developed for meristematic or young cells must be questioned and examined with care. Fortunately, several recent and thorough investigations (Smillie and Krotkov, 1960; Kupila, Bryan, and Stern, 1961) of the various methods available for nucleic acid analysis of plant tissues have been made. Although these

236

investigations did not deal with histochemical methods they should prove invaluable to the histochemist interested in the examination of nucleic acid content in a wide range of plant materials.

Each of the three major parts of the nucleic acid molecule can be used as a means to estimate the amount of nucleic acid present. Each, however, has certain difficulties associated with it. Before examining the means available to extract the nucleic acids from the tissue, it is necessary to discuss the various assay procedures available. These procedures involve (1) the measurement of the sugar, (2) the measurement of the phosphate, and (3) the measurement of the purine and pyrimidine bases.

Excellent colorimetric procedures for deoxyribose exist (Dische, 1955; Burton, 1956), and these are probably the methods of choice in measuring DNA (Kupila, Bryan, and Stern, 1961). There appear to be no interfering substances present in the cell. Furthermore, deoxyribose is associated only with DNA under the conditions used for DNA extraction. Unfortunately, no similar test is available for RNA. The color methods available for the determination of ribose also react with other pentoses, including deoxyribose (Dische, 1955). Moreover, large amounts of pentose sugars, particularly xylose, are present in the cell wall. Some of these are usually extracted with the nucleic acids, which results in spurious values for RNA when pentose color reactions are used as a measure. This is not true for all tissues but must be constantly guarded against in using new material.

The phosphorus content of the nucleic acids may also be used to estimate their amount. Excellent colorimetric procedures for phosphorus analysis are given in Chapter 13. Here, as with the color methods for ribose, the procedure does not permit the estimation of one nucleic acid in the presence of the other; only the total amount can be obtained. All phosphorus compounds which may be extracted from the cell under the conditions used to extract the nucleic acids must be removed before the nucleic acids are extracted, or they will increase the value of the nucleic acid analysis. The removal of these compounds is not particularly difficult in meristematic tissue of vascular plants but becomes a problem in certain algae in which phosphate deposits exist (Smillie and Krotkov, 1960).

The purines and pyrimidines are measured on the basis of their absorption of ultraviolet light, which results from the double bonds they contain. This measure is, again, an estimate of the total nucleic acid content if DNA and RNA are present in the same solution. Only if the DNA and RNA are extracted separately will ultraviolet absorption serve as a measure of the individual nucleic acids. Again, as in the case of both the pentose and phosphorus determinations, the possibility exists that there may be interference from other compounds found in the cell. This does not seem to be a problem in meristematic tissue (Ogur and Rosen, 1950) but may be a problem in leaves.

These are the major means of estimating the nucleic acid content of extracts from tissues. Additional methods exist, such as Hoff-Jorgensen's (1952) microbiological assay based on deoxyribonucleosides, but these are much less frequently used, although they are of great value in some problems, particularly in developing a method of nucleic acid extraction (Kupila, Bryan, and Stern, 1961). Each of the methods discussed has advantages and disadvantages, and each must be considered in terms of the extraction procedure used to remove the nucleic acids from the tissue.

Four extraction procedures are given in this chapter. They are (1) the perchloric acid extraction procedure of Ogur and Rosen (1950); (2) the trichloroacetic acid extraction procedure of Schneider (1945); (3) the hot salt extraction method of Kupila, Bryan, and Stern (1961); and (4) the alkaline hydrolysis method of Scott, Fraccastoro, and Taft (1956). As with the measurement procedures, the extraction methods each offer advantages and disadvantages, making it impossible to recommend one for all plant material.

With all of the extraction procedures the tissue is first treated with ethyl alcohol, methyl alcohol, or methyl alcohol containing 0.05 M formic acid, to remove pigments and similar interfering substances. The tissue is then extracted with ethyl alcohol, ether mixtures, or other organic solvents to remove the lipids. The removal of the lipids aids in the subsequent extraction of the acid-soluble phosphates and the nucleic acids, probably through the destruction of membranes and structural elements within the cell (Smillie and Krotkov, 1960). The tissue is also extracted with dilute acid to remove acid-soluble phosphates which may interfere with the subsequent measurement of the extracted nucleic acid. This step is an important one, since the extraction of acid soluble phosphates must be complete.

The perchloric acid extraction procedure (Ogur and Rosen, 1950) is based on the selective removal of, first, RNA with cold 0.5 M perchloric acid and then of DNA with warm 1 M perchloric acid. The basis for this procedure is the difference in size, and probably in structure, of the two nucleic acids, whereby RNA is more easily hydrolyzed than DNA. Since the two nucleic acids are removed separately, the nucleic acid content of each extract can be measured by ultraviolet absorption, pentose content, or phosphorus content. Inasmuch as few of the substances extracted from meristematic tissues absorb in the ultraviolet range under these conditions, ultraviolet absorption has been used more extensively as a measure of nucleic acid content.

The Ogur and Rosen (1950) perchloric acid extraction procedure was designed for the meristematic tissues (particularly root tips) of vascular plants. For this type of tissue the procedure works well, the DNA and RNA being differentially extracted relatively easily and completely. With other tissues and plants, however, the method is less successful. Kupila, Bryan, and Stern (1961) found that perchloric acid extraction of DNA from wheat leaves was never complete. Smillie and Krotkov (1960) failed to obtain differential extraction of the nucleic acids with perchloric acid in *Euglena*.

The trichloroacetic acid (TCA) method of Schneider (1945) is based on the extraction of DNA and RNA with warm 1 M TCA. Trichloroacetic acid removes the nucleic acids by hydrolyzing them to soluble nucleotide units. Aliquots of this extract are measured for total nucleic acid content by determining total pentose or total phosphate content. The amount of DNA present is measured by determining the deoxyribose content. The difference between the total nucleic acid content and the DNA content is the measure of RNA present. Since TCA absorbs in the ultraviolet, the amount of purines and pyrimidines cannot be measured this way.

Perchloric acid may be used in place of TCA in the Schneider method (Smillie and Krotkov, 1960). In this case the extraction is not differential as in the Ogur and Rosen perchloric acid procedure. The use of perchloric acid in place of TCA permits the measurement of ultraviolet absorption. The work of Smillie and Krotkov (1960) indicates that, under conditions such that DNA and RNA are moved simultaneously, perchloric acid extraction is the method of choice in work on many plants, including the algae. To determine the amount of DNA and RNA present in pea leaves and beet roots, they recommend extraction of the tissue with 5% perchloric acid at 90°C for 15 minutes, followed by the measurement of ultraviolet absorption, total phosphorus content and deoxyribose content of the extract. In *Euglena* the presence of polyphosphates eliminates the use of total phosphorus to indicate total nucleic acid. Consequently, four measurements must be made on the extract: ultraviolet absorption, ribose content, deoxyribose content, and total phosphate. The ribose-plus-deoxyribose estimate of RNA and DNA should equal the estimate of nucleic acid content based on ultraviolet absorption. Subtracting the total nucleic acid content from the total phosphorus estimate yields the amount of phosphate present as polyphosphate. Smillie and Krotkov (1960) present a generalized scheme of nucleic acid extraction which includes the use of an ion exchange column to remove various interfering substances. This has not yet been used in quantitative histochemistry but is an excellent suggestion.

Perchloric acid is not, however, the answer to all nucleic acid extraction problems, as shown by the work of Kupila, Bryan, and Stern (1961). As noted earlier, they were unable to obtain complete extraction of DNA in wheat leaves with perchloric acid even after prolonged extraction. They did find, however, that they could quantitatively extract the nucleic acids with 10% NaCl at 100°C for 30 minutes. Since their work was primarily concerned with DNA, they measured only deoxyribose as a means of estimating the DNA content of the extract. The procedure can be used, however, to estimate the content of both DNA and RNA in the extract, employing techniques similar to those discussed above. The salt extraction procedure appears to be an excellent, simple method for the extraction of the nucleic acids, particularly from mature tissues, as well as from root tips and embryos (Kupila, Bryan, and Stern, 1961). However, it does not appear to be the method of choice with algae (Smillie and Krotkov, 1960). In algae the extraction of the nucleic acids appears to be incomplete by the salt procedure.

The final extraction procedure given is based on the use of NaOH. In the Schmidt and Thannhauser (1945) procedure nucleic acids are removed by hydrolysis with NaOH, followed by acid precipitation of DNA. Scott, Fraccastoro, and Taft (1956) have modified this procedure and reduced it to the histochemical scale. This method is based on the observation that, after treatment with NaOH, RNA becomes readily acid soluble, whereas DNA does not. Consequently, the tissue is first treated with NaOH, which makes the RNA soluble in cold dilute HCl. The DNA, which is still in the tissue, is removed with hot perchloric acid. This method, according to the data of Scott, Fraccastoro, and Taft (1956), yields a sharper separation of RNA and DNA than does the differential perchloric acid extraction procedure of Ogur and Rosen (1950). The amount of nucleic acid present in the extracts can be measured by ultraviolet absorption, phosphorus analysis, or sugar analysis, the ultraviolet absorption measurement being recommended by Scott, Fraccastoro, and Taft (1956).

From this discussion of the various means available for the extraction and measurement of the nucleic acids, it should be clear that no single method offers a final answer to the multitude of problems presented by plant tissue. The age and condition of the cells must always be taken into account with regard to the extraction of the nucleic acids. The possibility of contamination of the extracts with ultraviolet-absorbing substances, pentose sugars, and phosphorus not a part of the nucleic acids must be guarded against. In working with the nucleic acids, there is no substitute for careful, thorough preliminary studies.

So far there have been few attempts to apply the procedures of chromatography and electrophoresis to the histochemistry of nucleic acids in plants. Animal histochemists, however, have made developments with regard to these techniques. An extremely interesting procedure developed by Edstrom (1952, 1953, 1960a,b) permits the measurement of purine-pyrimidine bases from a single cell or cell part by means of a microchromatographic procedure. This procedure has never been used on plant tissue, but is clearly of great potential value in many problems in plant development.

Procedures

1. DNA and RNA—Perchloric Acid Extraction
(JENSEN, 1956; OGUR AND ROSEN, 1950)

A. Use fresh, freeze-dried, or freeze-substituted tissue sectioned at 25–200 μ in thickness. If paraffin embedded material is used, remove the paraffin with toluene, rinse the tissue with absolute ethyl alcohol, and proceed as with fresh tissue.

B. Add 95% ethyl alcohol, and drain.

C. Add ethyl alcohol and ether in a 1:3 mixture, and heat to 60°C for 10 minutes.

D. Drain the tissue, chill to 0°C, and keep in a chilled aluminum block.

E. Add cold 0.2 M perchloric acid, agitate, and drain at once.

F. Add 0.2 ml of 1 M perchloric acid, and leave overnight in a refrigerator. Remove extract, and save.

G. Add 0.2 ml of fresh 1 M perchloric acid, leave in refrigerator for 4 hours, and remove extract. Add this extract to the extract from step F. Together they constitute the RNA fraction.

H. Wash residue with 0.5 M perchloric acid.

I. Add 0.2 ml of 0.5 M perchloric acid, and heat at 70°C for 20 minutes. Remove the extract, and save.

J. Add 0.2 ml of 0.5 M perchloric acid, and repeat step I. Remove the extract, and combine with the extract from step I. This constitutes the DNA fraction.

K. To determine the amount of DNA and RNA present in the extracts, measure the absorption of the extracts at 260 mμ in a spectrophotometer equipped with an ultraviolet attachment and with quartz or fused-silica microcuvettes. To measure the phosphorus content, use the procedure given in Chapter 13; to measure the ribose and deoxyribose content use the methods given in Procedure V.

L. Use purified samples of DNA and RNA to make the standard curves. To bring nucleic acids into solution, take them up in 0.04 M Na₂CO₃ in as small a volume as possible, neutralize them with 0.1 N HCl, and dilute.

II. DNA and RNA—Trichloroacetic Acid Extraction (SCHNEIDER, 1945; STEELE, SFORTUNATO, AND OTTOLENGHI, 1949)

A. Prepare the sections as in the first procedure.

B. Add cold 10% trichloroacetic acid (TCA), and drain.

C. Add fresh 10% TCA, and drain. (The two 10% TCA extracts can be combined, saved, and used to determine acid-soluble phosphorus compounds in the tissue. (See Chapter 13 for the phosphorus procedure).

D. To the residue add 80% ethyl alcohol, and drain.

E. Resuspend in 95% ethyl alcohol, and drain.

F. Boil the residue 3 times, 3 minutes each time, in a 1:3 mixture of alcohol and ether. (The extracts may be combined and the phosphorus content measured as a means of determining the phospholipid content of the tissue.)

G. Resuspend the residue in cold 5% TCA (or 5% perchloric acid), and drain.

H. Resuspend the residue in 0.2 ml of 5% TCA (or 5% perchloric acid) at 90°C for 15 minutes. Cool, remove, and save the extract.

I. Rinse the residue with 0.2 ml of 5% TCA (or 5% perchloric acid), and add the extract to that of step H. The combined extracts contain the nucleic acids. Analyze aliquots for total phosphorus, total pentose, and deoxyribose content. If perchloric acid is used, ultraviolet absorption may also be measured. The amount of RNA and DNA present may be calculated from these measurements (see text).

III. DNA—Salt Extraction (KUPILA, BRYAN, AND STERN, 1961)

A. Use freeze-dried, freeze-substituted, or fresh tissue.

B. Place the tissue in a pyrex ignition tube, and use toluene to remove any paraffin present. Rinse with absolute methyl alcohol.

C. Extract the tissue with cold methyl alcohol containing 0.05 M formic acid. Repeat this extraction twice, and discard the extract.

D. Add to the tissue a 2:1 mixture of ethyl alcohol and ethyl ether, and heat at 50°C for 30 minutes. Discard the extract.

E. Extract the nucleic acid from the tissue by adding a minimal volume of 10% NaCl containing 0.05 M tris (hydroxyamino) methylmethane (tris) buffer at pH 7.0.

F. Place the tube in a boiling water bath. After about 1 minute, tightly stopper the tube.

G. Heat the stoppered tube at 100°C for 30 minutes, and then cool.

H. Remove the extract containing the nucleic acids. The extraction procedure (steps E–H) may have to be repeated one or more times depending on the tissue.

I. Make the extract 0.5 N with respect to perchloric acid, and heat to 70°C for 20 minutes.

J. Measure the amount of DNA present by using the diphenylamine method for deoxyribose given in Procedure V.

This procedure is recommended for leaves, stems, and similar mature tissues of vascular plants.

IV. DNA and RNA—Alkaline Hydrolysis (SCOTT, FRACCASTORO, AND TAFT, 1956)

A. Use freeze-dried, freeze-substituted, or fresh tissue.

B. Place sections in reaction tubes (4 × 25 mm) and remove paraffin, if present, with toluene. Rinse in absolute ethyl alcohol.

C. Add 50 μl of cold 0.3 N perchloric acid. Stir, and remove. Keep the tubes in racks and in an ice water bath until step G.

D. Repeat step C. The extracts may be saved and used to measure acid soluble phosphates by the phosphorus method.

E. Add 100 μl of cold 80% alcohol. Stir and remove. Discard.

F. Wash in three successive 100-μl aliquots of a 3:1 mixture of 95% ethyl alcohol and ethyl ether. Stir, remove, and discard.

G. Add 50 μl of 1 N NaOH. Stir, and allow to stand for 1 hour at room temperature.

H. Add 10 μl of 6 N HCl. Stir, cool in an ice water bath, centrifuge 1 minute at 850 g or until the supernatant is clear.

I. Remove the supernatant with a 100-μl pipette. Retain the solution in the pipette.

J. Add to the sediment 25 μl of a 5:1 mixture of 1 N NaOH and 6 N HCl. Stir, and centrifuge.

K. Remove the supernatant by drawing it into the same 100-μl pipette.

L. Fill the pipette to volume with the NaOH-HCl mixture. This is the RNA fraction. Measure in a microcuvette at 260 mμ. Use the NaOH-HCl mixture as a blank.

M. To the sediment add 25 μl of 0.3 N perchloric acid. Stir, and remove immediately. Discard.

N. Add 50 μl of 1.6 N perchloric acid to the sediment. Stir, and heat at 60°C for 7 minutes. Cool immediately, and centrifuge.

O. Remove the supernatant with a 100-μl pipette. Retain the solution in the pipette.

P. Add 25 μl of 1.6 N perchloric acid to the sediment. Stir, and centrifuge.

Q. Remove the supernatant by drawing it into the same 100-μl pipette.

R. Fill the pipette to volume with 1.6 N perchloric acid. This is the DNA fraction. Measure in a microcuvette at 260 mμ. Use the 1.6 N perchloric acid as a blank.

V. Colorimetric Methods for Deoxyribose and Ribose

A. DEOXYRIBOSE—CYSTEINE REACTION (DISCHE, 1955)

1. To 50 μl of the extract add 50 μl of a freshly prepared 5% solution of cysteine hydrochloride solution and 0.5 ml of 75% H_2SO_4.

2. Shake vigorously, and allow to cool at room temperature.

3. Measure the optical density at 490 mμ in a Beckman spectrophotometer or similar instrument after 10–15 minutes.

B. DEOXYRIBOSE—DIPHENYLAMINE REACTION (BURTON, 1956; KUPILA, BRYAN, AND STERN, 1961)

1. Prepare the reagent by dissolving the entire contents of a newly opened bottle of diphenylamine in glacial acetic acid at a final concentration of 100 g/l of solution. If stored in a dark bottle in a refrigerator, the solution will remain stable for 6 months. Prepare a stock reagent by diluting 60 ml of this solution to 400 ml with glacial acetic acid and adding 6 ml of concentrated H_2SO_4. Keep this solution at room temperature. Immediately before using add 0.1 ml of an acetaldehyde solution (16 mg/ml of water) to each 20 ml of stock reagent.

2. Add 2 volumes of reagent to one volume of extract.

3. Incubate for 18 hours at 25–30°C.

4. Measure the optical density at 600 mμ and at 540 mμ in a suitable spectrophotometer. The difference between the two readings is the measure of DNA in the sample.

5. Run a standard with each determination. Polymerized commercial

DNA may be used, but Kupila, Bryan, and Stern (1961) found a solution of deoxyadenosine in 50% ethyl alcohol more reliable. They used a final concentration of 0.5 μmoles/ml, 0.1 ml of which was used in each set of analyses. One μmole of deoxyadenosine is equivalent to 2 μmoles of DNA-P.

If this procedure is used in conjunction with the hot salt extract procedure for DNA, it is important that the chloride ion concentration not exceed 0.7% in the final mixture, or the color intensity will be reduced. If the chloride concentration is too high, lyophilize the extract, and wash the dry residue with cold 0.72 N TCA to remove the NaCl. Then suspend the washed residue in 0.5 N perchloric acid, heat for 20 minutes at 70°C, cool and centrifuge. The supernatant fluid is used in the analysis.

C. RIBOSE—H_2SO_4—CYSTEINE REACTION (DISCHE, 1955)

Measure total pentose in the nucleic acid extract by the H_2SO_4—cysteine reaction given on p. 184. This may be used as a measure of RNA, since deoxyribose reacts so much more slowly than does ribose that it does not interfere appreciably. However, pentoses other than ribose, such as xylose and arabinose, will react, and may be present in the extract as cell wall components. Always keep in mind that pentose polysaccharides are present in the cell wall.

D. RIBOSE—ORCINOL REACTION (MARKHAM, 1955)

1. Prepare the orcinol reagent by mixing 10 ml of a 1% orcinol solution in water, 40 ml of concentrated HCl, and 1 ml of 10% $FeCl_3$ in water. This reagent should be used fresh.

2. To 20 μl of a solution containing 0.5–5 μg of pentose add 0.2 ml of the reagent.

3. Stopper the tube, and heat for 8 minutes in a water bath at 100°C.

4. Cool the tube, and measure the optical density at 640 mμ with a spectrophotometer or colorimeter. If the color is too dense, dilute with *n*-butanol.

Microscopic Histochemistry

In microscopic histochemistry the same component parts of the nucleic acids can be used in their localization as are used in their measurement in quantitative histochemistry. Owing to their absorption of ultraviolet light, the purine and pyrimidine bases can be used to localize the nucleic acids. The sugars, or rather the deoxyribose of DNA, can be utilized by the formation of aldehydes which can be colored with fuchsin. Finally, the phosphates in the nucleic acids have the capacity to bind certain basic dyes and present a different way to localize both DNA and RNA.

The ultraviolet microscope was discussed briefly in Chapter 3. In ultraviolet microscopy the absorption of ultraviolet light by a substance is used to differentiate it from a nonabsorbing background. Compounds high in double bonds, such as nucleic acids and lignin, readily absorb ultraviolet light. Ultraviolet light, however, is difficult to use in microscopy. First, it is absorbed by glass, making it necessary to use quartz or fused silica in all the optics. Such optics are expensive. Second, the eye is not sensitive to ultraviolet light, thus requiring the use of a fluorescent viewer and photographs for observations. Critical observations must be made from photographs.

Aside from the difficulty of working with ultraviolet light there are certain inherent difficulties in the technique. Proteins, as well as nucleic acids, absorb in the ultraviolet, and although they have different absorption maxima, they complicate the picture. More important than the absorption by the proteins is the fact that absorption maxima for DNA and RNA are the same. It is therefore impossible to differentiate between them, thus the end result is the localization of total nucleic acid.

The ultraviolet absorption technique was perfected by a group of Swedish workers led by Caspersson (1950). They brought the method to the peak of usefulness by using ultraviolet monochromators and sensitive receptors and obtained absorption curves for various parts of the cell. In their hands the method has been made to yield important information which has done much in formulating the current concepts of the role of the nucleic acids in cell function and growth. Owing to the difficulties involved in the technique and to the high cost of the equipment, the technique has been relatively little used in other laboratories. Since the procedure will not be given in detail here, the interested reader is referred to two very excellent reviews by Nurnberger (1955) and Walker (1956).

The deoxyribose present in DNA is the basis for one of the most famous histochemical procedures ever devised—the Feulgen reaction (Gomori, 1952). In this procedure the tissue is treated with warm HCl, which hydrolyzes the purine-deoxyribose linkages, thus exposing free aldehyde groups (Lessler, 1953). These groups then form a highly colored complex with fuchsin in a reaction identical to that discussed in carbohydrate localization by the periodic acid-Schiff's reaction. The acid hydrolysis must be long enough but not so long that the DNA becomes soluble. As it appears that almost any acid hydrolysis will cause some loss of DNA, the length of hydrolysis is always a compromise between these two considerations.

Some plants appear to exhibit very faint Feulgen staining; chief among these are some algae (*Oscillatoria, Spirogyra*) and some bryophytes (*Marchantia polymorpha*). The reason for such weak Feulgen staining was studied by Hillary (1939), Ishida (1961), and Milovidov (1949), and proved to be highly complex. In some nuclei the concentration of DNA was simply too low to give much color (Hillary, 1939). In other nuclei the DNA appeared particularly susceptible to extraction with HCl. Ishida (1961) has shown this to be the case for *Oscillatoria*. Another complicating factor is the presence of proteins, which interfere with color development (Ishida, 1961), and tannins, which may interfere with color development and develop color themselves (Ishida, 1961; Milovidov, 1949). Lignin, as noted in Chapter 8, will give a positive test with Schiff's reagent without prior hydrolysis.

The Feulgen reaction for DNA is of great interest to microscopic histochemists because it is both specific and, under standard conditions, quantitative; the color produced is proportional to the amount of DNA present. Thus, by measuring the color of a nucleus stained with the Feulgen reaction it is possible to estimate the amount of DNA present. For the reasons given in Chapter 3, the amount of DNA present must be expressed comparatively. The measurement of DNA per nucleus by means of microspectrophotometers has added greatly to our knowledge of cell function and development.

The concept of DNA constancy was developed largely through research based on the microspectrophotometry of Feulgen stained nuclei; Swift's (1950) investigation of the DNA content of plant nuclei is an example of the kind of data obtained. The relation of DNA synthesis to mitosis has been studied in a number of plant tissues by these techniques. For example this relationship was examined in onion root tips by Patau and Swift (1953), in *in vitro* tobacco pith tissue cultures by Patau and Das (1961), and in the root tip of *Vicia faba* by Deeley, Davies, and Chayen (1957). The relation of nucleic acid and protein metabolism during the mitotic cycle in *Vicia faba* has recently been studied with microspectrophotometric methods, not only for DNA but for RNA and protein as well (Woodard, Rasch, and Swift, 1961). These measurements were combined with data obtained with autoradiographs of cells similar to those used in the microspectrophotometric analyses. Another example of combined data from Feulgen measurements and autoradiographs is the work of Das and Alfert (1961) regarding the effect of X-irradiation on DNA synthesis in onion root tips. These are but a few examples of the many types of investigations in which an important role is played by the quantitative estimation of DNA through the Feulgen reaction.

As a result of the phosphates present, the nucleic acids have a marked tendency to bind basic dyes at an acid pH. The dye-binding is ionic in nature; the nucleic acid molecule is anionic, or positively charged, and the dye molecule is cationic, or negatively charged (Kurnick, 1955a; Singer, 1954). Although the mechanism of the reaction is not completely understood, these methods are useful when coupled with extraction procedures, particularly when these extractions are specific for one or the other of the nucleic acids. (Brachet, 1953).

Methyl green is a basic dye that binds selectively to DNA. This specificity of the dye appears related to the high degree of polymerization of DNA, inasmuch as depolymerized DNA will not stain. To achieve maximum effectiveness, the proper pH must be used, and the dye must be pure. The dye must be extracted with ether or chloroform to remove all purple impurities (Taft, 1951). The extraction of the dye with ether or chloroform should be continued until no more color appears in either the ether or the chloroform. There is some evidence that under certain conditions the dye binding is quantitative and may be measured microspectrophotometrically (Kurnick, 1950, 1955a).

Pyronine, when combined with controls in which RNA has been removed, can be used as a stain for RNA. Although the specificity of this dye has been doubted at times, it is usually quite effective and specific, particularly when used with methyl green (Brachet, 1953). The combination of methyl green and pyronine is known as Unna's stain. Cells treated with Unna's stain have red cytoplasms and nucleoli and blue nuclei—a very striking combination.

The methyl green-pyronine stain combination has been studied in some detail, with regard to both specificity and standardization. Difficulties in staining certain materials and in employing some brands of dyes have been reported (Jordan and Baker, 1955), but if the methyl green is purified, the proper buffer and pH used, and care taken with the various steps of the procedure, excellent preparations may be obtained (Taft, 1951; Brachet, 1953).

Azure B is a very useful stain for the nucleic acids and illustrates a phenomenon not yet discussed—metachromosia (Kramer and Windrum, 1955; Schubert and Hamerman, 1956). When Azure B is used, the nucleic acids stain two different colors, thus the dye is termed metachromatic. Metachromatic dyes, of which there are several, usually have two absorption peaks, with a third appearing as the concentration of the dye increases. The color of the dye solution is termed the orthochromatic shade; the second color, formed in certain parts of the cell, is called the metachromatic shade. With Azure B the metachromatic shade is a dark blue, and the orthochromatic shade is blue-green. At *p*H 4.0 Azure B stains RNA blue and DNA a blue-green, but leaves the proteins essentially negative (Flax and Himes, 1950, 1952). Cell walls do not stain unless they contain lignin, in which case they appear green. Cuticle and sieve plates often appear reddish, which is the third color peak.

Metachromosia detects high-molecular-weight substances having free anionic groups. These include many mucopolysaccharides, the nucleic acids, and some anionic lipids capable of polymerizing into units of high molecular weight. Owing to the importance of the mucopolysaccharides in animal tissue, the use of metachromatic dyes is much more widespread in animal histochemistry than in plant histochemistry. The metachromatic properties of the nucleic acids have not been explored until recently. In addition, the metachromatic nature of lignin in Azure B is little known or appreciated by botanists.

The mechanism of metachromosia is not completely understood and has been the source of conflicting opinions. (Schubert and Hamerman, 1956). Perhaps the most accepted theory states that metachromatic dyes are capable of forming polymers that are different in color from the monomers. The amount of the polymer formed is a function of both the chemical characteristic of the sites and the geometry of the sites. The more closely spaced sites there are, the more metachromatic color is formed. The dye-binding sites involved are ester sulfates, carboxylates, and phosphates. The phosphates in the nucleic acid are thus the bases for the action of the dye. Presumably, the arrangement of the phosphates is tighter in the highly polymerized DNA than in the RNA, with the result that DNA is metachromatic.

With regard to each of the methods discussed above, it is necessary to run proper controls based on the differential extraction of the nucleic acids. The same chemical means can be used as in the histochemical procedures. Perchloric acid is particularly useful and can be used in the same fashion as in the histochemical procedures (Erickson, Sax, and Ogur, 1949). Another method of extraction is the use of the enzymes ribonuclease (RNA'ase) and deoxyribonuclease (DNA'ase) (Brachet, 1953). When highly purified preparations are used under optimum conditions, these enzymes are highly specific and are of great value as controls. The two enzymes differ markedly from one another in physical characteristics. Ribonuclease is of very small molecular weight for an enzyme, is remarkably heat resistant, and is known to enter living cells.

Deoxyribonuclease, on the other hand, is a large molecule, is easily denatured, and is not believed to penetrate living cells.

Before leaving a discussion of the nucleic acids the importance of autoradiographic procedures (Chapter 16) in the study of both DNA and RNA in the cell must be mentioned. The use of labeled specific precursors has opened up interesting and important areas of research. Great use has been made of the differences in the pyrimidine bases between the two nucleic acids: labeled thymidine (the base thymine plus the sugar) has been used to study DNA synthesis in relation to chromosome structures; and labeled uridine (the base uricil plus the sugar) has been used to study the site of synthesis of RNA in the cell.

Procedures

I. DNA—Feulgen Method (GOMORI, 1952)

A. Use freeze-dried, freeze-substituted, or chemically fixed material. If chromic acid was present in the fixative wash the tissue overnight in running water.

B. Section, mount, deparaffinize, and bring to water.

C. Hydrolyze sections in N HCl at 58–62°C for 10–15 minutes.

D. Wash in tap water, and then follow the procedure for staining in Schiff's reagent as given for histochemical localization of polysaccharides (p. 199).

E. Counterstaining is not usual, although the cell walls may be stained with ruthenium red, or the cytoplasm may be stained with orange G. Structures containing DNA will stain violet.

II. DNA and RNA—Methyl Green and Pyronine Method (BRACHET, 1953)

A. Section the paraffin-infiltrated tissue, mount the sections, and remove the paraffin. Then bring the tissue to water.

B. Place the tissue in a solution composed of 0.15 g of methyl green, 0.25 g of pyronine B, and 100 ml of acetate buffer at pH 4.7. Make the buffer by adding 1.65 g of sodium acetate and 10 ml of HCl to 1000 ml of water. Test the pH, and *dilute 4 times* before using. (Extract the methyl green with ether or chloroform in a separatory funnel before using in this solution. Repeat the extraction until fresh ether or chloroform does not take on a purple color.)

C. Leave the tissue in stain for 20 minutes, and then wash in rapidly running tap water until the water is no longer red in color.

D. Differentiate in 95% alcohol if necessary. Then pass rapidly through absolute alcohol to xylene, and mount.

DNA-containing structures will stain blue; RNA-containing structures will stain red. Thus the nucleus is blue with a red nucleolus and is surrounded by red cytoplasm. For a modified procedure using pyronin Y, see Kurnick (1955b).

Use one of the extraction procedures given below (Procedure V or VI) as a control on the specificity of the reaction.

III. DNA and RNA—Methyl Green and Pyronine Method
(TAFT, 1951)

A. Fix, dehydrate, paraffin infiltrate, and section the tissue.

B. Remove the paraffin, and hydrate the tissue.

C. Place the material in stain for 3–5 minutes. Prepare the stain by dissolving 0.5 g of methyl green in 100 ml of 0.1 M acetate buffer at pH 4.4. Extract this solution repeatedly with chloroform to remove residual methyl violet. As many as 8 extractions may be necessary (Jordan and Baker, 1955). Then dissolve 0.2 g of pyronine B in the solution of methyl green. If the methyl green solution is stored for several months methyl violet will again appear as an impurity.

D. Rinse the tissue briefly, and blot.

E. Before the tissue is completely dry, immerse in a differentiating solution of tertiary butyl alcohol and absolute ethyl alcohol (3:1) for 2 minutes or longer.

F. Clear in xylene, and mount.

Use one of the extraction procedures (Procedure V or VI) as a control on the specificity of the reaction.

IV. DNA and RNA—Azure B Method
(FLAX AND HIMES, 1952)

A. Use freeze-dried, or freeze-substituted material. Chemically fixed tissue may also be used if chromic acid or other heavy metal ions are not present.

B. Section the paraffin infiltrated material at 10 μ. Mount, deparaffinize, and hydrate in the usual manner.

C. Place the tissue in an 0.25 mg/ml solution of Azure B in citrate buffer at pH 4.0 for 2 hours at 50°C.

D. Wash in water, and place in pure TBA for 30 minutes. Then take through two more changes of pure TBA for 30 minutes or longer. If the stain is too deep leave in TBA overnight if necessary.

E. Pass through xylene, and mount.

DNA will appear a green-blue; RNA will appear purple or dark blue. Sieve plates will appear a cherry red, and lignin will appear green. Use one of the extraction procedures (Procedure V or VI) as a control on the specificity of the reaction.

V. Differential Extraction of DNA and RNA—Perchloric Acid Method (ERICKSON, SAX, AND OGUR, 1949)

A. Section the paraffin infiltrated tissue, mount on slides, and deparaffinize. It may be necessary to coat the sections with celloidin.

B. Bring the sections to water, and place in 1 N perchloric acid. Leave the sections in the perchloric acid for 12–24 hours in a refrigerator at 4°C. This step removes the RNA.

C. Wash well in running water.

D. Place the sections in 0.5 N perchloric acid at 70°C for 20 to 40 minutes. This step removes the DNA.

E. Immerse the sections in a 1% sodium carbonate solution for 5 minutes, and then wash in running water.

F. Stain using Procedure II, III, or IV.

VI. Differential Extraction of DNA and RNA—Enzyme Method (BRACHET, 1953)

A. Use freeze-dried, freeze-substituted, or formalin-fixed tissue. Avoid fixatives containing heavy metals. It is also well to avoid adhesives to which preservatives have been added.

B. Section the tissue, and mount on three slides.

C. Remove the paraffin from the tissue, and bring to water.

D. Place one slide in an 0.1% ribonuclease solution at pH 6.8 for 1 hour at 40°C. In making the RNA'ase solution do not use a buffer; adjust the pH with a minimum of NaOH. The length of time in the RNA'ase is variable, depending on the tissue. Try several time periods. This treatment removes the RNA.

E. Place the second slide in a solution consisting of 0.2 mg/ml of deoxyribonuclease in an 0.003 M magnesium sulfate solution at pH 6.5 for 1 hour at 25°C. As in the RNA'ase solution, do not use a buffer. The time in this solution is also variable; longer times in the DNA'ase may be necessary. This treatment removes the DNA.

F. Place the third slide in water at pH 6.5 for 1 hour. This is a control of the effect of the pH on the removal of the nucleic acids.

G. Wash all slides well, and stain by Procedure II, III, or VI.

Both DNA'ase and RNA'ase can be obtained commercially. Worthington Biochemicals, Freehold, N. J., is recommended as a source. The enzyme solutions may be frozen and stored in a deep freeze, thus allowing them to be used more than once.

The enzymatic removal of DNA by DNA'ase is the only means by which DNA can be extracted without also extracting the RNA.

LITERATURE CITED

Brachet, J., 1953. The use of basic dyes and ribonuclease for the cytochemical detection of ribonucleic acid. *Quart. J. Microscop. Sci.*, **94**:1–10.

Burton, K., 1956. A study of the conditions and mechanism of the diphenylamine reaction for the colorimetric estimation of deoxyribonucleic acid. *Biochem. J.*, **62**:315–323.

Caspersson, T., 1950. *Cell Growth and Cell Function*. Norton, New York.

Das, N. K., and M. Alfert, 1961. Accelerated DNA synthesis in onion root meristem during X-irradiation. *Nat. Acad. Sci. (U.S.)*, **47**:1–6.

Deeley, E. M., H. G. Davies, and J. Chayen, 1957. The DNA content of cells in the root of *Vicia faba*. *Exptl. Cell Research*, **12**:582–591.

Dische, Z., 1955. New color reactions for the determination of sugars in polysaccharides. *Methods of Biochem. Anal.*, **2**:313–358.

Edstrom, J. E., 1952. A chromatographic method for the analysis of nucleic acids in microgram amounts. *Biochem. et Biophys. Acta.*, **9**:528–530.

———, 1953. Ribonucleic acid mass and concentration in individual nerve cells. A new method for quantitative determinations. *Biochem. et Biophys. Acta.*, **12**:361–386.

———, 1960a. Extraction, hydrolysis, and electrophoretic analysis of ribonucleic acid from microscopic tissue units (microphoresis). *J. Biophys. Biochem. Cytol.*, **8**:39–46.

———, 1960b. Composition of ribonucleic acid from various parts of spider oocytes. *J. Biophys. Biochem. Cytol.*, **8**:47–51.

Erickson, R. O., K. B. Sax, and M. Ogur, 1949. Perchloric acid in the cytochemistry of pentose nucleic acid. *Science*, **110**:472–473.

Flax, M. H., and M. H. Himes, 1950. A differential stain for ribonucleic and desoxyribonucleic acid. *Anat. Record*, **108**:529.

———, 1952. Microspectrophotometric analysis of metachromatic staining of nucleic acids. *Physiol. Zool.*, **25**:297–311.

Gomori, G., 1952. *Microscopic Histochemistry, Principles and Practice.* Univ. of Chicago Press, Chicago.

Hillary, B. B., 1939. Use of the Feulgen reaction in cytology. I. Effect of fixations on the reaction. *Botan. Gaz.*, **101**:276–300.

Hoff-Jorgensen, E., 1952. A microbiological assay of deoxyribonucleosides and deoxyribonucleic acid. *Biochem. J.*, **50**:400–403.

Holmes, B. E., L. K. Mee, S. Hornsey, and L. H. Gray, 1955. The nucleic acid content of cells in the meristematic elongating and fully elongated segments of roots of *Vicia faba*. *Exptl. Cell Research*, **8**:101–113.

Ishida, M. R., 1961. A cytochemical

study of nucleic acids in plant cells. VII. Causal analysis of negative Feulgen staining. Memoirs of the College of Science, Univ. of Kyoto, Series B, Vol. XXVIII, No. 1.

Jensen, W. A., 1956. On the distribution of nucleic acids in the root tip of *Vicia faba*. *Exptl. Cell Research*, 10:222–226.

————, 1958. The nucleic acid and protein content of root tip cells of *Vicia faba* and *Allium cepa*. *Exptl. Cell Research*, 14:575–583.

Jordan, B. M., and J. R. Baker, 1955. A simple pyronine/methyl green technique. *Quart. J. Microscop. Sci.*, 96:177.

Kramer, H., and G. M. Windrum, 1955. The metachromatic staining reaction, *J. Histochem. and Cytochem.*, 3:225–237.

Kupila, S., A. M. Bryan, and H. Stern, 1961. Extractability of DNA and its determination in tissues of higher plants. *Plant Physiol.*, 36:212–215.

Kurnick, N. B., 1950. The quantitative estimation of desoxyribose nucleic acid based on methyl green staining. *Exptl. Cell Research*, 1:151–158.

————, 1955a. Histochemistry of nucleic acids. *Intern. Rev. Cytol.*, 4:221–268.

————, 1955b. Pyronin Y in the methyl green-pyronin histological stain. *Stain Technol.*, 30:213–230.

Lessler, M. A., 1953. The nature and specificity of the Feulgen nucleal reaction. *Intern. Rev. Cytol.*, 2:231–247.

Markham, R., 1955. Nucleic acids, their components and related compounds, pp. 246–304. In *Modern Methods of Plant Analysis*, Vol. 4. K. Paech and M. V. Tracey (Editors). Springer-Verlog, Berlin.

Milovidov, P. F., 1949. Physik und chemie des zellkernes. *Protoplasma-Monographien*, 20.

Nurnberger, J. I., 1955. Ultraviolet Microscopy and Microspectroscopy. In *Analytical Cytology*. 1st ed. R. C. Mellors (Editor). McGraw-Hill, New York.

Ogur, M. and G. Rosen, 1950. The nucleic acids of plant tissues. I. The extraction and estimation of desoxypentose nucleic acid and pentose nucleic acid. *Arch. Biochem.*, 25:262–276.

Patau, K. and N. K. Das, 1961. The relation of DNA synthesis and mitosis in tobacco pith tissue cultured *in vitro*. *Chromosoma*, 11:553–572.

Patau, K. and H. Swift, 1953. The DNA-content (Feulgen) of nuclei during mitosis in a root tip of onion. *Chromosoma*, 6:149–160.

Schmidt, G. and S. J. Thannhauser, 1954. A method for the determination of deoxyribonucleic acid, and phosphoproteins in animal tissues. *J. Biol. Chem.*, 161:83–89.

Schneider, W. C., 1945. Phosphorus compounds in animal tissues. I. Extraction and estimation of desoxypentose nucleic acid and of pentose nucleic acid. *J. Biol. Chem.*, 161:293–303.

Schubert, M., and D. Hamerman, 1956. Metachromosia; Chemical theory and histochemical use. *J. Histochem. and Cytochem.*, 4:158–189.

Scott, J. F., A. P. Fraccastoro, and E. B. Taft, 1956. Studies in histochemistry. I. Determination of nucleic acids in microgram amounts of tissue. *J. Histochem. and Cytochem.*, 4:1–10.

Singer, M., 1954. The staining of basophilic components. *J. Histochem. and Cytochem.*, 2:322–333.

Smillie, R. M. and G. Krotkov, 1960. The estimation of nucleic acids in some algae and higher plants. *Can. J. Bot.*, 38:31–49.

Steele, R., T. Sfortunato, and L. Ottolenghi, 1949. A micromethod for the determination of the nucleic acids. *J. Biol. Chem.*, 177:231–235.

Swift, H., 1950. The constancy of desoxyribosenucleic acid in plant nuclei. *Proc. Nat. Acad. Sci. (U.S.),* **36**:643–654.

Taft, E. B., 1951. The problem of a standardized technic for the methyl-green-pyronin stain. *Stain Technol.,* **26**:205–212.

Walker, P. M. B., 1956. Ultraviolet absorption techniques, pp. 402–487. In *Physical Techniques in Biological Research,* Vol. III. G. Oster and A. W. Pollister (Editors). Academic, New York.

Woodard, J., E. Rasch, and H. Swift, 1961. Nucleic acid and protein metabolism during the mitotic cycle in *Vicia faba. J. Biophys. Biochem. Cytol.,* **9**:445–462.

CHAPTER 12

Lipids

Quantitative Histochemistry

Lipids are difficult substances to work with histochemically. Simple methods, such as weighing the tissue before and after extraction with one or more organic solvents, are not completely acceptable for a number of reasons. One is the difficulty in making the measurements with sufficient accuracy. Another reason is that the organic solvent removes not only the lipids but removes a number of nonlipid substances as well. These include amino acids, various nitrogen bases, some sugars, and other substances. Despite these difficulties, this is one of the ways in which total lipid content can be at least roughly estimated. Ether-alcohol and pyridine are both excellent solvents for use in extracting total lipids.

A procedure is given for the determination of total lipid by extraction (Glick, Swigart, Nayyar, and Stecklein, 1955). Since this method was developed for work with animal tissue, care should be used in applying it to plant material. It does, however, illustrate one approach to the problem of weighing and extracting small pieces of tissue. A similar approach, although different in detail, is that of Lowry (1953). In this approach a quartz-fiber balance is employed, permitting the use of smaller samples.

Lipids are usually first extracted and then purified before being measured or identified by a series of techniques. Even on the macro scale lipids are difficult to work with, hence these difficulties are compounded on the reduced scale of histochemical work. However, some histochemical methods have been developed for the measurement of lipids, all of which have been developed for use with animal tissue but have not been applied to plants. The methods of Schmidt-Nielsen (1942, 1944a,b), although elaborate and difficult, are excellent techniques. Unfortunately we cannot assume that these procedures are directly transferable from animal to plant material, thus they are not given here. Those interested in histochemical methods for the measurement of lipids should use the papers of Schmidt-Nielsen as a guide and model for this type of work.

The phospholipids may be approached by measuring the amount of phosphorus in extracts of organic solvents. The trichloroacetic acid extraction procedure given in Chapter 11 may be used for this. The tissue is first extracted with cold 10% trichloroacetic acid to remove the acid-soluble phosphate and is then extracted with a 1:3 solution of alcohol and ether to remove the lipids. The phosphorus content of this extract is then measured using the phosphorus procedure given in Chapter 13.

A great deal more information is required on the lipids content and metabolism of plant cells. Histochemical procedures for the measurements of lipids in plant tissues are urgently needed.

Procedures

I. Determination of Total Lipids by Extraction
(GLICK, SWIGART, NAYYAR, AND STECKLEIN, 1955)

A. Section the tissue when fresh, after rapid freezing in a cryostat at −20°C. Other methods of sectioning fresh material may also be used. Sections should be as thin as possible.

B. Place the sections on filter paper in a Petri dish, and keep them at −20°C until used.

C. Make an aluminum plate for holding the tissue sections by drilling three rows of 14 holes each, 4.5 mm deep by 8 mm in diameter, in a block of aluminum 20 × 5 cm by 0.6 cm thick. These measurements may be varied to suit the needs. Use a paper punch to cut some small discs of aluminum foil. Use these to hold and transport the sections. Turn up a corner of each disc to serve as a handle. Number the holes in the aluminum plate, and place one aluminum foil disc over each hole.

D. Place the sections on the discs, and allow them to dry for 4 hours in the cryostat. Then dry them in a vacuum desiccator. A freeze-dry apparatus could also be used.

E. Weigh the discs and dried sections rapidly on a Roller-Smith torsion balance with a total scale of 3 mg and a sensitivity of 2 μg.

F. Tease the tissue off the disc into the hole in the aluminum block on which the disc was resting. Weigh the disc, and place it over the corresponding hole in a second plate in order that the arrangement will not be lost.

G. Place the plate containing the sections in a shallow aluminum tray, and carefully fill each hole with a fat solvent, such as a mixture of equal volumes of absolute ethyl alcohol and acetone or petroleum ether. The sections must remain at the bottom of their holes. Carefully pour more fat solvent into a corner of the tray until the plate is covered. Now cover the tray with a glass plate.

H. Leave the tray and sections at room temperature for 30 minutes.

I. Remove the glass plate from the tray, and carefully remove the aluminum plate from the tray.

J. Remove the solvent from the holes very carefully by means of a drawn out pipette and gentle suction.

K. A second extraction can be performed by repeating steps F to I if desired.

L. Place the plate in a dustproof container, and allow it to air-dry for 1 hour.

M. Use a teasing needle to transfer the sections back to their original aluminum discs.

N. Weigh the discs plus extracted tissue as in step E. The first weight minus the weight of the disc represents the dry weight. The second weight minus the weight of the disc is the weight of the lipid-free tissue. The first weight minus the second is the weight of the lipids and fats present in the tissue.

The extracted tissue can be used for other determinations. The conditions of extraction and the solvents will, of course, have to be altered to suit the various plant materials and the aim of the experiment. For a slightly different approach to the same technical problems of handling the tissue for weighings and extractions, see Lowry (1953).

Microscopic Histochemistry

One of the principal difficulties in the localization of the lipids lies in their solubility in organic solvents. The standard histological procedures are all based on the use of organic solvents. Thus, the fact that lipids are soluble in organic solvents rules out the use of paraffin unless the lipids have been rendered insoluble to organic solvents by fixation. In the discussion of fixatives in Chapter 4, it was pointed out that one of the actions of a fixative was to make the chemical constituents of the cell insoluble. In the discussion of chemicals commonly employed in fixatives, all except osmium tetroxide were noted as being rather poor fixatives for lipids. But for the reasons given in Chapter 4, osmium tetroxide is not a preferred fixative for paraffin work. When used with a calcium salt, formalin does not make the lipids insoluble, but is generally believed to reduce the movement of lipids in the cell and is often used as a fixative in conjunction with sectioning on a freezing microtome. In a recent and careful study LaCour, Chayen, and Gahan (1958) found that most common fixatives, including formalin-calcium, actually resulted in the removal of lipids from the cell. However, they also found that Lewitsky's fluid, a fixative composed of chromic acid and formalin, made lipids insoluble. By using this fixative they were able to use paraffin and still obtain positive staining for lipids (or at least for phospholipids). The action of this fixative is probably based on the combination of the chromate ion with the lipids, making them at least partially insoluble.

Another approach to the problem of lipid solubility is to avoid the use of organic solvents. In the search for alternate infiltration and imbedding media, use has been made of the polyethylene glycols or carbowaxes (Firminger, 1950). These water-soluble compounds range from liquid to solid at room temperature, depending on molecular weight. The usual procedure has been to fix the tissue in a fixative such as formal-calcium, which does not contain organic solvents and which is believed to fix the lipids. (See LaCour, Chayen, and Gahan, 1958.) The tissue is next placed in a solution of carbowax, which infiltrates the tissue. This is then replaced by other carbowaxes of higher molecular weight until the tissue is infiltrated and embedded in a carbowax that is solid at room temperature. Heat is usually necessary in the final steps. The material can then be sectioned on a microtome. Good sections can be obtained, but the technique is reasonably tricky and is sometimes unreliable. There is the possibility that freeze-dried tissue may be infiltrated with carbowax. One ingenious method used with animal tissue involves freeze-drying the tissue; infiltrating it with ethylene glycol, which is a very poor lipid solvent and which is liquid at low temperatures; and then sectioning the tissue on a freezing microtome (Hack, 1952). It is important to remember that many lipids have melting points around room temperature. This means that any heating may cause the loss or dislocation of some lipids.

The easiest, safest, and most widely used method of obtaining sections for lipid localization is simply to section the fresh material. This is the principal method used at present. It yields reasonable results, but thinner, more precisely and uniformly cut sections will ultimately be required.

The actual localization procedures fall into two classes: (1) those based on the selective solubility of the dye in the lipids, or the so-called physical methods, and (2) those based on chemical reactions with lipids, or the chemical methods. The famous Sudan stains, Nile blue, and the fluorescence dyes are in the first group, whereas osmium tetroxide, acid haematein, orange G, and peracetic acid-Schiff's are in the second.

In the Sudan stains (Sudan B, Sudan III, and Sudan IV) the dye is dissolved in alcohol, triethylphosphate, propylene, or ethylene glycol (Baker, 1946; Chiffelle and Putt, 1951; Gomori, 1952). Alcohol (usually 70% ethyl alcohol) was the first solvent used with the Sudan stains and is still the most commonly used. However, the lipids of the cell are highly soluble in alcohol, and there is always some loss of lipids when the dyes are used in alcohol solution. Triethylphosphate is probably the best solvent for the dye in that it is the poorest lipid solvent. The basis of the action of the Sudan dyes is that they are more soluble in the lipids than they are in the solvent in which they are initially dissolved; the tissue is simply placed in the stain, and the lipids accumulate the dye. Several factors influence the accumulation of the dye by the lipids. One is the solubility of the dye in the solvent relative to the solubility of the dye in the lipid. If the dye is more soluble in the solvent than in the lipid it will not tend to accumulate the lipid. This consideration rules out the use of certain solvents. Another factor is the physical state of the lipid. Oils tend to accumulate the dye much more readily than do fats, thus the solid lipid formations may stain poorly with the Sudan stains.

The Sudan stains have different staining capacities. Sudan III and Sudan IV stain fats, oils, waxes, and free fatty acids blue to black without coloring the phospholipids. Sudan black B stains all the lipids of the cell, including the phospholipids. All the Sudan stains are specific for lipids.

Nile blue is used in a manner similar to the Sudan stains, but differs from them in that it is a water-soluble dye. Actually, Nile blue consists of a mixture of two dyes: oxazin, which is blue, and oxazone, which is red (Cain, 1947). Fats, oils, and waxes take up the oxazone and stain red, whereas free fatty acids and phospholipids react with the oxazin and stain blue. The blue color is actually the product of two reactions (Lillie, 1956). The first involves the solubility of the dye in the oil, the deep blue color being determined by the indicator properties of the dye. The second is a salt reaction common to basic dyes, which results in a lighter, greener color. The principal difficulty with Nile blue is that it also acts as a basic dye, and will stain nucleoprotein and other similar substances, as well as lipids. Controls in which the lipids are extracted should be run as a necessary part of this staining procedure.

A number of fluorescent dyes have also been used as lipid stains. Two of the most promising are 3:4 benzpyrene (Berg, 1951; Chayen, LaCour and Gahan, 1957) and Phosphine 3R (Popper, 1944). Both are aqueous stains and are absorbed by the lipids. Benzpyrene stains all lipid compounds of the cell, as well as sterols, whereas the Phosphine 3R stains all lipids except free fatty acids and sterols. The fluorescent dyes are highly sensitive methods which allow for considerably more precise localization than do the Sudan stains or the Nile blue.

Tissue stained with any of the dyes discussed above cannot be dehydrated and mounted in balsam. Such treatment would remove the lipids and result in loss of color. The sections must therefore be mounted in glycerine-gelatin or in some similar aqueous mounting medium.

The second group of staining procedures for lipids is based not on solubility differences but on chemical reactions. There are relatively few of these reactions, and even fewer have been applied to plant material.

The oldest of the chemical methods is that employing osmium tetroxide. The use of osmium tetroxide as a fixative has already been discussed. As a lipid stain, osmium tetroxide is believed to oxidize the double bonds present in unsaturated fatty acids in the lipid molecule (Cain, 1950; Lison, 1953; Pearse, 1953). A black compound of osmium is formed which indicates the location of lipids that have a relatively large number of double bonds. These are primarily the phospholipids and the sterols. Osmium tetroxide will react with a large number of other substances in the cell if allowed enough time. It is therefore essential to use precisely defined conditions and extraction controls. Even under the best conditions, however, the procedure is not completely reliable. Great care must also be taken in working with osmium tetroxide as it is an extremely dangerous compound, the vapors of which cause blindness.

A more specific test for phospholipids is Baker's (1946, 1947) acid haematein method, originally developed for animal tissue. In the original procedure the tissue was first fixed in formalin-$CaCl_2$, which was believed to immobilize rather than fix the phospholipids. The tissue is then placed in a dichromate-calcium mixture. The dichromate oxidizes the lipids and, in turn, is reduced to an insoluble compound. This insoluble chromium compound then combines with acid haematoxylin, with the result that the site containing the phospholipids is stained blue-black. LaCour, Chayen, and Gahan (1958) developed a modification of this procedure for use with plant material. They used a chromic acid-containing fixative in place of the formalin-$CaCl_2$ and thus combined the first two steps. They also made a change in the times used. Both methods are given in the Procedures section of this chapter.

The acid haematein method is quite specific when used correctly. The time in the chromate is important, since other cell constituents will react if given enough time. Even at the proper times other nonlipid parts of the cell will stain with the acid haematein. An extraction control is therefore a necessary part of this procedure. Baker used warm pyridine, which is highly recommended. Only those sites that stain before extraction and lose their ability to stain after extraction can be considered as containing phospholipids.

In a fairly recent method proposed by LaCour, Chayen, and Gahan (1958), the tissue is fixed in a chromic acid fixative and is stained with orange G-aniline blue. The orange G acts as a lipid stain under these conditions, possibly because of the chromium compound present. The aniline blue acts primarily as a counter stain in this procedure, staining nucleoproteins and proteins. The parts of the cell that stain orange in this procedure are the same as those that stain blue-black in the acid haematein procedure. The orange color appears specific for phospholipids. Extraction controls must be run as in the acid haematein method. The orange G-aniline blue method is quite new, and, although it holds promise, must be used with care (LaCour, and Chayen, 1958).

Finally, there is the peracetic acid-Schiff's reaction for unsaturated lipids (Lillie, 1952; Pearse, 1951). This test follows the general pattern of the other Schiff's reactions discussed thus far. The peracetic acid, a rather mild oxidant, attacks the double bonds present in the unsaturated lipids, resulting in the formation of an aldehyde. This is then colored by the Schiff's reagent. The peracetic acid will not attack carbohydrates, whereas under some conditions the periodic acid used in the carbohydrate procedure will attack the unsaturated lipids. Hence, the peracetic acid can be used as a control for the periodic acid oxidation in the carbohydrate test. An excellent control for the peracetic acid-Schiff's reaction consists in treating the sections with bromine. The bromine blocks the double bonds, thus the peracetic acid has no effect. However, bromine will not affect the periodic acid-Schiff's reaction.

Anyone considering research problems involving the localization of lipids should consult the excellent review by Cain (1950). The problem of lipid localization has been generally neglected in plant histochemistry. Thorough, critical studies of the type undertaken by Cain and Baker on animal tissue are needed in botanical studies. New techniques are needed for the handling of tissue prior to localization. New reactions are needed for both localization and identification of various types of lipids within the plant cells.

Procedures

1. Use of Polyethylene Glycols or Carbowaxes as Embedding Media (FIRMINGER, 1950)

A. Fix the tissue in 10% formalin.

B. Wash the tissue, and place it directly in carbowax. A mixture of carbowax 1500 (low melting point) and carbowax 4000 (high melting point) is commonly used in a ratio of 1 or 2:10; the higher the room temperature the sectioning is to be done in, the lower the amount of carbowax 1500. Since carbowax is hygroscopic, it should be heated to approximately 175 °C for 30 seconds and stored at 56 °C until used.

C. Leave the tissue in carbowax for 1–4 hours, and then embed as in the paraffin method. Do not use water to shorten the time of hardening. Use a refrigerator for this purpose.

D. During preparation of the tissue for sectioning, and during sectioning, handle the tissue in the same manner as for paraffin embedded tissue.

E. Try various methods of attaching the tissue to the slide.

1. Float sections on 5–10% carbowax in 4% formalin on a slide coated with Haupt's adhesive. Use no heat.

2. Place the sections directly on a slide coated with Haupt's adhesive, and suspend them in a covered dish with 40% formalin on the bottom. The moisture from the formalin will flatten the sections, and the formalin fumes will harden the gelatin of the adhesive. An exposure of 30–40 minutes is usually sufficient for flattening the sections.

F. Remove the carbowax with warm water, and stain the tissue. An alternate procedure involves placing the unfixed tissue directly into molten carbowax 4000. Mount the tissue immediately on a freezing microtome, using the CO_2 only to solidify the carbowax. Do not freeze the tissue. This is essentially another way to fresh-section the material.

II. Fixatives Recommended for Lipids

A. FORMAL-CALCIUM (BAKER, 1946)

1. Fix the tissue for 6–24 hours in a mixture composed of 10 ml of 40% formalin, 10 ml of 10% $CaCl_2$ in water, and 80 ml of distilled water. Add a piece of chalk to keep the pH neutral.

2. This fixative does not prevent the lipids from dissolving in organic solvents but may help prevent their movement in aqueous solutions.

B. LEWITSKY'S FLUID (LACOUR, CHAYEN, AND GAHAN, 1958)

1. Fix the tissue in a mixture composed of 50 ml of 1% chromic acid in water and 50 ml of 10% formalin. This fixative is good for phospholipids, since it fixes them well enough to permit paraffin infiltration and embedding.

III. Extraction Procedures for Lipids

A. PYRIDINE METHOD (BAKER, 1946)

1. Use fresh or formalin-fixed tissue.
2. Place the tissue in pyridine at room temperature for 30 minutes.
3. Then place in fresh pyridine at 60°C for 24 hours.
4. Wash in running water for 2 hours. All classes of lipids should be extracted. Pyridine is a strong base and causes changes in other cell constituents besides the lipids. It is not recommended as a control for Nile blue, although it is an excellent control for most of the other procedures.

B. ETHER-ALCOHOL METHOD (PEARSE, 1953)

1. Use fresh tissue.
2. Place the tissue in a Coplin jar in a mixture of three parts ether and one part ethyl alcohol for 1 hour at 60°C. Seal the top of the Coplin jar with silicone grease to prevent excess evaporation.
3. Repeat the extraction with fresh ether-alcohol two more times.
4. Wash the tissue in running water for 1 hour.
5. An alternate procedure consists in placing the tissue in a microsoxlet apparatus and extracting by a continuous process. This extraction procedure will remove all classes of lipids.

IV. Total Lipids—Sudan Dyes (BAKER, 1947; GOMORI, 1952)

A. Use fresh sections.
B. Place the sections in 50% ethyl alcohol for a few minutes.
C. Stain the sections in a saturated and filtered solution of Sudan III, Sudan IV, or Sudan black B in either 70% ethyl alcohol or 60% triethylphosphate for 5–20 minutes.
D. Differentiate in 50% ethyl alcohol for about 1 minute.
E. Mount in glycerine-gelatin.

An alternate method, developed by Chiffelle and Putt (1951), involves the following steps.

A. Use fresh sections.
B. Place the sections in pure propylene or ethylene glycol for 3–5 minutes, shaking occasionally.
C. Transfer the sections to a staining solution made by dissolving 0.7 g of the Sudan dye in 100 ml of propylene or ethylene glycol. Heat the solution to 100–110°C, and stir thoroughly for several minutes. Filter the hot solution through Whatman No. 2 paper, cool, and filter again.
D. Stain the sections for 5–7 minutes.

E. Transfer the sections to 85% propylene or ethylene glycol and water, and agitate gently for 2–3 minutes.

F. Wash with distilled water for 3–5 minutes, and then mount in glycerine-gelatin.

By either method the Sudan III and Sudan IV will stain the fats and oils and the waxes. In addition to these, Sudan B will stain the free fatty acids and the phospholipids. The preparations are not permanent.

V. Total Lipids—Nile Blue Procedure (CAIN, 1947)

A. Use fresh tissue or tissue fixed in Lewitsky's fluid.

B. Section the tissue by hand.

C. Stain in 1% Nile blue at 37°C for 30 seconds.

D. Differentiate in 1% acetic acid at 37°C for 30 seconds.

E. Wash in distilled water, and mount in glycerine-gelatin.

Fats, oils, and waxes (the neutral lipids) stain red; the free fatty acids and phospholipids (the acidic lipids) stain blue. Structures that stain blue do not necessarily contain lipids; the blue dye (oxazine) is also a basic dye, and will bind at a number of sites in the cell. The red dye (Oxazane) is present only at higher concentrations of Nile blue (1%). Oxazane is formed by hydrolysis of oxazine and is water-insoluble, although slightly soluble in strong solutions of Nile blue. If only the blue dye (oxazine) is required, use an 0.02% solution of Nile blue.

VI. Lipids and Sterols—3:4 Benzpyrene-Caffeine Method (BERG, 1951)

A. Use fresh sections cut as thin as possible. Fixation in Lewitsky's fluid is recommended, but not in formal-calcium.

B. Stain for 20 minutes in a benzpyrene solution made as follows: prepare a saturated solution of caffeine in water at 20°C (about 1.5% caffeine); to 100 ml of the filtered solution add 2.0 mg of 3:4 benzpyrene, and keep at 37°C for 2 days; filter the solution, add 100 ml of distilled water, let stand for 2 hours, and refilter. The solution is now ready for use, and will remain stable for several months.

C. Wash in water, and mount in glycerine.

D. Examine under an ultraviolet fluorescence microscope.

Lipids and sterols give a blue or bluish-white fluorescence. The preparations obtained are not stable, and will fade relatively rapidly. For controls use unstained sections and sections stained after pyridine extraction. The caffeine is used only to get the dye into solution and does not contribute to the color.

VII. All Lipids Other Than Fatty Acids, Soaps, and Sterols—Aqueous Phosphine 3R (POPPER, 1944)

A. Use fresh sections cut as thin as possible.

B. Stain the sections for 3 minutes in an 0.1% aqueous solution of Phosphine 3R at room temperature.

C. Rinse briefly in water.

D. Mount in 90% glycerine.

E. Examine with the ultraviolet fluorescence microscope. Lipids will appear as a clear, silvery-white fluorescence. The fatty acids, soaps, and sterols will not be fluorescent. Use unstained sections and sections stained after pyridine extraction as controls.

VIII. Unsaturated Lipids—Osmium Tetroxide Method (CAIN, 1950)

A. Fix the tissue in formal-calcium fixative for not more than 6 hours. Avoid fixatives containing dichromate.

B. Place the tissue in a 1% solution of osmium tetroxide in water for 1 hour at room temperature. Keep and use all osmium tetroxide solutions in a hood as they are dangerous, particularly to the eyes.

C. Wash well in running water for one-half hour.

D. Section the tissue when fresh, either free hand or on a freezing microtome.

E. Mount in glycerine-gelatin or other aqueous medium. Avoid the use of alcohol.

F. Unsaturated lipids will appear black.

IX. Phospholipids—Acid Haematein Method (BAKER, 1946)

A. Fix small pieces of tissue for 6–18 hours in formal-calcium fixative.

B. Transfer to a dichromate-calcium solution [5 g of potassium dichromate, 1 g of $CaCl_2$ (anhydrous), and 100 ml of distilled water] for 18 hours at 22°C.

C. Transfer to a second dichromate-calcium solution (same as in B) for 24 hours at 60°C.

D. Wash well in distilled water.

E. Cut frozen sections at 10 μ.

F. Mordant in dichromate-calcium solution for 1 hour at 60°C.

G. Wash in distilled water.

H. Transfer to acid haematein solution for 5 hours at 37°C. To make the haematein solution, place 0.05 g of haematoxylin in a flask, and add

48 ml of distilled water and 1 ml of 1% $NaIO_4$. Heat until boiling, cool, and add 1 ml of glacial acetic acid. Use the same day.

I. Rinse in distilled water.

J. Transfer to borax-ferricyanide solution (0.25 g of potassium ferri-cyanide, 0.25 g of sodium tetraborate, and 100 ml of distilled water) for 18 hours at 37°C. Keep this solution in the dark.

K. Wash in water.

L. Mount in glycerine-gelatin.

It is absolutely necessary to run a control of tissue previously extracted with pyridine. Only the substances that stain dark blue or blue-black in the unextracted material and which do not stain in the extracted tissue are phospholipids. Nucleoprotein will stain the same as the phospholipids but will not be extracted with pyridine.

X. *Phospholipids—Acid Haematein Method* (LACOUR, CHAYEN, AND GAHAN, 1958)

A. Fix the tissue in Lewitsky's fluid for 18 hours.

B. Embed the tissue in paraffin. Before embedding, pass the tissue through chloroform. Section at 7 μ.

C. Remove paraffin from sections, and bring to water.

D. Place sections in dichromate-calcium solution (see preceding procedure) at 60°C for 5 hours.

E. Wash in distilled water.

F. Transfer to acid haematein solution (see preceding procedure) for 5 hours at 37°C.

G. Wash in distilled water.

H. Mount in glycerine-gelatin.

A pyridine extraction control must be used; the results should be the same as in Procedure IX.

XI. *Phospholipids—Orange G-Aniline Blue Method* (LACOUR, CHAYEN, AND GAHAN, 1958)

A. Fix tissue in Lewitsky's fluid for 18 hours.

B. Paraffin infiltrate and embed the tissue. Pass the tissue through chloroform prior to paraffin infiltration. Section at 7 μ.

C. Remove the paraffin, and bring the sections to water.

D. Stain for 2–3 minutes in a staining mixture made by dissolving 2 g of orange G and 0.5 g of aniline blue (water soluble) in 100 ml of 0.1 M citrate buffer at pH 3.

E. Rinse for 30 seconds in the citrate buffer used to make the stain.

F. Carefully blot the sections, and rinse them rapidly in equal parts of absolute ethyl alcohol and tertiary butanol.

G. Rinse in tertiary butanol for 2–3 minutes and mount in Euparal. Phospholipid containing structures will appear yellow; the rest will appear blue.

XII. Unsaturated Lipids—Peracetic Acid—Schiff's Method (LILLIE, 1952; PEARSE, 1951)

A. Use formalin-fixed, paraffin-infiltrated tissue. Fresh tissue may also be used.

B. Remove the paraffin from the sections, and bring them to water.

C. Treat with 40% peracetic acid for 2–5 minutes.

D. Wash in running water for 2–5 minutes.

E. Place in Schiff's reagent for 30 minutes.

F. Wash in running water for 10 minutes.

G. Mount in glycerine jelly.

Unsaturated lipids stain red. The only other positive reaction is given by DNA. As a control, treat sections with bromine (1 ml of bromine in 39 ml of CCl_4) for 1 hour, and then run through procedure. A negative reaction should be obtained. This reaction and the bromine control should be used as a control on the periodic acid-Schiff's reaction for carbohydrate. A positive periodic acid-Schiff's reaction after the bromine treatment clearly indicates that the color is due to carbohydrates and not to lipids.

LITERATURE CITED

Baker, J. R., 1946. The histochemical recognition of lipine. Quart. J. Microscop. Sci., 87:441–471.

———, 1947. Further remarks on the histochemical recognition of lipine. Quart. J. Microscop. Sci., 88:463–465.

Berg, N. O., 1951. A histological study of masked lipids. Stainability, distribution, and functional variations. Acta Pathol. Microbiol. Scand. Suppl., 90: 1–192.

Cain, A. J., 1947. The use of Nile blue in the examination of lipids. Quart.

J. Microscop. Sci., 88:383–392.

———, 1950. The histochemistry of lipids in animals. Biol. Rev. Camb. Phil. Soc., 25:73–112.

Chayen, J., L. F. LaCour, and P. B. Gahan, 1957. Uptake of benzpyrene by a chromosomal phospholipid. Nature, 180:652–653.

Chiffelle, T. L. and F. A. Putt, 1951. Propylene and ethylene glycol as solvents for Sudan IV and Black B. Stain Technol., 26:51–56.

Firminger, H. I., 1950. Carbowax embedding for obtaining thin tissue sections and study of intracellular lipids. *Stain Technol.*, **25**:121–123.

Glick, D., R. H. Swigart, S. N. Nayyar, and H. R. Stecklein, 1955. Flame photometric determination of potassium in microgram quantities of tissue and the distribution of potassium and lipid in the adrenal of the monkey and guinea pig (Studies in histochemistry, XXXII). *J. Histochem. and Cytochem.*, **3**:6–15.

Gomori, G., 1952. *Microscopic Histochemistry, Principles and Practice*. Univ. of Chicago Press, Chicago.

Hack, M. H., 1952. A new histochemical technique for lipids applied to plasmal. *Anat. Record*, **112**:275–302.

LaCour, L. F. and J. Chayen, 1958. A cyclic staining behaviour of the chromosomes during mitosis and meiosis. *Exptl. Cell Research*, **14**:462–468.

LaCour, L. F., J. Chayen, and P. S. Gahan, 1958. Evidence for lipid material in chromosomes. *Exptl. Cell Research*, **14**:469–485.

Lillie, R. D., 1952. Ethylenic reaction of ceroid with performic acid and Schiff reagent. *Stain Technol.*, **27**:37–45.

———, 1956. The mechanism of Nile blue staining of lipofuchsins, *J. Histochem. and Cytochem.*, **4**:377–381.

Lison, L., 1953. *Histochimie et Cytochimie Animales, Principes et Méthodes*. 2ᵉ ed. Gauthier-Villars, Paris.

Lowry, O. H., 1953. The quantitative histochemistry of the brain—Histological sampling. *J. Histochem. and Cytochem.*, **1**:420–428.

Pearse, A. G. E., 1951. The histochemical demonstration of keratin by methods involving selective oxidation. *Quart. J. Microscop. Sci.*, **92**:393–402.

———, 1953. *Histochemistry, Theoretical and Applied*. J. and A. Churchill, London.

Popper, H., 1944. Distribution of vitamin A in tissue as visualized by fluorescence microscopy. *Physiol. Rev.*, **24**:205–224.

Schmidt-Nielsen, K., 1942. Microtitration of fat in quantities of 10^{-5} gram. *Compt. rend. trav. lab. Carlsberg, Sér. chim.*, **24**:233–247.

———, 1944a. Micro determination of the iodine number of fat in quantities of 10^{-5} gram. *Compt. rend. trav. lab. Carlsberg, Sér. chim.*, **25**:87–96.

———, 1944b. Extraction and fractionation of the lipids in 1 mg of tissue. *Compt. rend. trav. lab. Carlsberg, Sér. chim.*, **25**:97–104.

CHAPTER 13

Minerals

Quantitative Histochemistry

Minerals occur in plant cells in large numbers and in diverse forms. They may be soluble, insoluble, or part of complex organic molecules. Histochemically they are not very difficult to work with as most form highly colored compounds with a variety of easily obtained reagents. The methods developed by the mineral nutrition plant physiologists and the soil experts are usually based on the assumption that these minerals exist in solution in an ionic form. The extraction of soluble minerals presents no problem; nor is the extraction of insoluble minerals, since it is usually simply a matter of choosing the proper extraction medium and the best pH. However, the minerals that are part of organic molecules can be liberated only by the destruction of these molecules. This can be best accomplished either by acid digestion or by ashing. Acid digestion may be carried out as for nitrogen determinations or by using the sealed-tube method given in this chapter. For nonvolatile minerals, such as calcium, boron, or iron, ashing is usually the easiest procedure. The fresh or paraffin-embedded sections are placed in pyrex tubes in an aluminum block and are heated in a muffle furnace. The heat causes the destruction of the organic matter and drives off the carbon, hydrogen, oxygen, and other volatile substances, leaving only the heavier metals. These are then taken up in acid, and the test is run.

On the whole, the reactions used in measuring the minerals once they are in solution are straightforward, resulting in a specific color which is measured in a spectrophotometer or colorimeter. Most of the reactions are very sensitive; the only difficulty that may be encountered is the possible interference from other minerals. This interference may come either in the form of other minerals present in the tissue or from minerals present in the solution used in making the determination. Actually, con-

270

tamination with minerals in the water used in making up the various test solutions may be a serious one for certain tests. It is also possible that contamination with outside minerals may occur in the sectioning of the material. For this reason it is sometimes necessary in exceedingly sensitive histochemical procedures to use a glass knife (made by standard procedures used in electron microscopy) in place of the ordinary metal microtome knife or razor blade. In any case it is best to use water of as high a purity as is obtainable (preferably deionized or triple-distilled water) and to use extreme caution throughout the entire analysis to avoid contamination with dust and dirt. One source of contamination must never be forgotten, namely, dirt settling out of the air. This is a particularly marked danger in highly industrialized locations, where atmospheric contamination may be considerable.

One of the most important inorganic constituents of the cell is phosphorus. Fortunately there are a number of good methods available for the determination of phosphorus. One procedure given here is a micro version of the famous molybdate reaction (Lundsteen and Vermehren, 1936). In this reaction the phosphorus combines with the molybdate to form phosphomolybdic acid, which is reduced by the amidol. The result is a deep blue color that is readily measured in a spectrophotometer. This procedure can be used either after digestion or directly on organic phosphate. It is highly reliable and should present no difficulties in use. Another excellent and highly sensitive phosphorus method is based on ammonium molybdate and stannous chloride. A micro adaptation of this method is given by Krugelis (1950). The version of the reaction presented here is that of Schaffer, Fong, and Kirk (1953). This method involves the extraction of the colored product, which reduces the interference from other colored materials that may be present in the sample, and increases the sensitivity of the reaction.

Phosphorus is such an important element and is present in so many compounds vital to the cell that phosphorus analyses are frequently made on various cell fractions. The methods used in obtaining such fractions are generally complex but yield a great deal of information. One such fractionation schedule is given in this chapter. This is the procedure used by Olney and Pollock (1960) in their work on cherry embryos and gives the following fractions: high-energy nucleotides, low-energy nucleotides, pentose and hexose phosphate, inorganic orthophosphate, and nucleic acid-phosphoproteins.

The calcium method given here is based on a different principle than are either of the phosphorus methods. In this procedure the calcium combines with a highly colored compound, chloranilic acid, decreasing the light absorption of the mixture. Thus, the greater the concentration, the lighter the color. The procedure given here is a histochemical adaptation of the method described by Tyner (1948). The major difficulty in working with calcium in plant tissue is that the high concentration of magnesium present in plant cells usually interferes with the determination unless removed. However, the removal of magnesium in small samples is not easy. The chloranilic acid procedure for calcium gives the least trouble with interference from magnesium and is therefore recommended. The problem of magnesium interference should always be kept in mind in making calcium determinations (see Gammon and Forbes, 1949).

The histochemical determination of boron is particularly difficult because of the contamination of the solutions by the boron present in pyrex glass. Great care must therefore be taken in the selection of glassware and in the purification of reagents. Another difficulty is that at temperatures above $300°C$ significant amounts of boron may volatize (Winsor, 1948). Consequently, temperatures above $300°C$ should be avoided. The procedure for boron given here is a histochemical modification of the standard quinalizarin method (Berger and Truog, 1944). The procedure is based on the color difference between quinalizarin, which is reddish, and the boron-quinalizarin complex, which is blue.

A similar procedure is used to measure copper (Turkington and Tracy, 1958). The solution containing copper is mixed with 1,5-diphenylcarbohydrazide and the resulting color measured. The method is simple and straightforward; chromium is the only interfering ion.

The procedure given for zinc has been used only on animal tissue (Malström, 1956; Malström and Glick, 1951). The way in which the method has been worked out, however, is a fine example of the direction in which further research on mineral determinations in plant tissue should go. Zinc is not an easy element to work with, and great care should be taken in attempting to measure it in biological material. In the procedure given, the zinc is extracted from the ashed sample and is then allowed to react with dithizone, which is in an organic solvent. The complex formed between the dithizone and the zinc is retained in the organic solvent and the resulting color measured.

The flame photometer is a very versatile tool for the analysis of many minerals, including potassium, sodium, calcium, boron, lithium, and others. The mineral is first combusted in a flame, and then the emission at a wave length characteristic for the mineral in question is measured. The procedure given here (Glick, Swigart, Nayyar and Stecklein, 1955) is for potassium, and can be used as a model for other elements. The method is highly sensitive and is capable of measuring unusually small amounts of potassium. The flame photometer used is a Beckman spectrophotometer model DU with flame-photometer and photomultiplier attachments. Other types of flame photometers can, of course, be used. If very small amounts of fluid containing the mineral are to be measured, the modified flame photometer of Solomon and Caton (1955) should be used. They modified the Beckman flame photometer (Model DU) such that only 0.25-ml samples were necessary, which permitted the measurement of 1 μM Na/liter or 0.6 μM K/liter. Thus they were able to measure the potassium and sodium in a single kidney tubule of *Necturus*. A colorimetric procedure for potassium that appears to be quite useful is the chloroplatinate method developed by Eckel (1952).

A method for the histochemical determination of magnesium may possibly be developed by scaling down Sterges and MacIntire's (1950) thiazole yellow procedure. This test appears to be quite specific, and there should be little trouble in reducing it at least 10 times. Another procedure that appears potentially capable of being developed into a histochemical procedure for iron in plant material is the spectrophotometric method of Severn and Peterson (1958). An interesting sulfur method based on the use of the Cartesian diver is given by Holter and Løvtrup (1949).

An excellent source of analytical procedures, particularly for the minerals, is the journal *Analytical Chemistry*. This publication frequently contains articles and papers of great value to the histochemist.

Procedures

1. Digestion for Phosphorus and Nitrogen Determinations
(GRUNBAUM, SCHAFFER, AND KIRK, 1952)

A. Place the tissue or extract in tubes (approximately 45 mm long with an outside diameter of 7 mm) sealed at one end.

B. Dry the liquid samples by placing the tubes in a vacuum desiccator.

C. Add to the tubes 10–25 μl of concentrated H_2SO_4. Do not allow the acid to contact the sample.

D. Seal the open ends of the tubes by heating the ends with a gas-oxygen torch until white hot. Using a hot pair of forceps, press the edges together. Anneal the ends briefly in a gas flame.

E. To wet the samples with the H_2SO_4 give the sealed tubes a quick jerk, to move the acid to the sample.

F. Place the tubes in a brass block in a muffle furnace preheated to

450°C. Set the block at an angle in the furnace, and place asbestos pads in the bottom of the holes to act as cushions.

G. Heat the tubes for 30 minutes.

H. Centrifuge the tubes immediately after removing from the furnace, to force the H_2SO_4 to the bottom of the tubes.

I. Scratch the tubes with a sharp file or glass knife, and break into two pieces. Place the pieces in a drying oven at 90°C for a few minutes. Olney and Pollock (1960) recommend opening the tubes under pressure (approximately 30 psi) and then reducing the pressure.

J. With a pipette, transfer the digest to vessels suitable for phosphorus or nitrogen analyses.

II. Phosphorus Determination (SCHAFFER, FONG, AND KIRK, 1953)

A. METHOD FOR PHOSPHORUS DETERMINATION IN THE RANGE 0.1–5 μg

1. Add the sample to the upper part of the large extractor shown in Fig. 13-1.

2. Next, add 50 μl of molybdate reagent, made by dissolving 2 g of ammonium molybdate in 40 ml of either water or 2 N sulfuric acid. Store the reagent in polyethylene bottles. The reagent will remain stable for several months. With acidic samples (about 100 μeq of acid) use the aqueous reagent; with neutral samples use the acid reagent.

3. Centrifuge the mixture to the lower bulb.

4. Add 200 μl of octyl alcohol with a special centrifugal pipette (Fig. 13-1) or with an ordinary transfer pipette.

5. Centrifuge again.

6. Cut a hard rubber stopper to form a pentagon, and mount in the shaft of a laboratory motor. Extract the phosphomolybdic acid by holding the lower bulb of the extractor against the stopper for 15–30 seconds.

7. Wash and displace the alcohol phase by adding enough 1 N HCl (approximately 300 μl) to bring the interface near the upper end of the capillary, and then centrifuge.

8. Use a capillary pipette to transfer the octyl alcohol to a glass-stoppered, 4-ml volumetric flask, and add 2 μl of a dilute stannous chloride solution prepared by diluting 0.25 ml of stock solution with 1 ml of water. Make the stock solution by dissolving 4 g of stannous chloride in 10 ml of concentrated HCl. Store the stock solution in a brown, glass-stoppered bottle. The stock solution will remain stable for a week, but the diluted solution should be prepared daily.

9. Rinse the upper chamber of the extractor several times with butyl alcohol, and transfer to a volumetric flask.

10. Shake the flask to develop color, and add about 200 μl of ethyl alcohol to assure the dissolution of any aqueous droplets present.

11. Use butyl alcohol to adjust the volume of the solution in the flask.

12. Measure the optical density at 725 mμ with butyl alcohol as the blank.

B. METHOD FOR PHOSPHORUS
   DETERMINATION IN THE
   RANGE 0.1–0.8 μg

1. Repeat steps 1–3 of A.

2. Add 200 μl of octyl alcohol by centrifugation from a special centrifuge pipette which is seated by means of a plastic collar in the top of the extractor and is discharged by centrifugal force.

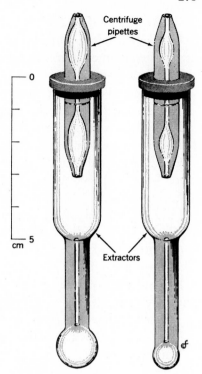

Figure 13-1

Extractors and centrifuge pipettes used in the phosphorus method of Schaffer, Fong, and Kirk (1953). [Redrawn from Schaffer, Fong, and Kirk, Anal. Chem. **25**, *1953.]*

3. Displace the alcohol phase with 1 *N* HCl as above, and add 2 μl of dilute stannous chloride solution.

4. Mix to develop color by rotating the extractor while holding it at an angle or by holding it against the shaker (see step 6 in A).

5. Centrifuge the extractor to separate aqueous droplets and to collect the alcohol-molybdenum blue solution.

6. Remove a sufficient quantity of the blue solution, and measure in a spectrophotometer.

A method for phosphorus determination in the range 0.002–0.08 μg P is also given by Schaffer, Fong, and Kirk (1953). This method involves the same principles.

III. *Phosphorus—Molybdate Test* (*Modified from* LUNDSTEEN AND VERMEHREN, 1936)

A. Use 50–200-μ sections of fresh or freeze-dried tissue. Place tissue in 10-mm tubes. If freeze-dried material is used remove the paraffin with toluene, and rinse with absolute alcohol.

B. Add 50 μl of 50% H_2SO_4 to the tissue.

C. Place tubes in aluminum blocks with shallow ($\frac{1}{4}$ inch deep) holes, and place on an electric hot plate. Heat slowly to 200°C.

D. Keep tissue at 200°C for at least 4 hours. Avoid temperatures above 200°C. At higher temperatures phosphorus may be lost from the sample.

E. Cool the tubes and the aluminum block.

F. Add 20 μl of superoxal (30% H_2O_2), and reheat at 200°C for 2 hours. The solution should be colorless. If it is not, repeat this step.

G. Cool the tubes and samples, and add 0.4 ml of molybdate reagent, made by mixing 100 ml of 7.5% ammonium molybdate, 45 ml of 10 N sulfuric acid, and 105 ml of water.

H. Add 0.1 ml of amidol solution. To make the amidol solution dissolve 15 g of sodium sulfite and 1.5 g of amidol in 100 ml of water, and dilute 4 times with water before using. Never use an amidol solution more than a day old.

I. Read the color after 10 minutes at 660 mμ in a Beckman spectrophotometer model DU equipped with microcuvettes.

J. For the determination of soluble phosphorus start with step G.

K. Use KH_2PO_4 to obtain a standard curve.

The range of this procedure is 1–25 μg P.

IV. Fractionation of Phosphorus
(OLNEY AND POLLOCK, 1960)

A. Dissect the axis and leaf primordia of five cherry embryos, and quickly freeze them in dry ice in a mortar made from thick-walled pyrex capillary tubing (35 × 2 mm I.D.).

B. Rub the frozen tissue into suspension in 50 μl of 10% perchloric acid (PCA) with a pyrex rod.

C. Centrifuge at room temperature for 1 minute at 1000 g.

D. Transfer the supernatant to a 6 × 45 mm reaction vessel.

E. Wash the precipitate twice with 50-μl aliquots of 5% PCA, and add the washings to the supernatant.

F. Dry the residue, which represents the acid-insoluble phosphorus, and analyze for phosphorus content.

G. Add to the combined supernatant approximately 1 mg of specially purified Norite A carbon. Stir, and remove by centrifugation.

H. Wash the carbon precipitate with 100 μl of glass-distilled water 3 times, and combine the supernatants.

I. Divide the combined supernatant into two equal aliquots. Analyze one directly for orthophosphate. Dry the second aliquot, and determine the total phosphorus content, using Procedure II. This analysis represents the acid soluble nonnucleotide phosphorus residue.

J. The charcoal residue (H) contains the nucleotides. Hydrolyze these in 75 μl of 1 N HCl at 100°C for 12 minutes. Remove the supernatant, wash the tissue once with 100 μl of water, and combine the tissue with the supernatant. Analyze the combined supernatant for total phosphorus. This represents the high-energy nucleotide phosphorus.

K. The phosphorus remaining associated with the charcoal represents the low-energy nucleotide phosphorus. Measure the amount of phosphorus in the charcoal after complete digestion in 25 μl of N-PCA (2.5 volumes of nitric acid to 1 volume of 70% perchloric acid). The five phosphorus fractions collected are:

1. High-energy nucleotides (adenosine di- and tri-phosphate) (step J).
2. Low-energy nucleotides (adenosine monophosphate) (step K).
3. Acid-soluble residue (chiefly pentose and hexose phosphate) (step I).
4. Acid-insoluble residue (chiefly nucleic acids and phosphoproteins) (step F).
5. Inorganic phosphate (inorganic orthophosphate) (step I).

This procedure has been used only on cherry embryos, but it should be applicable to all types of plant tissues.

V. Calcium (Modified from TYNER, 1948)

A. Place fresh tissue or sections of freeze-dried or freeze-substituted material in pyrex tubes. Do not deparaffinize the sections.

B. Put the tubes in an aluminum block, place in a muffle furnace, and ash at 450°C.

C. Cool the tubes carefully, add a small drop of triple-distilled water, and then dissolve the ash in dilute (1:3) HCl.

D. Next, evaporate the sample to dryness in an oven or steam bath.

E. Take up the residue in 50 μl of 0.1 N acetic acid, and warm carefully for a few minutes.

F. Add 200 μl of triple-distilled water and 100 μl of 0.1% chloralinic acid.

G. Allow to stand overnight. The time may be reduced to 3 hours if the tubes are agitated.

H. Measure in a spectrophotometer at 500 mμ.

I. Use as a blank 200-μl triple distilled water and 100 μl 0.1% chloranilic acid.

VI. Boron—Quinalizarin Procedure (Modified from BERGER AND TRUOG, 1944)

A. Follow steps A–E of the calcium procedure.

B. Add 300 μl of a quinalizarin solution made by dissolving 2.5 mg of quinalizarin in 100 ml of concentrated sulfuric acid.

C. After 5 minutes measure the color at 620 mμ in a spectrophotometer.

VII. Copper—1,5-Diphenylcarbohydrazide Method (TURKINGTON AND TRACY, 1958)

A. To 200 μl of a solution containing 0.01–0.26 μg of copper, which may be either an extract or a solution obtained from ashing (see steps A–E of the calcium procedure), add 200 μl of a buffer at pH 9.0.

B. Next, add 40 μl of an 0.1% solution of 1,5-diphenylcarbohydrazide solution in redistilled 95% ethyl alcohol, and thoroughly mix.

C. Read the color at 495 mμ in a spectrophotometer between 4 and 7 minutes after the solutions have been mixed.

D. Use triple-distilled water and borosilicate glassware.

VIII. Zinc (MALSTRÖM, 1956; MALSTRÖM AND GLICK, 1951)

A. Use freeze-dried, paraffin-infiltrated tissue. Cut the tissue with a glass microtome knife (see Latta and Hartman, 1950), and transfer to the reaction tubes on the tip of a drawn out borosilicate-glass rod. Use quartz reaction tubes with an inside diameter of 4 mm and a length of 25 mm. Fit the tubes with flat-topped, ground, borosilicate-glass stoppers to facilitate clamping in the extraction apparatus.

B. Place the tubes in a stainless steel block ($5 \times 7.5 \times 1.3$ cm) with holes 5 mm in diameter and 10 mm deep. Ash in a muffle furnace for 3 hours at 475°C. After ashing keep the tubes stoppered at all times, except when reagents are added.

C. Add 20 μl of 2N HCl to each tube, and let stand for 30 minutes with occasional mixing.

D. Then add enough 2 N NH$_4$OH (made by dissolving tank ammonia in deionized water) to each tube to bring the pH to 5.5, and mix (determine the volume required by previous titration).

E. Next, add 25 μl of a buffer solution to the mixture. Make this by dissolving 34 g of CH$_3$COONa·3H$_2$O, 20 g of Na$_2$S$_2$O$_3$·5H$_2$O, and 1.0 g of KCN in about 100 ml of deionized water; bring the pH to 5.5 with 15 N CH$_3$COOH, and make up to 250 ml with deionized water. Then make the buffer zinc-free by repeated shaking with dithizone solution in a separatory funnel until the dithizone solution remains pure green.

F. Finally, add 20 μl of 0.7 mg% dithizone to each sample.

G. Extract for 5 minutes at 650 rpm (30 g). The extraction apparatus is a modified clinical centrifuge in which the head is replaced by a rack that holds the reaction tubes horizontally and turns and spins them at the same time. The details of the construction of this machine are given by Malström and Glick (1951).

H. Transfer an aliquot of the organic phase to a capillary cuvette, and read the density at 620 mμ.

I. Run a blank by repeating the procedure without the sample.

This method is designed to measure millimicrogram quantities of zinc.

IX. *Potassium—Flame Photometry Method*
(GLICK, SWIGART, NAYYAR, AND STECKLEIN, 1955)

A. Prepare the tissue as described in Procedure I for total lipid determination in Chapter 12.

B. After determining the dry weight of the tissue, the tissue may either be extracted directly or it may be ashed.

1. To extract the potassium without ashing, transfer the tissue directly to a tube containing 1 ml of water. Remove the tissue from the water with a fine glass rod after a 1- to 2-hour extraction period at room temperature. Be careful not to fragment the tissue.

2. To ash the tissue, place the sections on the aluminum discs in a muffle furnace, and heat at 375°C for about 22 hours or until all carbon is lost. Then transfer each disc and sample to a tube containing 1 ml of water, cover with Parafilm, and centrifuge to bring down any undissolved material. Use the supernatant fluid in the determination.

C. Transfer the water solution of the potassium sample to the sample vessel in the flame photometer (a Beckman spectrophotometer model DU with flame photometer and photomultiplier attachment or other similar instrument). Measure the intensity of emission at 768 mμ, using a slit width of 0.62 mm, and measure the 0.1 sensitivity setting. Prepare a standard curve by making serial dilutions of a stock standard solution of potassium chloride in double-distilled water containing 10 meq of potassium/liter. The standard curve should cover a range of 0.01–0.10 meq of potassium/liter.

Glick, Swigart, Nayyar, and Stecklein (1955) found that ashing resulted in a loss of potassium; for this reason, they recommend direct water extraction. Keep in mind, however, that the tissue they used was frozen before it was dried and that this may have made extraction easier.

Microscopic Histochemistry

Minerals may be localized within the cell by microincineration, crystal formation, or coloration. Each of these methods has not only certain advantages but also disadvantages, with the result that precise localization and identification of minerals are difficult.

Microincineration offers by far the most precise localization. The procedure is simple and straightforward. The tissue is placed in paraffin, sectioned, and mounted as usual, freeze-dried material offering the best results. Next, the slide containing the tissue is placed in a muffle furnace and is heated to 650°C. This results in the total destruction of organic matter in the tissue, leaving only an ash of nonvolatile inorganic matter—the minerals. When viewed with dark-field illumination the mineral deposits can be clearly seen (Fig. 13-2). The question next arises as to the identification of minerals in the ash. The ash consists chiefly of sodium, potassium, calcium, magnesium, phosphorus, and iron. All are white when viewed with dark-field illumination, except iron which is yellow to red. Silicon, if present, may retain its crystalline structure and be double refractive in polarized light, but it may also fuse with calcium.

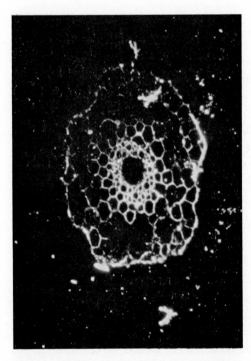

Figure 13-2
Microincineration of a section of barley root viewed under dark field illumination (100×). [*Courtesy of Dr. A. D. McLaren.*]

Detailed studies, principally by Scott (1933), indicate that there is little if any change in localization of insoluble or organically bound minerals during microincineration. The difficulty in the technique does not lie in the localization but in the identification of the minerals in the ash. As there is no satisfactory way to do this, the method is useful primarily in determining the general distribution of minerals, with the possible exception of iron which may be identified by the red color of its ash. For an excellent review of the work on the microincineration of plant tissues see Uber (1940).

Attempts have been made to localize and identify minerals by dissolving them, usually in dilute acid, and then adding an anion with which they form insoluble, characteristically shaped crystals. This has been done with both fresh material and microincinerated material. The method is quite specific, and a large number of characteristic crystals can be formed and identified (Chamot and Mason, 1958). The difficulty here, of course, is not one of identification but of localization. In most cases such information is of little value unless the mineral is not normally present in a cell. By carefully controlling the conditions under which the crystals are formed and counting them, the relative distribution of a mineral may be determined in the various tissues. This technique was used to study calcium-boron interrelations in cell growth (Marsh and Shive, 1941), and may have much wider use.

Finally, numerous attempts have been made to adapt various of the coloration reactions undergone by minerals to localization. On the whole these attempts have failed because (1) the colored product was not insoluble, (2) the soluble minerals were lost before the reaction, (3) the insoluble or organic bound minerals did not react, or (4) in attempting to liberate the insoluble and bound minerals, the site of localization was destroyed or drastically altered.

One of the more successful of these procedures is given in the magnesium test (Broda, 1939). In this method the magnesium forms a blue complex with the quinalizarin and a red complex with the Titian yellow. However, this procedure will yield results only if the concentration of the magnesium is high. The results should also only be accepted if the quinalizarin and Titian yellow data agree.

No good color test exists for the localization of calcium in plant cells unless the calcium is present in the form of insoluble calcium phosphate or calcium carbonate. If it is, the compound can be demonstrated by placing the tissue in silver nitrate. The silver replaces the calcium and forms silver phosphate or silver carbonate, which can be converted to metallic silver by the usual photographic development procedures (Gomori, 1952). The localization is sharp and clear. The tissue sections must be washed beforehand to remove soluble phosphate, carbonate, or chloride, which would give a false localization.

Actually, it is possible to work out a localization procedure for chloride, phosphate, and carbonate ions on the basis of their reaction with silver. If freeze-dried tissue is used, and if the paraffin is not removed, these water soluble substances should be retained in the tissue. By dissolving the silver nitrate in 95% ethyl alcohol instead of in water, silver chloride, phosphate, and carbonate can be formed without loss or movement. With the paraffin still in the tissue, the silver can be developed and the site localized. The chloride ion can be distinguished from the phosphate-carbonate ions by the use of alternate slides. One slide is placed in dilute nitric acid immediately after the step in which the tissue was in the silver nitrate. The alternate slide is merely placed in water. Both slides are put through the development steps. Since the silver phosphate and the silver carbonate are both acid-soluble, and the silver chloride insoluble, at least the chloride can be distinguished from the phosphate-carbonate.

The final method given is for the detection of calcium and magnesium phytates, which are organic phosphates (Persidsky, personal communication). The tissue or isolated particles are treated with ferric chloride or basic dyes at an acid pH. Tubiform outgrowths appear if the particle contains calcium or magnesium phytates. These growths, which are similar to the famous "chemical gardens," result from the precipitation of a membrane that forms around the dissolved particles of phytate after the phytate has been dissolved in the $FeCl_3$ or in the dye solution. This membrane breaks when the endosmotic pressure exceeds the strength of the membrane only to reform as the phytate solution comes in contact with the dye solution. Growth of a tube results, and a characteristic tubiform structure is formed. Work by Persidsky (personal communication) indicates that many difficult types of compounds may give this reaction in purified form, but only the calcium and magnesium phytates react in tissue sections or preparations.

Procedures

1. Total Minerals—Microincineration Method (SCOTT, 1937)

A. Use freeze-dried, paraffin-infiltrated tissue. The paraffin should be of high purity.

B. Section the tissue at 3–5 μ, and mount on slides without using an adhesive or employing water. Do not let the tissue come into contact with moisture or become dusty. Leave the paraffin in the tissue.

C. A good, clean laboratory muffle furnace with accurate temperature control should be used. Scott (1937) gives directions for making a special microincineration furnace, but the commercial muffle furnaces are completely suitable.

D. Place the slide containing the tissue on a quartz slide or slab. This is necessary because the glass slide becomes plastic at the high temperatures used in the oven.

E. Increase the temperature in the furnace slowly to about 200°C within 10–15 minutes. This period is the most critical, since the greatest shrinkage occurs at this time.

F. Then increase the temperature to 650°C in the next 30 minutes. Finally, shut off the furnace, and allow it to cool.

G. Now very carefully remove the slide from the furnace, and gently place a cover slip over the ash. Seal the edges of the cover slip with a beeswax-paraffin mixture (1:1).

H. Now examine the preparation under dark-field illumination. If the ash appears brownish or black, the carbon has not been completely removed, and the preparation is faulty. When the ash is free of carbon, the ash of sodium, potassium, calcium, magnesium, and phosphorus will appear white, hence there is no good way to identify the various minerals. Iron, however, appears yellow to deep red, thus it can frequently be identified with some degree of accuracy. Silicon can be identified by its crystalline structure and by its double refraction in polarized light.

II. Calcium—Calcium Sulfate Crystal Procedure
(MARSH AND SHIVE, 1941)

A. Fix the tissue in neutral 4% formalin, dehydrate, and paraffin-embed or use freeze-substituted or freeze-dried material. Fresh materials are also good.

B. Section and mount the tissue, and remove the paraffin.

C. Hydrate the sections to 40% alcohol, and place a cover slip over the tissue.

D. Now add 3% sulfuric acid.

E. If calcium is present, colorless monoclinic needles of calcium sulfate will form. This procedure can also be used with tissue ash after microincineration.

III. Boron—Crystal Formation Method
(MARSH AND SHIVE, 1941)

A. Use fresh, fresh-frozen, or freeze-dried tissue.

B. Section at 10 μ, and mount on clean slides without adhesive.

C. Microincinerate at 350°C for 3 hours. Avoid higher temperatures, since boron has a tendency to volatilize.

D. After the slide has cooled add a small drop of dilute HCl to make the boron soluble. Then add a drop of concentrated potassium periodate or potassium iodide.

E. After several hours add concentrated KCl, and, finally, stain the resulting crystals with 50% alcoholic alkaline tumeric acid.

IV. Magnesium—Quinalizarin-Titian Yellow Method (BRODA, 1939)

A. Use chemically fixed, freeze-substituted, or, preferably, freeze-dried tissue.

B. Section and mount the tissue on slides.

C. Add 1 or 2 drops of quinalizarin reagent. To make this, mix 100 mg of quinalizarin and 500 mg of sodium acetate, and then dissolve 500 mg of this mixture in 100 ml of 5% NaOH.

D. Next, add 1 or 2 drops of 10% NaOH. Magnesium will develop a blue color after several hours.

E. As a control, and for comparison, treat a different section with 1 or 2 drops of Titian yellow solution, followed by 1 or 2 drops of 10% NaOH. The magnesium should develop a brick-red color.

V. Calcium—Silver Method (GOMORI, 1952)

A. Use chemically fixed, freeze-substituted, or freeze-dried tissue.

B. Section the tissue, remove the paraffin, and rinse thoroughly in distilled water.

C. Place slides in an 0.5% solution of $AgNO_3$ for 10 minutes.

D. Wash thoroughly in distilled water.

E. Immerse the slides in 0.5% amidol solution for 2 minutes, and then rinse in distilled water.

F. Place the slides in a 2% thiosulfate (hypo) solution for several minutes, and then wash.

G. Dehydrate, stain lightly with fast green, and mount.

Deposits of metallic silver will indicate the sites of calcium carbonate or calcium phosphate. The only source of error lies in the presence of cells containing large amounts of uric acid. The leaves and seeds of some plants are the only tissues in which this may be a factor. If the presence of uric acid is suspected place the tissue at step C into a solution made by adding 5 ml of a 5% $AgNO_3$ solution to 100 ml of a 3% methenamine solution, and buffer to pH 9. Keep the solution at 37°C for 30 minutes, then rinse the slide, and place it directly into the thiosulfate solution. The uric acid is so highly argentaffinic that metallic silver is produced directly.

VII. Phosphate, Carbonate, and Chloride—Silver Method
(GERSH, 1938; GOMORI, 1952)

A. Use only freeze-dried tissue.

B. Section and mount the sections on alternate slides by pressing with the finger. Avoid using water or adhesives that contain metals.

C. Place the slides directly in an 0.5% solution of $AgNO_3$ in 95% ethyl alcohol at 5°C for 30 minutes. Do not remove paraffin.

D. Gently wash the sections in distilled water, and place one set of slides in 0.5% nitric acid and the other set in distilled water for 5 minutes.

E. Gently wash both sets, and place in 0.5% amidol solution for 2 minutes. Then rinse in distilled water.

F. Next, immerse the slides in 2% thiosulfate (hypo) solution for several minutes, and wash.

G. Dehydrate carefully, and remove the paraffin.

H. Stain lightly with fast green, and mount.

In the tissue not placed in acid, the sites of phosphate, carbonate, and chloride should be visible as black deposits of metallic silver, whereas in the acid-treated tissue only the chloride will be localized. Uric acid presents a problem here as well as in Procedure VI, and can be handled in the same way as in Procedure VI.

VIII. Calcium and Magnesium Phytates (PERSIDSKY, personal communication)

A. Use sections of tissue or smears of isolated globoids. Dry the preparations before adding the test solutions.

B. To the dry material add several drops of 20% $FeCl_3$ in water at pH 1.8 (adjust pH with KOH) or a 1% aqueous solution of basic fuchsin, Bismarck brown, safranin, or pyronin B at pH 3.5–3.8 (adjust pH with acetic acid).

C. Calcium and magnesium phytates form tubiform outgrowths which, in the dyes, are strongly stained.

LITERATURE CITED

Berger, K. C. and E. Truog, 1944. Boron tests and determinations for soils and plants. *Soil Sci.*, **57**:25–36.

Broda, B., 1939. Über die Verwendbarkeit von Chinalizarin, Titangelb und Azublau zum mikro-und histochemischen Magnesiumnachweis in Pflanzengeweben. *Mikrokosmos*, **32**: 184.

Chamot, E. M. and C. M. Mason, 1958. *Handbook of Chemical Microscopy.* 3rd ed. Wiley, New York.

Eckel, R. E., 1952. A photometric chloroplatinate method for ultramicrodetermination of potassium. *J. Biol. Chem.*, **195**:191–197.

Gammon, N., Jr. and R. B. Forbes, 1949. Determination of calcium on soil extracts and plant ash by chloralinic acid. Compensating errors caused by presence of magnesium and iron. *Anal. Chem.*, **21**:1391–1392.

Gersh, I., 1938. Improved histochemical methods for chloride, phosphate-carbonate, and potassium applied to skeletal muscle. *Anat. Record*, **70**: 311–329.

Glick, D., R. H. Swigart, S. N. Nayyar, and H. R. Stecklein, 1955. Flame photometric determination of potassium in microgram quantities of tissue and the distribution of potassium and lipid in the adrenal of the monkey and guinea pig (Studies in histochemistry, XXXII). *J. Histochem. and Cytochem.*, **3**:6–15.

Gomori, G., 1952. *Microscopic Histochemistry, Principles and Practice.* Univ. of Chicago Press, Chicago.

Grunbaum, B. W., F. L. Schaffer, and P. L. Kirk, 1952. Kjeldahl determination of nitrogen with sealed tube digestion. *Anal. Chem.*, **24**:1487.

Holter, H. and S. Løvtrup, 1949. Microdetermination of some sulfur compounds by means of the iodine-azide reaction. *Compt. rend. lab. Carlsberg, Sér. chim.*, **27**:72–78.

Krugelis, E. J., 1950. Properties and changes of alkaline phosphatase activity during amphibian development. *Compt. rend. trav. lab. Carlsberg, Sér. chim.*, **27**:273–290.

Lundsteen, E. and E. Vermehren, 1936.

Micro methods for the estimation of phosphatase in blood plasma and inorganic phosphorus in blood. *Compt. rend. trav. lab. Carlsberg, Sér. chim.*, **21**:147–166; *Enzymologia*, **1**:273–279.

Malström, B. G., 1956. Determination of zinc in biological materials. *Methods Biochem. Anal.*, **3**:327–352.

Malström, B. G., and Glick, D., 1951. Determination of zinc in millimicrogram quantities. *Anal. Chem.*, **23**: 1699–1703.

Marsh, R. P. and J. W. Shive, 1941. Boron as a factor in calcium metabolism of the corn plant. *Soil Sci.*, **51**: 141–152.

Olney, H. O. and B. M. Pollock, 1960. Studies of rest period. II. Nitrogen and phosphorous changes in embryonic organs of after-ripening cherry seed. *Plant Physiol.*, **35**:970–975.

Schaffer, F. L., J. Fong, and P. L. Kirk, 1953. Microgram and submicrogram determination of phosphate. *Anal. Chem.*, **25**:343–347.

Scott, G. H., 1933. A critical study and review of the method of microincineration. *Protoplasma*, **20**:133–151.

———, 1937. The microincineration method of demonstrating mineral elements in tissues, pp. 643–665. In *Microscopical Techniques.* 2nd ed. McClung, C. E. (Editor) Hoeber, New York.

Severn, M. and R. Peterson, 1958. Spectrophotometric determination of iron in urine using 4,7-diphenyl-1,10-phenanthroline. *Anal. Chem.*, **30**:2016–2018.

Solomon, A. K. and D. C. Canton, 1955. Modified flame photometer for microdetermination of sodium and potassium. *Anal. Chem.*, **27**:1849–1850.

Sterges, A. J. and W. H. MacIntire, 1950. Magnesium content of plant tissue. Microchemical determination through thiazole yellow procedure. *Anal. Chem.*, **22**:351–353.

Tyner, E. H., 1948. Determining small amounts of calcium in plant materials. *Anal. Chem.*, **20**:76–80.

Turkington, R. and F. Tracy, 1958. Spectrophotometric determination of ultramicro amounts of copper with 1,5-diphenylcarbohydrazide. *Anal. Chem.*, **30**:1699–1701.

Uber, F. M., 1940. Microincineration and ash analysis. *Botan. Rev.*, **6**:204–226.

Winsor, H. W., 1948. Boron micro-determination in fresh plant tissue. *Anal. Chem.*, **20**:176–181.

CHAPTER 14

Enzymes: Quantitative Histochemistry

The study of enzymes is one of the most exciting areas of quantitative histochemistry. Beginning with the work of Linderstrøm-Lang and Holter (1931) on dipeptidase activity, ingenious and effective methods have been developed for the histochemical study of enzymes.

The study of an enzyme usually involves a measurement of the activity of the enzyme rather than the direct measurement of the enzyme. Enzyme activity may be measured by the utilization of substrate, accumulation of an end product, or by some secondary effect which is directly proportional to enzyme activity. Many of the usual biochemical methods have been or can be adapted for histochemical use. No attempt will be made to list all the histochemical procedures. Instead, a group has been selected which illustrates the basic points of the most generally applicable methods. These include examples of titrimetric, gasometric, and colorimetric procedures.

Before discussing any of these procedures, however, it is necessary to discuss certain problems which arise when studying enzymes histochemically and which are common to all methods. One of these is the sampling of the tissue, a problem discussed in some detail in Chapter 7. The problems encountered in tissue preparation for enzyme investigations are usually greater than in other areas of histochemistry. For many botanical problems fresh dissected material can be used. Investigations on the metabolism of mature plant embryos (Pollock and Olney, 1959; Olney and Pollock, 1960), the physiology of shoot development (Sunderland and Brown, 1956; Sunderland, Heyes, and Brown, 1957), the rest period in the buds of maple (Pollock, 1953), and the metabolism of microspore development in anthers (Nasatir and Stern, 1959; Stern, 1958, 1960; Foster and Stern, 1959) were all made using fresh dissected material.

An interesting example of the combination of diverse techniques which may be employed in the preparation of the sample is the work of Holter and Pollock (1952) on the distribution of enzymes in the cytoplasm of the myxomycete, *Physarum polycephalum*. Pieces of the plasmodium were first centrifuged until the mitochondria and the nuclei moved to the centripetal pole. The piece was then cut in half and each half homogenized in a small homogenizer. The peptidase and succinic dehydrogenase activity were then measured. Holter and Pollock found that, although centrifugation did not change the distribution of peptidase, succinic dehydrogenase activity was concentrated in the half containing the mitochondria and nuclei. They concluded that peptidase was not associated with a granular component of the cytoplasm but that succinic dehydrogenase was.

Although many problems can be approached through the use of living material obtained by dissection, there are many problems in which sectioning of the tissue is necessary. Such problems as the (1) distribution of peptidase (Bottelier, Holter, and Linderstrøm-Lang, 1943), peroxidase (Jensen, 1955b), invertase (Wanner and Leupold, 1947), and oxygen uptake (Jensen, 1955a; Wanner, 1944) in roots; (2) peptidase distribution in *Avena* coleoptiles (Avery and Linderstrøm-Lang, 1940); and (3) amylase (Linderstrøm-Lang and Engel, 1937; Engel, 1947a), proteinase and dipeptidase (Engel and Heims, 1947), and esterase (Engel, 1947b) in barley seed are all involved in the use of sections.

In all of these problems the tissue was sectioned either fresh or fresh frozen. There is no reason why freeze-dried or even freeze-substituted tissue may not be used for some enzyme determinations. The use of freeze-dried or freeze-substituted tissue does, however, introduce the problem of paraffin infiltration. The introduction of the paraffin into the tissue is an advantage in that sections of any desirable thickness may be obtained. The heating of the tissue during infiltration and the exposure of the tissue to organic solvents during paraffin removal may cause considerable difficulty in working with some enzymes. Not all enzymes should be adversely affected, however, and for these freeze-drying may prove to be the best method of tissue preparation. When freeze-dried material is used, adequate controls must be run to test the effect of the procedure on the tissue. The enzyme activity of a sample should be determined on (1) fresh tissue, (2) freeze-dried tissue before paraffin infiltration, and (3) freeze-dried tissue after paraffin infiltration and removal. These determinations may be done biochemically as long as the freeze-drying technique is the same as will be used in the histochemical procedure.

An interesting approach to sampling for enzyme histochemistry is the dissection of freeze-dried tissue which has not been paraffin infiltrated. In this method small pieces or sections of tissue are freeze-dried and then dissected in the dry state. With this procedure it is possible to carry out dissections of complex tissue systems which may be too delicate to dissect in the fresh state. The method has been developed for animal tissue (Lowry, 1953) and has not been tried on plant material. Such an approach, however, could be useful in studies of embryo-sac development and in investigations involving the differentiation of tissue.

Another problem basic to most quantitative histochemical enzyme procedures is the extraction of the enzyme from the tissue or the diffusion of the substrate into the cell. If the substrate is a small, easily penetrating molecule there may be no difficulty, particularly if thinner sections or small pieces of tissue are used. Fresh material may be frozen and thawed out after being placed in the reaction vessel. This treatment causes disruption of the cell membranes and of the internal organization, causing the release of many enzymes and permitting easier diffusion of complex substrates. The use of ultrasonic treatment would have the same effect. A similar disruption of the cell membranes can be caused by placing the tissue in glycerol. Sections may be homogenized in scaled-down versions of tissue homogenizers, as noted earlier (p. 25). These work well and are useful in histochemical procedures, particularly when used in conjunction with a microcentrifuge. By using such apparatus very small amounts of tissue may be successfully handled in enzyme determinations. An important point that must be emphasized in relation to histochemical determinations is that all the care and controls used in biochemistry must be used in histochemistry. Time must be taken to find the pH and temperature optima. Various substrate systems should be tested, and adequate controls must be run. These include reaction mixture minus the substrate, complete mixtures with heat inactivated tissue, and complete mixtures with tissue inhibitors. Care must also be taken to prevent the denaturation of the enzymes at interfaces. Because the relative amount of enzyme to surface area is large in most histochemical determinations, the possibility of enzyme denaturation is great.

Now let us examine the principles of operation of the most important groups of histochemical enzyme procedures. Among these are the titrimetric and gasometric procedures as well as the colorimetric, spectrophotometric, and fluorimetric methods. Almost every enzyme that can be measured on the macro scale can be handled on the histochemical scale with the same degree of accuracy.

One of the earliest histochemical procedures developed was the titrimetric procedure. Initially developed during the 1930's by Linderstrøm-Lang and Holter at the Carlsberg Laboratory in Copenhagen, they have been widely used and extended since that time. Originally developed for use in measuring dipeptidase activity, the titrimetric procedures can be adapted to measure a large group of hydrolyzing enzymes. The original, classic procedure developed by Linderstrøm-Lang and Holter (1932) for dipeptidase activity, however, provides a fine example of the basic principles involved.

The enzyme to be measured is a dipeptidase that splits a dipeptide, such as alanylglycine, into two amino acids, alanine and glycine:

$$NH_3{}^+CHCO\!-\!NHCH_2COO^- \xrightarrow[H_2O]{Enzyme}$$

$$\underset{\text{alanylglycine}}{\overset{|}{CH_3}}$$

$$\underset{\text{alanine}}{NH_3{}^+CHCOO^-} + \underset{\text{glycine}}{NH_3{}^+CH_2COO^-}.$$

From this equation it is clear that the number of amino groups present after the reaction is greater than before and can be used as a measure of the reaction. The easiest way to determine the number of amino groups is by titration. The only problem lies in scaling down the methods.

A segment of fresh tissue is placed in a drop of glycerol-water in a reaction vessel. The purpose of placing the tissue in the glycerol is to cause the disruption of the cell membranes, permitting the enzyme and the substrate, which is added next, to come into contact. A flea is added and the mixture stirred by means of a magnet. The reaction vessel is capped and placed in a water bath at the temperature at which the reaction is to be run.

After the reaction has run a predetermined length of time, the reaction is stopped by the addition of a known amount of alcoholic hydrochloric acid. Next, acetone containing an indicator is added and the number of amino groups liberated determined by titration with HCl. A microburette and a microtitration stand is used in the titration. A control minus the substrate is run through the same procedure.

The titrimetric method can be used to measure a large range of enzyme reactions. It can also be used in the measurement of carbohydrates, lipids, and minerals, without reference to enzyme action. The two procedures given in detail are for dipeptidase, as outlined above, and for amylase (Linderstrøm-Lang and Engel, 1937).

In a series of studies on the enzymes of resting cereals, Engel made extensive use of titrimetric methods. The dry grains of wheat, rye, and barley were used and the tissue sectioned using the method devised by Linderstrøm-Lang and Engel (1937), described in Chapter 7. Using $25\text{-}\mu$ sections as the bases for their measurements, Engel and his co-workers studied the distribution of amylase (Engel, 1947a), proteinase and dipeptidase (Engel and Heims, 1947), and esterase (Engel, 1947b). From these determinations Engel and Bretschneider (1947) were able to characterize enzymatically the various cell types present in the grain and study the relation of the enzymes to the number of mitochondria present in the various cells. This series of papers represents another good example of the application of quantitative histochemical procedures to botanical problems.

Another set of important histochemical procedures is gasometric. The sensitivity range of these procedures is wide, and, as discussed in Chapter 2 in relation to the work of Pollock and Olney (1959) on cherry embryos, the choice of methods depends on the amount of tissue available, the metabolic activity of the tissue, and the object of the investigation. The variety of methods extends from adaptations of the standard Warburg apparatus through the differential capillary microrespirometer to the Cartesian diver microrespirometer. Since the Warburg apparatus, and the microadapters used with it, is treated in standard works, such as Umbreit, Burris, and Stauffer (1957), it will not be discussed here. Both the differential capillary and the Cartesian diver microrespirometers will, however, be discussed, since both are important to the botanical histochemist.

The differential capillary microrespirometer which is in general use was designed by Stern and Kirk (1948a) and was first used to measure oxygen uptake in single *Trillium* anthers (Stern and Kirk, 1948b). This instrument, commercially available from Microchemical Specialties Co., Berkeley, Calif., is both simple and effective. It consists of two chambers in a common metal block which are connected with a capillary. One chamber holds the tissue plus a small amount of sodium hydroxide used to absorb the CO_2 present. The other chamber holds only the sodium hydroxide. The oxygen consumption of the tissue is measured by the movement of a drop of kerosene in the capillary.

The sensitivity of the apparatus is determined by the size of the capillary and the chambers. Temperature control is necessary only in the most sensitive range, unless experimental conditions require it. The critical point with regard to temperature is that any change must be the same for both chambers. If this is not the case, the drop of kerosene would move as a result of changes in gas volume caused by this temperature differential rather than as a result of the tissue. The movement of the drop is independent of barometric changes.

The apparatus is simple to use and can be modified such that gases of known composition may be introduced into the chambers (Pollock, 1953). The sensitivity of the differential capillary microrespirometer is considerably less than the Cartesian diver microrespirometer but is far easier to use and less expensive to purchase.

The differential capillary microrespirometer was used by Stern (Stern and Kirk, 1948b) in his study of the relation of oxygen uptake to the stages of microspore development in *Trillium*. In this work Stern found the fresh weight of the anthers by using a quartz helix balance, measured the oxygen consumption, and determined the exact stage of microspore development in the anther by means of acetocarmine squashes. A modified differential capillary microrespirometer was used by Pollock (1953) to measure the effect of changes in gas content of dissected parts of *Acer* buds during the winter rest period.

An all-glass differential microrespirometer was designed by Grunbaum, Siegel, Schultz, and Kirk (1955) for use with animal tissue cultures and was used by Pollock and Olney (1959) in their investigation of afterripening cherry seeds. The principles involved in this microrespirometer are the same as those already discussed in the Stern-Kirk design. The all-glass construction has decided advantages in some types of experiments but also makes the apparatus more delicate to handle.

The Cartesian diver has also been used with plant material and, although more difficult to use and expensive to acquire than the differential capillary microrespirometers, is more sensitive and versatile. This ingenious device, developed at the Carlsberg Laboratory by Linderstrøm-Lang and Holter in the early 1940's, allows the histochemist to use almost all of the procedures developed for the Warburg apparatus, but on a scale reduced a thousand times (Waterlow and Borrow, 1949).

The Cartesian diver is based on very old physical principles and derives its name from the ancient toy known as the Cartesian devil or diver, the name having no known connection with the Cartesian philosophy of Descartes. The apparatus consists of a small gas-filled vessel—the diver—which floats submerged in a medium contained in a large glass container—the flotation vessel. This, in turn, is connected to a pressure regulator which can be used to regulate the pressure of the medium in the flotation vessel. A manometer is incorporated into the system to measure pressure changes.

The diver is open to the medium, such that when the pressure on the medium is increased, the gas in the diver is compressed, and some of the medium enters the diver. The diver, losing buoyancy, sinks. If the pressure on the medium is decreased, the gas in the diver expands, and the medium is pushed from the diver. The diver, now more buoyant, rises. For a diver with a given amount of gas there is an equilibrium pressure at which it will neither sink nor rise but will float at a given level. At equilibrium pressure the gas volume in the diver is a function of the density of the medium and of the weight and charge of the diver, provided that the temperature remains constant. If gas is evolved or consumed in the diver, the equilibrium pressure changes. This change is proportional to the change in the amount of gas in the diver or:

$$\frac{V_o}{V} = \frac{P_o}{P},$$

where V_o = change in gas volume, V = gas volume, P_o = change in equilibrium pressure, and P = equilibrium pressure.

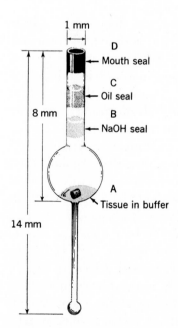

Figure 14-1
A "standard" diver fully charged for oxygen uptake measurement.

A standard diver is shown in Fig. 14-1. The total length, including the solid glass tail, is approximately 14 mm; excluding the tail, approximately 8 mm. The diameter is 1 mm; the total volume, roughly 10 μl. The diver is shown loaded for a respiratory or oxygen uptake determination. The tissue is in a drop at A; the drop, which fills the neck of the diver at B, and is thus termed a seal, is composed of NaOH, to absorb the CO_2. A paraffin-oil seal is placed at C to prevent water vapor from leaving the diver. The neck seal at D is composed of flotation medium. The flotation medium is a strong solution of sodium nitrate and sodium chloride. The gases in the diver are all highly water soluble and would leave the diver and be dissolved if water were used. This loss of gas would cause the diver to become steadily less buoyant and interfere with the measurement. By using a strong salt solution as the flotation medium the solubility of the gases, particularly oxygen, is reduced, thus decreasing the rate of change in the buoyancy of the diver. There is, nonetheless, always some change in the buoyancy of the diver with time, and this must be corrected by the use of a control diver. The control diver is prepared in the same manner as the divers containing the tissue but without the tissue.

When a reading is made the diver is carefully raised to a given mark, which may be either a mark on the side of the flotation vessel or a cross hair in a horizontal microscope, by adjusting the manometer. With careful adjustment the diver can be brought to the mark and held for 15–20 seconds. The manometer is then read and the diver allowed to sink. After a given length of time the procedure is repeated. Since the constants for the diver are known, the oxygen uptake can be measured. This method allows for the measurement of changes of the order of magnitude of 10^{-2} μl/hr for gas reactions.

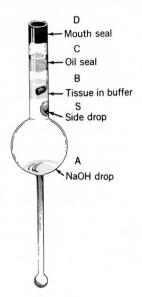

Figure 14-2
A standard diver with side drop.

Divers can be filled in a number of ways and are highly versatile as a result. One way is shown in Fig. 14-2. Here the tissue is placed in the seal b, the NaOH is then placed in the bottom a, and a side drop s is added. The side drop may contain an inhibitor in order that after an initial period in which normal oxygen uptake is measured, the inhibitor can be mixed with the tissue and the effect of the inhibitor on oxygen uptake can be measured. The mixing is accomplished by exerting an excess pressure, which moves all the seals down and causes the side drop to mix with the seal containing the tissue. Two side drops could be used if, say, reversal of inhibition by a substrate were to be tested. Similar methods are used if RQ is to be determined. To use side drops the divers must be coated with silicone (Schwartz, 1949).

The most complete description of the theory and use of the Cartesian diver is given in volume 24, numbers 17 and 18 of the *Comptes Rendus du Laboratoire Carlsberg, Série chimique*, 1943. This issue, often called the "diver Bible," contains a paper by Linderstrøm-Lang, "On the theory of the Cartesian diver microrespirometer" and one by Holter, "Technique of the Cartesian diver." Anyone seriously interested in using the Cartesian diver should procure a copy of this impressive publication. A shorter but excellent paper which includes discussion of other types of microrespirometers as well as the Cartesian diver is that by Holter, Linderstrøm-Lang, and Zeuthen, 1956.

The Cartesian diver has been used in a variety of botanical problems. Ball and Boell (1944) were among the first to use it in their work on the oxygen uptake of various segments of the shoots of *Lupinus albus* and *Tropaeolum majus*. Their problem was to determine whether or not a correlation existed between the differences in apical dominance and oxygen uptake by the apical tissues in the two species. Three segments were dissected from each shoot using a binocular dissecting microscope. One of these segments contained the shoot apex and the three youngest foliar primordia; a second was composed of maturing tissue immediately basal to the first segment; and the third contained still more mature tissue basal to the second segment. Oxygen uptake was measured in Cartesian divers and was expressed per segment, per microgram of dry weight, and per microgram of nitrogen. Although Ball and Boell were unable to find any correlation between the difference in oxygen uptake and apical dominance in the two species, they gained considerable data on the physiology of the shoot apex.

A more recent use of the Cartesian diver in the study of shoot development and physiology is found in the work of Sunderland, Heyes, and Brown (1957). They dissected the shoot of *Lupinus albus* into seven segments consisting of the apical dome and the one or more leaf primordia and internodes. The samples were obtained by using dissection methods developed by Sunderland and Brown (1956), described in Chapter 7. Cartesian divers were used to measure the amount of oxygen used by the various segments. The differences in size and rate of oxygen consumption required divers of two different sizes—one set with 3- to 7-μl volumes; and a second, with 20-μl volumes. The data obtained was expressed per segment, per cell, and per unit protein nitrogen. From their data, Sunderland, Heyes, and Brown concluded that respiration per unit nitrogen tends to increase in the primordia from the younger to the older, whereas in the internodes respiration is highest in the first three internodes, decreases abruptly from the third to the fourth, and then increases again. They were also able to draw conclusions as to the metabolic differences between the cells of the tunica and the corpus.

These examples are given to illustrate the way quantitative histochemical procedures, in this case, methods employing Cartesian diver microrespirometers, can be used to separate various units of a complex system and to analyze their role in the total process. The work of Pollock and Olney (1959), discussed in Chapter 2, makes the same point. Surely such procedures are the methods of choice in studies on the physiology of shoot and flower development, in which older tissues, such as the leaves composing the bud, contribute so much to the overall picture.

Among other examples of the use of Cartesian divers in the investigation of botanical problems are the work of Jensen (1955a) on the oxygen uptake of 200-μ segments of the root tip of *Vicia faba* and the work of Holter and Pollock (1952) on the measurement of succinic dehydrogenase activity in the halves of centrifuged plasmodium of *Physarum polycephalum*.

An important application of the diver principle is found in the Cartesian diver balance (Zeuthen, 1948). The diver (Fig. 14-3) is a thin inverted vessel completely filled with the flotation medium except for a small bubble of air which gives it buoyancy. Affixed to the top of the inverted diver is a small plastic cup. The air bubble is open to the flotation medium, thus the same principles which regulate the use of the diver function in the case of the diver balance. The diver balance differs from the diver in that different conditions cause the change in equilibrium pressure. In the diver the change is caused by a change in the volume of the gas; in the balance it is caused by the addition of a weight, which forces the diver balance down. To raise the loaded balance to the mark, the pressure on the medium is decreased, causing the air bubble to increase in volume and increasing the buoyancy of the balance. The weight of the object is proportional to the change in equilibrium pressure.

The flotation medium used in the diver balance can be any physiological solution that is desirable. This means that the tissue is not harmed by exposure to nonphysiological media in the process of weighing. The weight thus obtained is the reduced weight—the weight of the object minus that of an equal volume of water (see p. 27). For most tissues the reduced weight approximates the dry weight. Thus, the diver balance not only permits the accurate determination of the reduced weight (to 10^{-2} μg) but leaves the tissue undamaged and provides what is essentially the dry weight as well.

There is one serious limitation to the use of the Cartesian diver balance with plant tissue: the tissue must be free of air bubbles or trapped gases if the reduced weight is to be determined. For

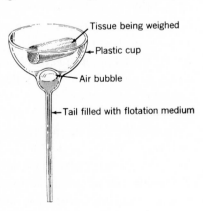

Figure 14-3
Cartesian diver balance.

meristematic tissues, on which the method has been used (see Jensen, 1955a; Pollock and Olney, 1959), this presents no problem. Many fungi (see, for example, Holter and Pollock, 1952) and algae should be suitable for weighing with a Cartesian diver balance. Mature plant tissues represent a real problem, however, and unless all the air can be removed from the tissue, they cannot be weighed by this method.

The third body of techniques important in the quantitative histochemistry of enzymes consists of the colorimetric, spectrophotometric, and fluorimetric methods.

The colorimetric procedures are a large group with wide application and continuing development. In recent years there has been a marked increase in interest in colorimetric and spectrophotometric procedures. This interest is the result of the general manipulative simplicity of the methods, their high accuracy and sensitivity, and the relative simplicity of the equipment required. The ease with which the spectrophotometer can be used in micro measurements is also an important factor.

Two colorimetric procedures for phosphatases are given to illustrate the variety of approaches open in these methods. In the first, the enzyme is given the usual substrate, glycerophosphate, from which it splits the phosphate. The increase in phosphate is then measured by the molybdate reaction used to measure total phosphorus. However, in this procedure the molybdate reagent is made in a form that reduces the tendency of the reagent to cause the breakdown of labile phosphates (Lowry and Lopez, 1946). The breakdown of labile phosphates would increase the values obtained for phosphatase activity, but usually this is not an important factor.

The second phosphatase procedure (Stern, 1961; Lowry, Roberts, Wu, Hixon, and Crawford, 1954) is based on the use of a substrate, nitrophenyl phosphate, which is colorless. When the phosphate is removed, however, the resulting nitrophenyl is highly colored and can be measured in a spectrophotometer or colorimeter. This method is simple and direct, avoiding the difficulties of the first while decreasing the number of steps.

The peroxidase method given is based on yet a different principle (Jensen, 1955b). In this method the enzyme is presented its substrate, hydrogen peroxide (H_2O_2), and oxygen is liberated. The oxygen released is measured by the conversion of lightly colored pyrogallol to the highly colored oxidation product, purpurogallin.

The procedure given for succinic dehydrogenase, developed by Defendi and Pearson (1955), introduces a new and exciting idea into enzyme histochemistry. In this method the tissue is placed on a slide and the slide is then placed in a reaction mixture containing a modified tetrazolium chloride. The enzyme converts the tetrazolium to the water insoluble formazan. The site of the enzyme can then be observed under the microscope if desired. The amount of formazan produced over short periods is proportional to enzyme activity. Thus, by simply extracting the formazan from the section with the proper solvent and measuring the amount of color present in a spectrophotometer, the amount of enzyme activity can be determined. This type of procedure thus permits both the localization and measurement of the enzyme in the same section. Doyle, one of the first to use this idea, developed a procedure for alkaline phosphatase (Doyle, Omoto, and Doyle, 1951). Other groups are also active in designing this type of technique; Glick and co-workers have developed some interesting procedures (Glick and Nayyar, 1956). None of these methods have been tried on plant tissue, but there is no reason why they should not work. The number of such methods is low, but they offer such excellent possibilities for expansion that it is expected that many more may be developed. Almost any microscopic histochemical enzyme procedure in which the color end product is proportional to enzyme activity has the potential for being developed into this type of histochemical procedure.

In fluorescence techniques it is not the absorption of light which is measured but the amount of fluorescent light emitted when visible or ultraviolet light is passed through the solution. The major advantage of fluorescence techniques lies in their great sensitivity. Owing to the nature of the technique, high dilutions must be used, thus placing the demands on the amount of material to be measured at a minimum. An example of the difference in sensitivity between spectrophotometric procedures and fluorescence procedures is given by Robins (1957), in which he compares the amount of tissue necessary for a given enzyme, malic dehydrogenase, by the two groups of procedures. A minimum of 0.01 μg of dried brain tissue is needed in the spectrophotometric techniques whereas only 0.00001 μg of tissue is needed in the fluorescence techniques.

In an excellent review of micro methods for enzymes, Lowry (1957) points to some of the peculiarities of fluorimetry. These include the fact that fluorescence is directly proportional to the exciting light intensity, thus proportionality between fluorescence and the material to be measured is possible only if absorption of the exciting light is negligible. Fluorescence may be affected by a variety of factors, including the possibility that the exciting and emitted light may be absorbed by the substance itself. Most of these difficulties can be overcome by dilution of the substance, which is a great advantage in histochemistry.

The fluorimetric method given here is for malic dehydrogenase. Both the spectrophotometric (Robins, Roberts, Eydt, Lowry, and Smith, 1956) and the fluorimetric (Lowry, Roberts, and Chang, 1956) methods are given, both of which are interesting studies in the methodology of enzymatic histochemistry. In the spectrophotometric procedure the tissue is given malate and DPN, the enzyme acting to produce oxalacetate and DPNH. The oxalacetate is then allowed to react with hydrazinoquinoline to form the quinolylhydrazone of oxalacetate. The absorption of this compound, which can be measured in a spectrophotometer at 305 mμ is proportional to the amount of enzyme action. In the fluorimetric procedure the reverse action is used. The tissue is given oxalacetate and DPNH, malate and DPN being produced. The DPNH in the solution is destroyed by the addition of HCl. The further addition of NaOH results in a fluorescent DPN product that, after dilution, can be measured in a fluorometer for fluorescence. The second method requires only a thousandth as much tissue as the first, and even more sensitive fluorescence methods are available (Lowry, Roberts, and Chang, 1956).

Unfortunately microfluorimetric procedures have not been used on plant tissue, although there is no doubt that they can be used. Lowry (1957) gives a number of excellent procedures. Even more important, however, is the potential development of techniques involving fluorescence. These possibilities have been emphasized by Robins (1957), who points out the interesting and important fact that the availability of methods for measuring DPN, TPN, DPNH, and TPNH at 10^{-8}M means that almost any enzyme reaction, with the addition of auxiliary enzymes, can be made to involve one of these compounds.

One of the most intriguing uses of fluorimetric methods is found in the work of Chance and Thorell (1959). They have adapted fluorometry to a true micro level, which has enabled them to study the localization and kinetics of reduced pyridine nucleotides in living cells. This application of microfluorometry, together with the recording microspectroscope of Thorell and Åkerman (1957), offers an interesting path for the future development of enzyme localization and measurement.

Finally, there is the possibility of combining chromatographic separation with spectrophotometric methods to measure enzyme activity. An example of this approach is found in the work of Hotta and Stern (1961) on the deamination of deoxycytidine and 5-methyldeoxycytidine by lily anther tissue. The reaction products were first separated by the use of descending paper chromatographs, located by ultraviolet light, and eluted. The absorbency of the eluates was then measured.

This brief survey of the methods available for enzyme assay on a quantitative level indicates both the diversity of the procedures available and the fact that many of the most sensitive and interesting procedures have not yet been applied to plant problems.

Procedures

I. Dipeptidase—Titrimetric Method (LINDERSTRØM-LANG AND HOLTER, 1932)

A. Place in a 6×25 mm reaction vessel 7 µl of 30% glycerol in 0.15 M phosphate buffer at pH 7.4.

B. Now add the dissected segments or sections of the fresh tissue; the smaller the piece, or the thinner the section, the better will be the extraction in later steps.

C. Put a flea in the vessel, and stir the solution.

D. Leave the vessel at room temperature for 1–2 hours. This is the period of enzyme extraction.

E. At the end of the extraction period add 7 µl of the substrate solution. This solution consists of 0.2 M alanylglycine or 0.18 M leucylglycine adjusted to pH 7.4 with NaOH.

F. Stir the reaction mixture, and cap the vessel with a piece of rubber tubing and a solid glass rod.

G. Suspend the capped vessel in a water bath at 25°C for 2–4 hours. Support the vessel with a loop of wire. Hook the wire over the side of the water bath such that the lower end of the vessel is suspended in the water.

H. At the end of the reaction period remove the vessel from the water bath, and uncap the vessel.

I. Stop the reaction by adding 30 µl of 0.05 N HCl in 95% ethyl alcohol. An automatic pipette is useful at this point (see p. 18).

J. Add 150 µl of acetone containing 2 mg/ml of naphthyl red. Using a microburette and a microtitration stand, titrate the solution to the orange end point with 0.05 N HCl in 95% ethyl alcohol. The standard for the end point is the color of the acetone-naphthyl red solution.

K. As a control carry one vessel complete with tissue through step E. Then, instead of adding the substrate solution to the tissue extract, place it on the side of the vessel, out of contact with the extract. To do this hold the vessel horizontal at all times. While adding the acid-alcohol (step I), mix the extract, substrate, and acid-alcohol. Titrate the control the same as the other samples.

L. With each tissue determine the extraction time, the reaction time, and the temperature experimentally. The sensitivity of the reaction is 5.6×10^{-5} mg of amino nitrogen.

II. Amylase—Titrimetric Method (LINDERSTRØM-LANG AND ENGEL, 1937)

A. Place 10–20 μl of 0.15 M phosphate buffer at pH 5.3 in a 6×25 mm reaction vessel.

B. To this add fresh sections of the tissue and a flea for stirring.

C. Leave the tissue in the buffer for 2–4 hours at room temperature. Stir occasionally to aid in the extraction of the enzyme. The proper extraction time must be determined experimentally for each tissue.

D. At the end of the extraction period remove 7–8 μl of the extract, and place it in the bottom of a 6×25 mm reaction vessel that has been silicone treated.

E. Next, add an equal volume of 1.5% soluble starch in 0.15 M phosphate buffer at pH 5.3.

F. Cap the vessel, and incubate in a water bath at 40°C for 2–4 hours. Again, as in C, the proper time must be determined for each tissue.

G. Remove the vessel from the water bath, uncap, add 10 μl of 0.4 M carbonate buffer at pH 10.2, and stir.

H. Add 6 μl of 0.1 M iodine in potassium iodide with an automatic pipette. Store this solution in a black bottle. The tip of the automatic pipette should be below the surface of the liquid in the vessel to prevent evaporation of the iodide.

I. Immediately place 10 μl of 1.2 M sulfuric acid across the neck of the tube to form a seal. Place a second seal of 10 μl of the starch solution above but not in contact with the acid seal. The two seals prevent the loss of iodine.

J. Stir, and let stand for 20 minutes at room temperature.

K. Cap the tube, and place in a centrifuge. Spin the tube just fast enough to collapse the seals and mix them with the reaction mixture.

L. Titrate the iodine with 0.02 M thiosulfate, using a microburette in which mercury does not contact the thiosulfate.

M. Use fresh phosphate buffer in the control.

N. Any method that will measure reducing sugars and which will not cause the breakdown of starch can be used in place of steps G–L.

Wanner and Leupold (1947) adapted this procedure for the study of invertase.

III. Differential Capillary Microrespirometer
(STERN AND KIRK, 1948a)

A. APPARATUS

A differential capillary microrespirometer consists of a block of Duralumin or brass with chambers of equal size drilled in the top (Fig. 14-4). The size and depth of the chambers are variable, depending on the size of the tissue to be used. The usual diameter is $\frac{3}{8}$ inch. The chambers are coated with lacquer to prevent reaction with the block if the NaOH used in most measurements is spilled. Openings into the chamber are controlled by small steel needle valves set in Teflon gaskets. The needle valves permit adjustment of the indicator droplet, equalizing the pressure, and changing the gas mixture used in the chamber (see Pollock, 1953). Each chamber also contains a small Teflon plastic cup to hold the NaOH or the tissue.

Figure 14-4. *A differential microrespirometer.*

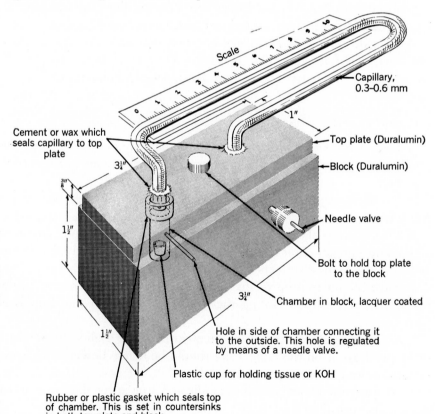

The chambers are sealed with a top plate made of the same material as the chamber block. A rubber or Teflon gasket is used to effect an air-tight seal. Capillary tubing connects the two chambers. Where the capillary joins the block another air-tight seal must be formed, either with a rubber gasket or with wax. The size of the capillaries varies, depending on the rate of respiration of the tissue. For work with lily anthers Stern and Kirk (1948b) used a 0.3-mm capillary. The capillary must be uniform in diameter, and the bends must be made with great care.

The capillary is equipped with a scale and is calibrated by introducing a thread of mercury in the capillary, measuring its length, expelling it, and weighing the drop on a microchemical balance (Kirk, 1950). In this way the volume per unit length may be calculated in relation to the scale.

An indicator drop of kerosene is placed in the capillary. The kerosene used must be carefully purified by being shaken over a period of several days with concentrated H_2SO_4. It is next separated from the acid, neutralized with NaOH, dried over anhydrous sodium sulfate, and distilled. The middle fraction is saved and stored over NaOH pellets.

Well-made commercial capillary microrespirometers are produced by Microchemical Specialties Co., Berkeley. They may also be hand made without great difficulty (Stern and Kirk, 1948a; Pollock, 1953).

B. PROCEDURE—OXYGEN UPTAKE

1. Place the tissue in the cup in one of the chambers. If the tissue is present in a solution, place this solution without the tissue in the second chamber.

2. To both chambers add a small piece of filter paper dipped in 1% NaOH.

3. Place the top plate with the capillary containing a drop of kerosene on the bottom plate. Bolt the top plate to the bottom securely. Leave the needle valves to the chambers open during this step.

4. Shift the index drop to the desired position on the scale by tilting the apparatus and then closing the needle valves when the drop is in place.

5. Place the respirometer in an incubator or in a shallow water bath or simply leave it on the table. Care should be taken, however, to avoid unequal heating of the apparatus.

6. Measure the movement of the indicator drop at regular intervals by reading the scale directly.

IV. *Differential Capillary Microrespirometer—All Glass Model* (GRUNBAUM, SIEGEL, SCHULTZ, AND KIRK, 1955)

A. APPARATUS

This differential capillary microrespirometer is, in general design, like the one described above except that two glass flasks (Fig. 14–5) serve as the chambers instead of a bored metal block. Side arms and openings near the ends of the capillary tubing replace the needle valves of the Stern-Kirk apparatus. The indicator drop and the scale arrangement are similar in the two designs. A small hook is provided on the end of the capillary tubing to hold a piece of filter paper containing the NaOH required in oxygen uptake studies.

These respirometers are also available from Microchemical Specialties Co., Berkeley, Calif.

B. PROCEDURE—OXYGEN UPTAKE

1. Introduce the indicator drop into the capillary, and clip the scale on the capillary.

2. Lubricate the ground glass connections with silicone grease.

3. Force filter paper disks on both glass hooks at the ends of the capillary.

4. Suspend the capillary by means of a two-finger prong, and add 10 μl of 10% KOH to each filter-paper disk.

5. Attach first the control vessel and then the vessel containing the tissue. The side arms must be in the open position (i.e., pointing away from each other in the apparatus shown in Fig. 14-5) such that atmospheric pressure exists on both sides of the kerosene drop.

6. Tilt the apparatus to bring the indicator drop to the second or third centimeter mark on the scale.

7. Close the side arm openings by rotating the vessels.

8. Adjust the temperature of the water bath, and slowly lower the apparatus into the bath to a point slightly below the side arm.

9. Make readings at known time intervals. Calculate the data for oxygen uptake by multiplying the distance which the index drop travels by a proportionality factor K, which is derived from the equation

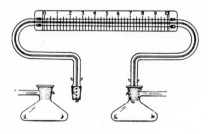

Figure 14-5
An all-glass differential microrespirometer.

$$K = \frac{273}{T} \left(\frac{P - P_w}{P_o} \right) A \left(\frac{V_g}{V_{gl}} + 1 \right),$$

where T = temperature (absolute), P = atmospheric pressure (mm Hg), P_w = vapor pressure of water at T (mm Hg), P_o = standard atmospheric pressure (mm Hg), A = cross-sectional area of capillary bore, V_g = volume of respiration chamber, and V_{gl} = volume of control chamber.

Compute the cross-sectional area of the capillary bore by drawing a thread of mercury into the bore, carefully measuring its length, removing it, and weighing it. Determine the volume of the chambers by using mercury.

In their work with cherry embryos, Pollock and Olney (1959) used capillaries of 0.8–1.0 μl/cm volume and flasks of approximately 1 ml volume.

V. Cartesian Diver (HOLTER AND LINDSTRØM-LANG, 1943)

A. APPARATUS

The basic parts of the Cartesian diver apparatus are shown in Fig. 14-6. The diver itself has already been discussed (p. 293), and can be seen in the flotation vessel, e. The flotation vessel is filled with a flotation medium consisting of a solution of 27.2 g of $NaNO_3$, 13.7 g of NaCl, and 0.2 g of sodium taurocholate in 59 ml of water. The flotation medium is filtered into the vessels and occasionally thereafter is shaken vigorously to saturate the solution with air. The flotation vessel has a ground glass joint at the top and is connected by a piece of heavy rubber tubing to the manifold. The manifold is constructed such that each flotation vessel is connected by a stopcock. The manifold is connected by a three-way stopcock to a manometer. The other end of the manometer is connected via a second three-way stopcock to an air bottle submerged in the same water bath as the flotation vessels, thus, the diver is independent of barometric pressure changes during the course of the measurements. The pressure regulator must have a coarse and a fine pressure adjustment.

The water bath should be provided with good temperature control, and a diffuse light source should be positioned behind the flotation vessels. The divers are observed in the vessels by means of a reading horizontal microscope with an ocular cross hair. By arranging the vessels at the same level in the water bath and by locking the vertical position of the microscope, the cross hair in the ocular can be used as the mark to which the divers are brought.

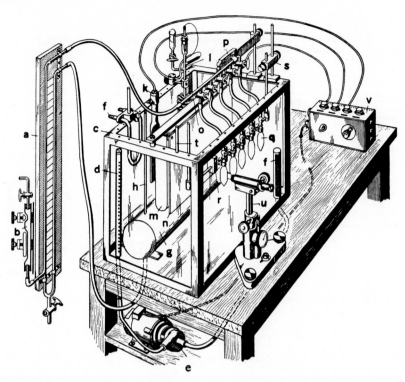

Figure 14-6. *A complete diver apparatus. a. Manometer after Holter. b. Pressure regulator. c. Water bath. d. Inlet tube. e. Circulation pump. f. Outlet filter tube. g. Pressure tank. h. Tube for tank. i. Thermostat. j. Cooling coil. k. Heater. m. Inside fluorescent lighting. n. Opal-glass plate. o. Stopcock manifold. p. Rack for manifold. q. Flotation vessel. r. Clamp for flotation vessel. s. Clamp for flotation vessels. t. Rod for thermometer. u. Cathetometer. v. Control box.* (Commerical model available from O. Dich, Copenhagen.)

There are many possible variations of the Cartesian diver apparatus. Tubes provided with rubber stoppers can be used for flotation vessels. Stopcocks are essential in connecting the vessels to the manifold, but the manifold may be different in construction. Five to seven vessels are usually used. If a large enough tank of water is used, and if temperature fluctuations are not great in the room being used, temperature control of the water bath may be unnecessary. The apparatus may also be made more elaborate, for example, by mounting the horizontal reading microscope on a lathe bench to facilitate its movement.

The divers themselves are made from glass tubing in which the ratio of wall thickness to the inside diameter of the tubing is 1:10. This tubing should then be drawn to the proper diameter; for a standard diver this is approximately 1 mm. The tubing must be free of air bubbles and must

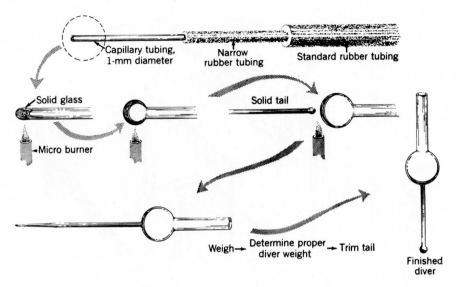

Figure 14-7. *Steps in making a Cartesian diver.*

have a specific gravity of approximately 2.40. To make the diver (Fig. 14-7) a piece of the capillary tubing is attached to a long, thin, rubber tube. The end of the capillary is then heated with a microburner and sealed by allowing a small excess of glass to collect. Next, by holding the end of the capillary with the sealed end in the flame, a bulb is blown that incorporates most of this excess glass. The bottom of the bulb should, however, be thicker than the sides. A solid thread of the same glass used in the diver is drawn. This thread must not contain air bubbles. This is attached to the thickened bottom of the diver by use of a microburner. This thread will form the tail of the diver; the amount of glass it contains will determine the weight of the diver. It is therefore necessary to calculate what the weight of the diver should be before the tail is finished. The final step in finishing the diver is to heat the glass in the tail such that a solid tail of reasonable size is formed instead of a long glass thread. Before this final step, however, the diver is cut to length (8 mm for the standard diver), its final weight calculated, and the weight adjusted by changing the tail of the diver.

To calibrate the diver the volume is found by weighing it when empty and when full of water. Next, it is necessary to decide what charge the diver is to receive. For most operations the charge would consist of the tissue drop in the bottom, the NaOH and oil neck seals, and the mouth seal. The desired weight is then calculated by the formula

$$g_D = \frac{V_T D_M - V_{oil} D_{oil} - V_W D_W - V_M D_M}{1 - \dfrac{D_M}{D_{gl}}},$$

where g_D is the desired weight of the diver; V_T is the total volume of the diver found by weighing, V_W is the total volume of water in the bottom plus the NaOH neck seal; V_{oil} is the volume of the oil seal in the neck; V_M is the volume of the mouth seal; and D_M, D_{oil}, D_w, D_{gl} are the densities of the medium, the paraffin oil, the water, and the glass of the diver.

After this calculation has been made, the weight of the diver is adjusted by adding or subtracting glass from the tail. The finished diver should be silicone-coated.

Divers can also be made by use of a jig designed by Claff (1948). The manipulations in making divers by hand, although requiring practice and some skill, are not overly difficult, and a jig, although it may be a convenience, is by no means necessary.

The filling of the divers is accomplished by holding the diver in a special clamp mounted on a movable platform (Figs. 14-8 and 14-9). The pipettes used in filling the diver are held stationary and are adjusted such that the tips of the pipettes are parallel to the sides of the neck of the diver. The divers are then positioned beneath the pipettes and the divers raised to the pipettes. A particularly fine design for a diver-filling apparatus that is available commercially is shown in Fig. 14-10. Any device, however, that meets these requirements can be used. The pipettes are made from thick-walled capillary tubing with a bore of 0.2–0.3 mm. To make the pipette a section of the capillary is heated and blown to form a bubble (Fig. 14-11). When the wall thickness is equal to half the diameter of the bubble, the capillary is given a slight pull, which produces a short section of capillary with a thinner wall. The center of this thin-walled section is then heated with a microburner and pulled to form the tip of the pipette. The inside diameter should be 0.07–0.12 mm; the outside diameter, 0.15–0.25 mm, depending on the size of the

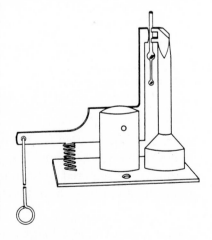

Figure 14-8
A diver clamp which is placed on a movable platform and used to hold the diver during filling.

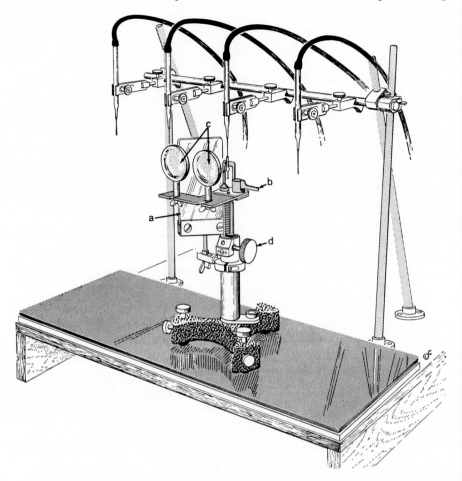

Figure 14-9. *Complete clamp stand for holding divers. a. Mirror. b. Handle for operating diver-clamp. c. Lenses. d. Vertical movement. The stand is shown with a rack which holds the micropipettes used to fill the diver.*

diver. The pipette used for the oil seal should have an inside diameter of no less than 0.15–0.18 mm. The pipette can be calibrated by a number of methods; the required graduations are obtained by attaching pieces of graph paper to the backs of the pipettes with Scotch tape.

B. PROCEDURE—OXYGEN UPTAKE

1. Use fresh tissue in the form of sections, homogenates, or cell suspensions.

2. Load the diver, using the apparatus described in the preceding section. Since the oxygen uptake of the tissue is to be measured, include NaOH as one of the seals. There are two major ways to fill the diver, depending upon the size and condition of the tissue.

a) If the tissue can be pipetted introduce it into the bottom of the diver in a given volume of fluid, usually 0.5 μl, with a breaking pipette.

Figure 14-10. *Stand for holding both micropipettes and diver for filling. a. Adjustable holder with ball-and-socket joint. b. Mirror. c. Diver clamp of stainless steel. d. Movable slide East-West. e. Movable slide North-South. f. Rubber tubing from mouth to selector-switch. g. Opal-glass. h. Lens. i. Movable slide vertical. k. Selector switch. (O. Dich, Copenhagen.)*

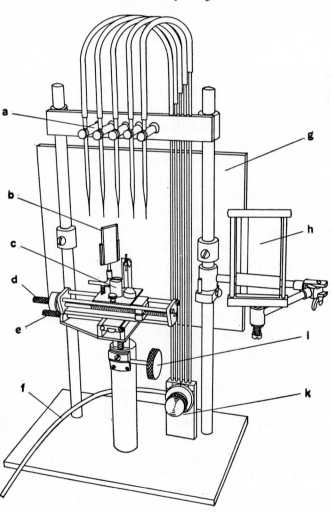

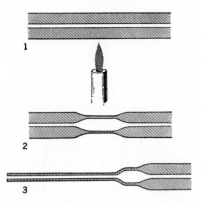

Figure 14-11
Steps in making a micropipette for filling divers.

Place the first, or lowest, neck seal, consisting of 0.6 μl of 0.1 *M* NaOH, using the micropipette described in section A. The seals are made as diagrammed in Fig. 14-12. Next, place the oil seal consisting of 0.6 μl of paraffin oil across the neck, again using a micropipette. Finally, place the mouth seal consisting of the flotation medium diluted 1:1 with water. To place the mouth seal, close the mouth of the diver with a drop of the flotation medium, and then move this drop into the desired position by sucking out the air in the space between the drop and the oil seal. The mouth seal is usually 2 mm long and should be measured with a horizontal microscope. Since it is used as a means of adjusting the initial equilibrium pressure of the diver, the length of the mouth seal will vary from one diver to another. If the diver is heavy, the mouth seal is made shorter; if light, it is made longer.

b) If the tissue is too large or too delicate to be pipetted, a different arrangement is used. Place the 0.6 μl of 0.1 *M* NaOH in the bottom of the diver, and completely fill the neck of the diver with the fluid that is to surround the tissue. Then add the tissue, and let it sink to the bottom by gravity. It may be necessary to push very large pieces of tissue to the bottom. Remove the excess fluid with a micropipette, and determine the volume of the tissue seal by measuring its length with a horizontal microscope. Then place the oil and mouth seals as described in part a of 2.

3. When the diver is filled transfer it to the flotation vessel with a wire loop and free it of any air bubbles that may adhere to the outside of the diver.

4. Shortly before the measurements begin, open the air bottle to the outside air by adjusting the three-way stopcock in the tube that connects the bottle to the manometer. This allows the pressure in the air bottle to equalize with the barometric pressure.

5. Measure the equilibrium pressure

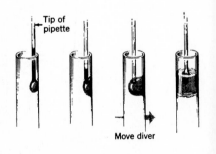

Figure 14-12
Steps in placing a neck seal.

of the diver at given time intervals, for example, every 15 minutes. Use a diver filled in the same manner but not containing the tissue as a control. In making these measurements carefully raise the diver to the cross hair in the ocular of the horizontal microscope. Read the manometer only when the diver remains stable for 10 seconds. When the reading is obtained produce a slight overpressure in the flotation vessel in order that the diver will sink to the bottom, and then close the stopcock at the top until the next reading.

6. When the readings are finished remove the diver from the flotation vessel with a wire loop and rinse it with water. Use thin rolls of lens paper to remove the seals. Then insert a thin-necked pipette into the bottom of the diver, and flush out the bulb and neck with a stream of water. *Caution:* Do not permit air to be introduced into the bottom of the diver at the end of the flushing. Then flush the diver once with acetone, once with toluene, again with acetone, and twice with double distilled water. Finally, dry the outside of the diver with lens paper, and then place it in an oven at 120°C. Store the divers in small, capped test tubes.

Use the following formula to convert the manometer readings to μl of oxygen used.

$$O_2 \text{ used } (\mu l) = \frac{V p T_0}{P_0 T},$$

where $V =$ the total gas space of the charged diver at equilibrium pressure (μl); $p =$ the change in pressure (cm of Brodie solution); $T_0 = 273°$K; $P_0 =$ normal barometric pressure (100 cm of Brodie solution); $T =$ temperature of the bath in °K ($273°$K $+$ temperature in °C).

This formula gives the oxygen uptake in terms of μl at zero degrees centigrade, which facilitates the comparison of data obtained at different temperatures. If this is not important, T_0 and T can be omitted and the oxygen uptake expressed at bath temperature.

In this formula, V is in fact the diver constant and can be calculated according to the following formula (Borei, 1948):

$$V = g_D \left(\frac{1}{d_M} - \frac{1}{d_{gl}} \right) + V_W \left(\frac{d_W}{d_M} - 1 \right) + V_{oil} \left(\frac{d_{oil}}{d_M} - 1 \right),$$

where $g_D =$ weight of the empty diver (mg); $d_M =$ density of the flotation medium (1.325 in the medium recommended, which is Holter's); $dgl =$ density of the glass in the diver; $V_W =$ volume of the aqueous charge of the diver (μl); (this includes the solution the tissue is in, the NaOH, and any other aqueous solutions present except the mouth seal); $d_W =$ density of the aqueous charge, usually approximated at 1;

V_{oil} = volume of the paraffin oil seal (μl); and d_{oil} = density of the paraffin oil, usually 0.87.

In making the calculation it is clear that the terms

$$V_W \left(\frac{d_W}{d_M} - 1 \right) \quad \text{and} \quad V_{oil} \left(\frac{d_{oil}}{d_M} - 1 \right)$$

become constants for any group of divers filled in the same way. The term

$$\frac{1}{d_M} - \frac{1}{d_{el}}$$

also becomes constant for any set of divers made from the same piece of glass tubing. Thus, the calculation of V is much easier than it first appears.

The formula given for the calculation of the oxygen uptake is good only if the solubility of all gases present in the diver is low. The only highly soluble gas present (CO_2) is taken out of the system by the NaOH. For the formula to be used when soluble gases are present see Holter (1943). If the CO_2 is present only for a short period and measured immediately, the oxygen-uptake formula is still good. This is also true if CO_2 loss from the diver is reduced. The reduction can be effected by the use of a hollow glass stopper or a modified oil seal (see Borrow and Penny, 1951).

With photosynthetic plant tissue it is necessary to consider the possibility that the light used in making the readings of the diver's position will affect the final result. Ball and Boell (1944) kept the diver dark except when making readings, whereas Pollock (1960) employed a green filter with the light used during measurement. Sunderland, Heyes, and Brown (1957) made their observations under overhead lighting, which, they were able to show experimentally, had no effect on their oxygen uptake data.

C. PROCEDURE—OXIDATIVE ENZYMES

1. Use fresh tissue in the form of sections, homogenates, or cell suspensions.

2. Load a silicone-coated diver as in procedure B, but place the NaOH in the bottom of the diver. At the base of the neck, place an 0.3-μl side drop (Fig. 14-13) consisting of the enzyme substrate. Above this, place the tissue seal, then the oil seal, and, finally, the mouth seal.

3. Place the diver in the flotation vessel, and make readings of the equilibrium pressure as in B to obtain the rate of oxygen uptake without the substrate.

4. When the substrate is to be mixed with the tissue, turn the three-way stopcock connecting the manometer to the manifold such that the manometer is disconnected from the manifold. Connect a rubber tube to the third arm of the stopcock such that, by blowing on it, a marked overpressure will be obtained in the flotation vessels. Apply this overpressure to each vessel, one at a time. The increased pressure will force the seals in the diver to move down while the side drop remains stationary. Thus, the side drop of substrate will be mixed with the tissue seal.

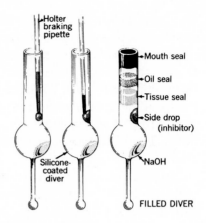

Figure 14-13
Steps in placing a side drop.

5. After all the divers have been handled in this way, return the stopcock to its normal position, and reestablish the equilibrium conditions.

6. Continue making readings of the equilibrium pressures until the new rate is established.

7. At the end of the run remove the divers from the flotation vessel, and clean and store them as in B.

8. The data are calculated by the oxygen-uptake formula given in B, except that in calculating the diver constant the increased volume of the aqueous phase due to the inclusion of the side drop must be taken into account.

9. Two side drops may be used if desired. These are often useful in inhibitor experiments in which it may be desirable to test the reversal of inhibition by the addition of a substrate.

D. PROCEDURE—RESPIRATORY QUOTIENT (RQ)—SINGLE-DIVER METHOD

1. Use fresh tissue in the form of sections, homogenates or cell suspensions.

2. Load the diver as in procedure B, but with the following modifications: at the base of the neck, place an 0.13-μl side drop of 1.67 N H_2SO_4; next, place the usual NaOH seal, then a second side drop of H_2SO_4, and finally the tissue seal. Place the oil and mouth seals as usual. Fill two divers in this manner. Use one as the control; use the second as the test diver.

3. Then place both divers in the flotation vessels, and after 20 min-

utes equilibration (counting from the time the oil seal is placed) read the equilibrium pressure of both divers.

4. Immediately after making this reading subject the control diver to an overpressure, as described in C, to mix the acid drops with the tissue and NaOH seal. This is done in order that the amount of CO_2 in the tissue can be corrected for in the final calculations.

5. After 30 or 60 minutes measure the equilibrium pressure of the test diver. The difference in equilibrium pressure is the measure of oxygen uptake.

6. Immediately apply an overpressure to the test diver to mix the acid with the NaOH and tissue seals. This results in the liberation of the CO_2 in the NaOH and of any in the tissue seal.

7. After 10 minutes read the equilibrium pressure again.

8. The decrease in gas volume during the initial period represents O_2 uptake by the tissue; the CO_2 liberated on addition of the acid, when corrected for the control, represents the respired CO_2. The equations given in B are applicable here because the time during which the CO_2 is present in the diver is considered too short to influence the calculations.

VI. Cartesian Diver Balance (ZEUTHEN, 1948)

A. APPARATUS

The basic parts of the Cartesian diver apparatus shown in Fig. 14-6 are used for the Cartesian diver balance. The only major difference is between the diver and the diver balance. In the diver balance an air bubble is contained in a glass chamber, the remainder of the chamber being filled with the normal physiological medium of the cells. A cup of polystyrene attached to the top of the chamber acts as a pan in which the material is weighed. Cartesian diver balances can be made to any range desirable by merely changing the size of the glass chamber and the cup. In fact, Løvtrup and Zeuthen (1951) demonstrated the versatility of the principle involved by constructing a Cartesian diver balance from an empty beer bottle, appropriately enough, a Carlsberg beer bottle.

To make a Cartesian diver balance in the micro range, thin capillaries are first drawn from the same type of glass as is used in the divers. One end is fused shut and the other attached by very thin rubber tubing to wider rubber tubing. The fused end is then heated, and a small bubble is blown. The bulb should be about 1 mm in diameter and the tail about 15 mm long. To test whether or not the bulb is the right size before the cup is attached, it should be placed in water in a suction flask and air drawn out until an air bubble $\frac{1}{3}-\frac{1}{2}$ the size of the bulb remains in the bulb at normal pressures. If the bulb then floats suspended in the water or slowly sinks or rises, it can be used. If, however, it sinks or rises rapidly it should be discarded. It is possible to adjust the weight of the balance somewhat by changing the size of the air bubble and shortening the tail.

The construction of the cup is shown in Fig. 14-14. A vertically mounted breaking pipette holds the plastic dissolved in benzene. The plastic used is polystyrene, which has a density of 1.05. It is important to keep the density of the plastic low to keep the weight of the cup down. The lighter the cup, the more sensitive the balance. The diver bulb is held in a clamp on a movable platform. The bulb is introduced into the polystyrene solution and is then slowly removed, drawing the plastic with it. A polystyrene bubble is formed by blowing through the pipette. When the bubble is uniformly thin the blowing and downward movement of the bulb is stopped and the plastic allowed to harden. When the plastic is dry, the balance cup is cut off with a razor. A small air pump, such as an aquarium pump, may be used as a source of air pressure in blowing the cup (Løvtrup, 1950).

The finished diver should be stored underwater. The diver is balanced by gradually removing air through the tail. In usual practice, the divers do not need to be cleaned. Occasionally it is necessary to clean them, in which case a short period in 50% H_2SO_4, followed by rinsings in water, is recommended.

Standard weights for calibrating the diver balances are 0.1- to 0.2-mg polystyrene beads of known weight and density. The reduced weight

Figure 14-14. *Steps in making the cup of a Cartesian-diver balance.*

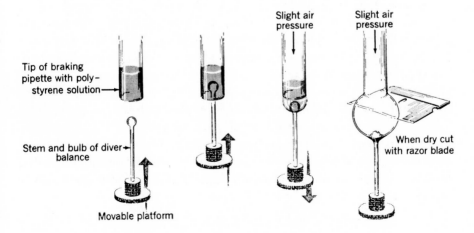

Tip of braking pipette with poly-styrene solution→

Stem and bulb of diver→ balance

Movable platform

Slight air pressure

Slight air pressure

When dry cut with razor blade

(RW) of the standard is calculated from the weight (W) of the standard obtained by weighing on a micro balance, the density of the medium (d_m) and the density of the standard (d_o), according to the relation

$$RW = W\left(\frac{1 - d_M}{d_o}\right).$$

These standards are handled by means of a breaking pipette.

The flotation medium used in the flotation vessels can be almost any medium that is desired. Usually a salt solution is employed, although water and other solutions can be used. For some measurements soluble starch solutions are very useful.

B. PROCEDURE FOR THE DETERMINATION OF REDUCED WEIGHT, USING THE CARTESIAN DIVER BALANCE

1. Introduce the diver balance into the flotation vessel by using a piece of wire with an open loop at the end. If the diver is too light, air can be drawn from the tail by reversing the procedure used to apply overpressures to the divers (p. 315).

2. Measure the equilibrium pressure of the empty diver.

3. Add the polystyrene standard by use of a breaking pipette and measure the equilibrium pressure again.

4. Remove the standard, and again determine the equilibrium of the empty diver.

5. Repeat steps 3 and 4 for the tissue.

6. Calculate the reduced weight (RW_t) of the tissue in mg from the formula

$$RW_t = \left[\frac{RW_{st}(P - \Delta P_{st})}{\Delta P_{st}}\right]\left(\frac{\Delta p_t}{P - \Delta p_t}\right) = K\left(\frac{\Delta p_t}{P - \Delta p_t}\right),$$

where RW_{st} = reduced weight of the standard (mg); ΔP_{st} = the numerical change in equilibrium pressure (cm), resulting from loading the empty diver with the standard; Δp_t = the numerical change in equilibrium pressure (cm) resulting from loading the empty diver with the tissue; and P = equilibrium pressure of the diver balance.

7. Since the reduced weight is not normally influenced by changes in water content of the cell, and can be obtained repeatedly on the same cell, it has many applications other than as a simple weight measure. However, the sample must be free of air bubbles or the weight will be incorrect.

C. PROCEDURE FOR THE DETERMINATION OF THE VOLUME, SPECIFIC GRAVITY, AND WET WEIGHT OF A TISSUE SAMPLE WITH THE CARTESIAN DIVER BALANCE

1. First, weigh the tissue in the normal fashion, using a diver balance floating in a normal physiological medium whose density is known or assumed to be that of water.

2. Repeat the weighing in a medium with a much higher density but of low osmotic activity and viscosity. The medium used by Zeuthen was one containing soluble starch, 3.3 g of Zulkowsky soluble starch (Merck) in 100 ml of glass-distilled water. The density of this solution was 1.0121.

3. From the reduced weight obtained from these two weighings, RW_w in the first and RW_s in the second, the volume (V), specific gravity (ϕ_c) and wet weight (g) of the tissue can be found, using the following equations:

$$V \text{ (volume)} = \frac{RW_w - RW_s}{\phi_s - \phi_w},$$

$$\phi_c \text{ (specific gravity)} = \frac{RW_w \phi_w}{V},$$

$$g \text{ (wet weight)} = \frac{RW_s \phi_s - RW_s \phi_w}{\phi_s - \phi_w},$$

where ϕ_w = density of the aqueous medium, and ϕ_s = density of the starch medium.

Thus, from this procedure it is possible to obtain the wet weight and the reduced weight of the tissue (which is essentially the dry weight) and still have the tissue physiologically active.

VII. Phosphatase—Spectrophotometric Method
(LOWRY AND LOPEZ, 1946)

A. Use fresh or freeze-dried tissue, and place in reaction vessels. Then place the vessels in an ice bath.

B. Use 0.1 M disodium-β-glycerophosphate as the substrate. The buffer will be determined by the phosphatase to be investigated. For alkaline phosphatase, use tris buffer at pH 9; for acid phosphatase use succinate buffer at pH 5–6. To the substrate solution add 1 M MgCl$_2$ in an amount equal to 0.2% of the total volume.

C. To the tubes containing the tissue in the ice bath add 100 μl of the chilled substrate.

D. Transfer all tubes at zero time to a water bath at the temperature desired for the reaction, and leave them there for 30 minutes to 8 hours.

E. At the end of this time add 20 μl of cold 30% trichloroacetic acid, and centrifuge out the precipitate.

F. Add 100 μl of the supernatant to 1 ml of a molybdate reagent, made by combining 2 ml of 2.5% ammonium molybdate, 46 ml of 0.1 M acetate buffer at pH 4, and, immediately before use, 2 ml of 1% ascorbic acid.

G. Stir very promptly. A stream of air or nitrogen can be used very effectively.

H. Measure the optical density at 870 mμ (any wave length between 650 and 950 mμ is satisfactory).

I. Use standards and blanks consisting of 10 μl of 15 mM KH$_2$PO$_4$ or water carried through from the beginning.

This procedure may be used for the measurement of adenosinetriphosphatase activity by substituting the proper substrates and buffers (Lowry, Roberts, Wu, Hixon, and Crawford, 1954). To measure ATP'ase use a reagent consisting of equal parts of (a) 5 mM adenosinetriphosphate (ATP) and (b) buffer containing 0.03 M tris (hydroxymethyl) aminomethane, 0.03 M 2-amino-2-methyl-1,3-propanediol, 0.03 M HCl, and 2 mM MgCl$_2$. The final pH is 8.4.

For another excellent phosphatase procedure of this type, see Taft and Scott (1958).

VIII. Phosphodiesterase (STERN, 1961)

A. Use homogenized tissue, such as fresh lily anthers, or fresh sections. Freeze-dried tissue should also be suitable for assay.

B. Make a solution of 0.01 M p-nitrophenyl phosphate (either the Na- or Ca-salt) in 0.01 M acetate buffer at pH 4.7. Dilute this solution threefold with water before using.

C. Pour 0.75 ml of the diluted solution into a tube, and add 0.25 ml of 0.5 M acetate buffer at pH 4.7, and 0.1 ml of the tissue homogenate or extract.

D. Incubate the mixture at 25 °C. At the beginning and after 10 minutes, pipette 0.25 ml into a cuvette containing 100 μl of 0.2 N NaOH. Repeat again in another 10 minutes.

E. Read the absorption immediately at 440 mμ.

This procedure was used by Lowry, Roberts, Wu, Hixon, and Crawford (1954) for measuring alkaline and acid phosphatase activity. They used disodium-p-nitrophenyl phosphate as the substrate. For alkaline phosphatase they used equal parts of a 16 mM solution of the substrate and a solution consisting of 1 M buffer at pH 10.0, made by mixing 8.9

g of 2-amino-2-methyl-1-propanol, 45 ml of 1 N HCl, and water to make 100 ml. They also added 1 M MgCl₂ to the extent of 0.2% of the total volume. For acid phosphatase they employed 0.1 M succinate as a buffer in the range pH 5–6 and 0.1 M acetate for more acid pH's.

IX. Peroxidase—Colorimetric Procedure (JENSEN, 1955b)

A. Use relatively thick (200 μ), fresh sections.

B. Place the sections in 10×75 mm tubes, and wash briefly with water.

C. Add 500 μl of 0.02 M phosphate buffer and 50 μl of 0.1 M H₂O₂.

D. At zero time add 50 μl of 0.01 M pyrogallol.

E. After 2 minutes rapidly and thoroughly remove the solution from the tissue with a straight, drawn-tip pipette.

F. Immediately after the reaction solution is withdrawn, add 500 μl of 1% HCl-acetone.

G. After 10 minutes withdraw this solution.

H. Determine the absorption of the reaction solution and of the HCl-acetone at 420 mμ in a Beckman spectrophotometer with a microcuvette attachment.

I. Obtain a standard curve based on dilutions of a standard purpurogallin solution. Express the data in micromoles of purpurogallin produced.

X. Succinic Dehydrogenase—Colorimetric Method
(DEFENDI AND PEARSON, 1955)

A. Cut sections using a cryostat at 5μ. Fresh sections or pieces of tissue may also be used.

B. Mount the sections on glass slides, and perform the reactions for succinic dehydrogenase by placing the slides in the following reaction mixture: 5 ml of an 0.1 M phosphate buffer at pH 7.4, 5 ml of 0.1 M sodium succinate, and 5 ml of 1 mg/ml 2-(p-iodophenyl)-3-(p-nitrophenyl)-5-phenyl tetrazolium chloride.

C. Leave the slide in the reaction mixture for 5 minutes to an hour.

D. Rinse the tissue, and observe it under a microscope. It may also be photographed, the localization being clear and accurate.

E. Dry the section, and extract the reduced tetrazolium with 3–5 ml of ethyl acetate.

F. Read the amount of absorption at 494 mμ in a spectrophotometer.

G. Use (1) sections incubated without substrate, and (2) substrate-incubated without tissue as controls. Heat inactivated tissue and inhibitors should be used as additional controls.

Glick and Nayyar (1956) have developed this procedure to a still smaller scale. They carried out a very careful study of the procedure, in which they used tetrachloroethylene as the extraction solvent. Both they and Defendi and Pearson used only animal tissue.

XI. Malic Dehydrogenase—Spectrophotometric Method
(ROBINS, ROBERTS, EYDT, LOWRY, AND SMITH, 1956)

A. Use freeze-dried tissue or homogenates.

B. Place the tissue in small reaction vessels, and place in an ice bath.

C. Add 10 μl of buffer-substrate reagent, made by mixing 1 ml of buffer (0.1 M 2-amino-2-methyl-1-propanol, pH 10.6), 50 μl of 1 M potassium L-malate, and 1.5 mg of DPN+.

D. Cover the tubes with Parafilm or some other kind of cap, and incubate for 30 minutes at 38°C.

E. Return the tubes to the ice bath, and add 10 μl of 0.5 mM 3-quinolyhydrazine in 0.21 N HCl.

F. Mix the contents of the tube, and allow to stand for 1 hour at room temperature.

G. Dilute with 100 μl of 0.01 N HCl.

H. Measure the absorption at 305 mμ in a spectrophotometer.

I. Run standards by incubating extra tubes with 1 μl of 1, 2, and 4 mM oxalacetic acid.

J. For blanks, use 1 μl of H$_2$O or simply an empty tube.

This procedure has been developed for brain tissue and may require changes when used with plant tissue. Lactic dehydrogenase and glutamic dehydrogenase can also be measured by this method.

XII. Malic Dehydrogenase—Fluorometric Method
(LOWRY, ROBERTS, AND CHANG, 1956)

A. Use freeze-dried tissue or homogenate.

B. Place the tissue in the bottom of a small reaction vessel, and add 0.25 μl of ice-cold buffer-substrate reagent, consisting of 0.5 mM oxalacetate, 0.25 mM DPNH, and 0.05% bovine albumin in 0.1 M tris buffer at pH 8.6. Keep the tubes in an ice bath.

C. Cover the substrate solution with several millimeters of hexane, and incubate for 60 minutes at 38°C.

D. Return the solution to the ice bath, and use a fine pipette to remove the hexane; remove the last traces by drawing air through the pipette while holding it just above the aqueous layer.

E. Add 1 μl of 0.2 N HCl (to destroy the DPNH), and mix gently.

F. Develop fluorescence by adding 5 μl of 8 N HCl and incubating for 60 minutes at room temperature.

G. Add 5 μl of this solution to 50 μl of water in a fluorometer tube, and measure the fluorescence using a microadapter with the Farrand fluorometer (Lowry, Roberts, Leiner, Wu, and Farr, 1954).

H. Run blanks of the reaction mixture minus tissue, and use a standard based on DPN.

This procedure has also been developed for brain tissue, and is given as an example of what can be done rather than as a procedure that is immediately adaptable to plant tissue. The publications of Lowry and co-workers (1954, 1956) are very important in fluorimetric enzyme histochemistry.

XIII. Deamination of Deoxycytidine and 5-Methyldeoxycytidine (HOTTA AND STERN, 1961)

A. Homogenize the tissue in 2 ml of 0.1 M tris buffer (pH 7.6).

B. Add 0.1 ml of deoxycytidine or 5-methyldeoxycytidine (5 mg/ml) to 0.2 ml of the suspension.

C. Incubate at 25°C for 30 minutes.

D. Stop the reaction with 0.3 ml of absolute methyl alcohol, and heat the mixture to 60°C for 2 minutes.

E. Cool in an ice bath, centrifuge, and streak on Whatman No. 1 filter paper.

F. Use a descending technique for separating the products of the reaction. As solvent systems, use either n-butanol and water (86:14 by volume) or a mixture of n-butanol and 0.1 M or 0.05 M ammonium formate (pH 9.0). Prepare the latter mixture by adding to 10 ml of ammonium formate enough n-butanol (approximately 68 ml) to bring all the components into solution. Place a layer of n-butanol at the bottom of the tank and place two Petri dishes containing ammonium formate in the butanol. This latter solvent system is recommended by Hotta and Stern, since it appears to best separate the deoxyribosides.

G. Locate the reaction products with an ultraviolet lamp, and elute with 0.1 N HCl. Read the absorbancy of the eluates at 262 and 280 mμ for deoxycytidine-to-deoxyuridine transformations and at 267 and 290 mμ for 5-methyldeoxycytidine-to-thymidine transformations.

Other deoxyribonucleotides may be used as the substrate (Stern, 1961).

LITERATURE CITED

Avery, G. S., Jr. and L. Linderstrøm-Lang, 1940. Peptidase activity in the *Avena* coleoptile, phytohormone test object. *Compt. rend. trav. lab. Carlsberg, Sér. chim.*, **23**:219–234.

Ball, E. and E. J. Boell, 1944. Respiratory rates of the shoot tips and maturing tissues in *Lupinus albus* and *Tropaeolum majus. Proc. Natl. Acad. Sci.* (US), **30**:45–50.

Borei, H., 1948. Respiration of oöcytes, unfertilized eggs and fertilized eggs from *Psammechinus* and *Asterias. Biol. Bull.*, **95**:124–150.

Borrow, A. and J. R. Penney, 1951. Further observations on biological reactions by the Cartesian diver technique—with special reference to mammalian tissue. *Exptl. Cell Research*, **2**:188–206.

Bottelier, H. P., H. Holter, and K. Linderstrøm-Lang, 1943. Determination of peptidase activity, nitrogen content and reduced weight in roots of the barley, *Hordeum vulgare. Compt. rend. trav. lab. Carlsberg, Sér. chim.*, **24**:289–313.

Chance, B. and B. Thorell, 1959. Localization and kinetics of reduced pyridine nucleotide in living cells by microfluorometry. *J. Biol. Chem.* **234**:3044–3050.

Claff, C. L., 1948. Method for making Cartesian divers. *Science*, **107**:202–203.

Defendi, V. and B. Pearson, 1955. Quantitative estimation of succinic dehydrogenase activity in a single microscopic tissue section. *J. Histochem. and Cytochem.*, **3**:61–70.

Doyle, W. L., J. H. Omoto, and M. E. Doyle, 1951. Estimation of phosphatase in histological preparations. *Exptl. Cell Research*, **2**:20–38.

Engel, C., 1947a. The distribution of the enzymes in resting cereals. I. The distribution of the saccharogenic amylase in wheat, rye, and barley. *Biochim. Biophys. Acta.*, **1**:42–49.

———, 1947b. The distribution of the enzymes in resting cereals. III. The distribution of esterase in wheat, rye, and barley. *Biochim. Biophys. Acta.*, **1**:278–279.

Engel, C. and L. H. Bretschneider, 1947. The distribution of the enzymes in resting cereals. IV. A comparative investigation of the distribution of enzymes and mitochondria in wheat grains. *Biochim. Biophys. Acta.*, **1**:357–363.

Engel, C. and J. Heims, 1947. The distribution of the enzymes in resting cereals. II. The distribution of the proteolytic enzymes in wheat, rye, and barley. *Biochim. Biophys. Acta.*, **1**:190–196.

Foster, T. and H. Stern, 1959. The accumulation of soluble deoxyribosidic compounds in relation to nuclear division in anthers of *Lilium longiflorum. J. Biophys. Biochem. Cytol.*, **5**:187–192.

Glick, D. and S. N. Nayyar, 1956. Studies in histochemistry. XLII. Further studies on the determination of succinic dehydrogenase in microgram amounts of tissue and distribution of activity in bovine adrenal. *J. Histochem. and Cytochem.*, **4**:389–396.

Grunbaum, B. W., B. V. Siegel, A. R. Schultz, and P. L. Kirk, 1955. Determination of oxygen uptake by tissue grown in an all glass differential microrespirometer. *Mikrochimica Acta.*, 263:1069–1075.

Holter, H., 1943. Technique of the Cartesian diver. *Compt. rend. trav. lab. Carlsberg, Sér chim.*, 24:399–478.

Holter, H. and K. Linderstrøm-Lang, 1943. On the theory of the Cartesian diver microrespirometer. *Compt. rend. trav. lab. Carlsberg, Sér chim.*, 24:334–398.

Holter, H. K. Linderstrøm-Lang, and E. Zeuthen, 1956. Manometric techniques for single cells. In *Physical Techniques in Biological Research*, Vol. III. G. Oster and A. W. Pollister (Editors). Academic, New York.

Holter, H. and B. M. Pollock, 1952. Distribution of some enzymes in the cytoplasm of the Myxomycete, *Physarum polycephalum. Compt. rend. lab. trav. Carlsberg, Sér. chim.*, 28: 221–245.

Hotta, Y. and H. Stern, 1961. Deamination of deoxycytidine and 5-methyldeoxycytidine in developing anthers of *Lilium longiflorum. J. Biophys. Biochem. Cytol.*, 9:279–284.

Jensen, W. A., 1955a. A morphological and biochemical analysis of the early phases of cellular growth in the root tip of *Vicia faba. Exptl. Cell Research*, 8:506–522.

———, 1955b. The histochemical localization of peroxidase in roots and its induction by indolecetic acid. *Plant Physiol.*, 30:426–432.

Kirk, P., 1950. *Quantitative Ultramicroanalysis.* Wiley, New York.

Linderstrøm-Lang, K., 1943. On the theory of the Cartesian diver microrespirometer. *Compt. rend. trav. lab. Carlsberg, Sér chim.*, 24:333–398.

Linderstrøm-Lang, K. and C. Engel, 1937. Über die Vertsilung der Amylase in den aussern Schicten des Gerstenkornes. *Enzymologia*, 3:138–146;

Compt. rend. trav. lab. Carlsberg, Sér. chim., 21:243–258 (1938).

Linderstrøm-Lang, K. and H. Holter, 1931. Contributions to the histological chemistry of enzymes. I. The estimation of small cleavages caused by enzymes. *Compt. rend. trav. lab. Carlsberg, Sér. chim.*, 19:1–39.

———, 1932. Contributions to the histochemistry of enzymes. II. The distribution of peptidase in the roots and sprouts of malt. *Compt. rend. trav. lab. Carlsberg, Sér. chim.*, 19:1–39; *Physiol. Chem.*, 204:15–33.

Løvtrup, S., 1950. Observations on the Cartesian diver balance technique. Determination of density of amoebae by means of a starch density gradient. *Compt. rend. trav. lab. Carlsberg, Sér. chim.*, 27:125–144.

Løvtrup, S. and E. Zeuthen, 1951. Cartesian diver balance. *Science*, 113: 661–662.

Lowry, O. H., 1953. The quantitative histochemistry of the brain—Histological sampling. *J. Histochem. and Cytochem.* 1:420–428.

———, 1957. Micromethods for the assay of enzymes, pp. 366–381. In *Methods in Enzymology*, Vol. IV: Colowick and Kaplan (Editors). Academic, New York.

Lowry, O. H. and J. A. Lopez, 1946. The determination of inorganic phosphate in the presence of labile phosphate esters. *J. Biol. Chem.*, 162: 421–428.

Lowry, O. H., N. R. Roberts, and M-L. Chang, 1956. The analysis of single cells. *J. Biol. Chem.*, 222:97–107.

Lowry, O. H., N. R. Roberts, K. Y. Leiner, M. Wu, and A. L. Farr, 1954. The quantitative histochemistry of brain. I. Chemical methods. *J. Biol. Chem.*, 207:1–17.

Lowry, O. H., N. R. Roberts, M-L. Wu, W. S. Hixon, and E. J. Crawford, 1954. The quantitative histochemistry of brain. II. Enzyme measurements. *J. Biol. Chem.*, **207**:19–37.

Nasatir, M. and H. Stern, 1959. Changes in the activities of aldolase and D-glyceraldehyde-3-phosphate dehydrogenase during the mitotic cycle in microspores of *Lilium longiflorum. J. Biophys. Biochem. Cytol.*, **6**:189–192.

Olney, H. O. and B. M. Pollock, 1960. Studies of rest period. II. Nitrogen and phosphorus changes in embryonic organs of after-ripening cherry seed. *Plant Physiol.*, **35**:970–975.

Pollock, B. M., 1953. The respiration of *Acer* buds in relation to the inception and termination of the winter rest. *Physiol. Plantarum*, **6**:47–64.

——, 1960. Studies of rest period. III. Respiratory changes in leaf primordia of maple buds during chilling. *Plant Physiol.*, **35**:975–977.

Pollock, B. M. and H. O. Olney, 1959. Studies of the rest period. I. Growth, translocation, and respiratory changes in the embryonic organs of the after-ripening cherry seed. *Plant Physiol.*, **34**:131–142.

Robins, E., 1957. Some extensions of the Linderstrøm-Lang and Holter quantitative histochemical method for the localization of enzymes and other constituents in cells and tissues. *Exptl. Cell Research, Suppl.*, **4**:241–253.

Robins, E., N. R. Roberts, K. M. Eydt, O. H. Lowry, and D. E. Smith, 1956. Microdetermination of α-keto acids with special reference to malic, lactic, and glutamic dehydrogenases in brain. *J. Biol. Chem.*, **218**:897–909.

Schwartz, S., 1949. The use of a silicone coating on the Cartesian diver microgasometer. *Compt. rend. trav. lab. Carlsberg, Sér. chim.*, **27**:79–92.

Stern, H., 1958. Variations in sulfhydryl concentration during microsporocyte meiosis in anthers of *Lilium* and *Trillium. J. Biophys. Biochem. Cytol.*, **4**:157–161.

——, 1960. Biochemical sequences in mitosis. In *Developing Cell Systems and Their Control.* 18th Symposium, Society for the Study of Development and Growth. D. Rudnick (Editor). Ronald, New York.

——, 1961. Periodic induction of deoxyribonuclease activity in relation to the mitotic cycle. *J. Biophys. Biochem. Cytol.*, **9**:271–277.

Stern, H. and P. L. Kirk, 1948a. A versatile microrespirometer for routine use. *J. Gen. Physiol.*, **31**:239–242.

——, 1948b. The oxygen consumption of the microspores of *Trillium* in relation to the mitotic cycle. *J. Gen. Physiol.*, **31**:243–248.

Sunderland, N. and R. Brown, 1956. Distribution of growth in the apical region of the shoot of *Lupinus albus. J. Exptl. Botany*, **7**:127–145.

Sunderland, N., J. K. Heyes, and R. Brown, 1957. Protein and respiration in the apical region of the shoot of *Lupinus albus. J. Exptl. Botany*, **8**:55–70.

Taft, E. B. and J. F. Scott, 1958. Studies in histochemistry. II. Quantitative histochemical estimation of activities of alkaline and acid phosphomonoesterases. *J. Histochem. and Cytochem.*, **6**:340–346.

Thorell, B. and L. Åkerman, 1957. Recording microspectroscopy for the study of intracellular reactions. *Exptl. Cell Research, Suppl.*, **4**:83–85.

Umbreit, W. W., R. H. Burris, and J. F. Stauffer, 1957. *Manometric Techniques and Related Methods for the Study of Tissue Metabolism.* Burgess, Minneapolis.

Wanner, H., 1944. The zonal gradiation of respiratory intensity in the root. *Arkiv. Botan.* **31A**:1–9.

Wanner, H. and U. Leupold, 1947.

Über die longitudinale Verteilung der Saccharaseaktivität in der Wurzelspitze. *Ber. Schweiz. Botan. Gesellschaft,* **57**:156–163.

Waterlow, J. C. and A. Borrow, 1949. Experimental observations on the Cartesian diver technique. *Compt. rend. trav. lab. Carlsberg, Sér. chim.,* **27**:93–123.

Zeuthen, E., 1948. A Cartesian diver balance weighing reduced weights (R.W.) with an accuracy of ± 0.01 gamma. Reduced weight and volume during starvation of the amoeba *Chaos chaos* L. Metabolism and Reduced weight in starving *Chaos chaos. Compt. rend. trav. lab. Carlsberg, Sér. chim.,* **26**:243–296.

CHAPTER 15

Enzymes: Microscopic Histochemistry

The localization of enzyme activity within the cell is a challenging and difficult problem in histochemistry. The field of enzyme localization itself is not particularly new, inasmuch as peroxidase activity was localized in plant tissues by Raciborski as early as 1898. However, the first of the modern enzyme procedures was developed independently by Gomori and Takamatsu in 1939 for the enzyme alkaline phosphatase. The development of techniques for enzyme localization, although slowed during World War II, was rapid during the 1950's and is almost exponential at present. This growth of localization procedures paralleled the development of cell homogenation and differential centrifugation methods. For a while it appeared as if the difficulties which were being encountered in enzyme microscopic histochemistry were so great, and the successes obtained by differential centrifugation procedures so striking, that enzyme microscopic histochemistry would always occupy a secondary role in cell research. As research continued, however, the balance shifted, and in recent years the complementary nature of the two groups of techniques has been recognized by an increasingly large number of workers (Novikoff, 1955).

The aim of enzyme microscopic histochemistry is the localization of enzyme activity within tissues and cells. This means that it is possible to draw two types of conclusions, as, for example, in Avers' (1958) work on the development of epidermal cells in grasses. On the tissue level Avers was able to show that certain cells—those which will form root hairs—possess much higher enzyme activity than do the cells which do not form root hairs. She was also able to demonstrate the particulate localization of the enzyme studied. Not all microscopic histochemical procedures for enzymes are exact enough to permit conclusions on a cell level. The peroxidase methods used by Van Fleet (1947) and Jensen (1955) allow conclusions only on the tissue level, because the end product is too soluble for precise localization. Yet the procedure has been used to advantage, particularly by Van Fleet (1947), in studies of tissue differentiation in roots and stems.

The methods of differential centrifugation of cell homogenates, in contrast to the procedures of microscopic histochemistry, permit conclusions only on the cell level. This point has been discussed in Chapter 8, but must be emphasized in relation to enzyme localization studies. Thus, by the techniques of differential centrifugation an enzyme may be located quite precisely in the cell, within the limitations discussed in Chapter 8. Tissue differences are completely lost, however, and the type of data obtained by Avers (1961), Van Fleet (1950), and Wilson (1949) in their respective studies of cell development is unobtainable by this technique. On the other hand, detailed biochemical studies can be made on isolated cell parts; such studies, however, cannot be made using microscopic histochemical techniques. Consequently the two sets of procedures, differential centrifugation and microscopic histochemistry, are complementary and frequently overlap. The investigator must recognize the limitations of each method and the effect these will have on the data collected.

The problems involved in the localization of enzyme activity differ considerably from, and are more complex than, those found in dealing with other components of the cell. There are four major problems to be faced in enzyme localization studies: (1) maintenance of enzyme activity, (2) maintenance of cytological sites, (3) precision of the localization procedure, and (4) specificity of the reaction. All four of these points are interrelated, but to gain an understanding of the procedures and of the problems, they will be discussed one at a time.

Maintenance of Enzyme Activity

Enzymes are proteins, and to be active they must not be denatured in the preparation of the tissue. Many enzymes can be localized only in living, unfixed material. This is particularly true for the respiratory enzymes, which include the dehydrogenases, cytochrome oxidase, and succinoxidase (Van Fleet, 1952). Frequently, fresh material can be used to advantage not only for those enzymes which are easily inactivated but for other enzymes as well. Thus, in her studies on epidermal development in roots, Avers (Avers, 1958, 1961; Avers and King, 1960) used living roots. The roots were small enough such that they could be simply pressed out on a slide for examination. Sorokin (1955, 1956) has done considerable work with living cells from onion bulbs, and Van Fleet (1947, 1950) has used fresh, free-hand sections of many plants. But fresh tissue is not always the tissue of choice. Diffusion of substrates and other reactants into the living cell, as well as the diffusion of end products of the reaction from the site, are problems frequently met in the use of living tissues (Pearse, 1961). Moreover, thin sections are difficult to obtain, and permanent preparations are difficult to make.

Sections of tissue cut by means of cold microtomes (Chapter 6) are being used by an increasing number of investigators working with animal material (Pearse, 1961). As yet, no work has been reported in which this technique was used in conjunction with enzyme localization studies in plant tissue. There is no reason to believe, however, that the method should not prove effective in many problems involving botanical material, with the exception of those enzymes which are damaged in the initial freezing of the tissue.

The use of fixed material also poses problems. First and foremost is the inactivation of enzyme activity. This problem has been studied to some extent in animal tissues but not at all with regard to plant tissue. The data available from animal tissues have been summarized by Casselman (1959a). From these data and from some additional data already discussed in Chapter 5, the conclusion can be drawn that any method of tissue preparation that involves paraffin infiltration causes a marked loss, 50–100%, of enzyme activity, depending on the enzyme. Of the methods that are available, however, the best are freeze-drying and freeze-substitution, in that order. Acid phosphatase is known to be preserved in freeze-dried (Jensen, 1956) and freeze-substituted (Zalokar, 1960) plant material, and from data obtained from animal tissue it can be expected that alkaline phosphatase, esterase, and various hydrolyzing enzymes would also be preserved. Freeze-substitution with fixation during dehydration (Feder and Sidman, 1958) should also prove useful. Cold acetone-fixed and cold alcohol-fixed tissue have also been found to retain much enzyme activity (Taft and Scott, 1958), but the use of this type of tissue brings up the second problem.

Maintenance of Cytological Sites

The cell is a highly organized unit, and it is clearly one of the important aims of microscopic histochemistry to study and to appreciate this complexity. Therefore, as important as the preservation of enzyme activity is in histochemistry, at least equally important for many problems is the preservation of cellular structure. If enzyme activity remains whereas structure is lost, then microscopic histochemistry becomes a bizarre and unprofitable type of biochemistry if the aim of the investigation is the localization of the enzyme within the cell. Both cold acetone and cold alcohol, although they preserve enzyme activity, do great violence to cell structure. Erroneous conclusions can be drawn from the use of such material because enzymes, liberated from small cell organelles but not inactivated, can be absorbed on the remaining cell parts and give a false picture of their distribution.

This can be demonstrated with regard to acid phosphatase in plants. When living or freeze-dried tissue was used the enzyme was found associated with a cytoplasmic particle. This was shown to be the case for living pea roots (Dyar, 1950) and grass roots (Avers and Grimm, 1959) and for freeze-dried onion and bean roots (Jensen, 1956). When acetone or alcohol fixed material was used (Glick and Fischer, 1946; McGregor and Street, 1953; Sharma and Roy, 1956) the acid phosphatase was found associated primarily with the nucleus, whereas little, if any, was reported in the cytoplasm. The cells in these studies showed poor cytoplasmic fixation. In addition, Jensen (1956) was able to demonstrate that treatment of freeze-dried roots with alcohol produced a loss of the enzyme from the cytoplasm and positive reactions in the nuclei.

As regards cellular organization, either living or freeze-dried tissue is clearly the material of choice. Many enzyme localization procedures can be performed with the paraffin still in the tissue sections. This means that, when freeze-dried material is used, organic solvents do not come in contact with the tissue until after the reaction is complete. Care must be taken, regardless of the methods used, to demonstrate that, in the tissue employed, all possible sites of enzyme activity exist before a conclusion can be drawn as to the site of the enzyme in the living cell.

Precision of the Localization Procedure

The third major problem involved in the histochemical localization of enzymes lies in the nature of the techniques used in actually demonstrating the enzyme activity (Nachlas, Young, and Seligman, 1957). In most enzyme procedures the enzyme is presented a substrate on which it acts, liberating either an end product or the diffusion stain precursor of Holt (1956). This end product, usually soluble, then reacts with another substance present in the medium to form an insoluble precipitate or the visualizing substance of Holt (1956). The rate of diffusion of the soluble end product of the enzyme reaction and the rate of capture of this substance are very important. The lower the rate of diffusion, and the higher the rate of capture, the more precise will be the localization. The solubility of the precipitate is also of great importance, and should be extremely low. How these various factors interact to influence the data obtained from a given procedure will be discussed shortly under the various techniques.

Another factor which has been receiving increasing attention is the binding of the end product and the precipitate to proteins. This is an important factor in procedures involving organic dyes. These various factors interact and can balance one another. Thus, if the solubility of a precipitate is higher than desirable but the precipitate has a high protein binding capacity, the solubility is, in effect, reduced, and the procedure may give good localization. The size of the site is a factor in the precision of localization; the larger the site, the greater the ease of localization. These various factors have been admirably analyzed by Holt and O'Sullivan (1958).

When working with enzymes it must be kept in mind that many of the problems that exist in microscopic histochemistry also exist in quantitative histochemistry. Thus, when applying a new procedure to a new material it is necessary to find the proper pH, the optimum temperature, a suitable substrate concentration, and the other features of enzyme activity that are usually kept well in mind by biochemists but which are all too frequently forgotten by histochemists. The direct application of a procedure may yield some striking results, but what these results mean must frequently depend on the subsequent careful and detailed examination of the technique.

Specificity of the Reaction

The fourth major problem involved in enzyme histochemistry is that of specificity. When a given substrate is used at a particular pH, is a specific enzyme being localized by the reaction? This is an important question, and one that is frequently difficult to answer. The range of specificities of histochemical enzyme reactions is enormous. Some enzyme localization reactions are highly specific, such as the reaction for cytochrome oxidase, whereas the reactions for some of the esterases, for example, are very general. Specificity is usually difficult to prove. The procedure for localizing ATP'ase is an example of the difficulties involved in showing specificity (Novikoff, Hausman, and Podler, 1958). A modification of Gomori's alkaline phosphatase procedure was first proposed by Glick and Fischer (1945), but considerable debate ensued as to the specificity of the reaction (Padykula and Herman, 1955a,b). Only by working very carefully and by using comprehensive controls were Padykula and Herman (1955b) able to work out a procedure for ATP'ase in animal tissue that appears to be at least reasonably specific. Similarly, the enzymes actually being localized in the tetrazolium procedures have been widely debated. These will be discussed later. The question of specificity is an important one, and must never be overlooked. This is particularly true when procedures developed for animal tissues are modified for plant material.

How these four major problems of enzyme preservation, cell organization, localization precision, and reaction specificity interact and influence the final result can best be seen in a discussion of the various procedures given here.

Before discussing the various procedures, a word must be said concerning the adaption of microscopic histochemical enzyme procedures developed for animal tissues to plant material. The vast majority of enzyme localization procedures were first developed for animal tissue. One of the outstanding exceptions is the use of tetrazolium in localizing dehydrogenase activity. This procedure developed from the use of tetrazolium salts to test seed viability (Jensen, Sacks, and Baldawski, 1951). Some of these methods can be applied directly to plant tissue, as was the post-coupling procedure for acid phosphatase of Rutenberg and Seligman (1955), which was designed for animal tissue but applied to plant tissue by Zalokar (1960). However, the direct application of other procedures developed for animal tissue has yielded negative results. This is the case for the procedures for B-galactosidase (Avers, 1961), B-D-glucuronidase (Avers, 1961), and lipase (Glick and Fischer, 1946). Yet many methods can be modified such that they will work on plant tissues.

These modifications may take a number of forms, depending on the enzyme. For example, some substrates are utilized by animal tissues but not by plant cells. In other cases the *p*H must be modified, and different buffers must be used. The amount of substrate may also vary greatly; some plants contain such large reserves of substrate that added substrate does not affect the result. This is true in dealing with dehydrogenase activity. Both incubation temperature and time may also have to be modified. Many procedures developed for mammalian cells specify 37°C as the incubation temperature. This may also be suitable for some plants, but for many it is too high, and the temperature used should be closer to 20°C. A reduction in temperature may necessitate an increase in incubation time. Finally, activators or cofactors that were not required for animal cells may be necessary for plant tissues. However, the opposite may also be the case.

Any or all of these modifications may be necessary to adapt animal techniques to plants. Changes may also be necessary before procedures developed for use with roots can be used with leaves. Modifications of methods developed for use with vascular plants may be necessary if they are to be applied to cryptogams. However, so little work has been done with a wide range of plant tissues that it is difficult at this time to give definite suggestions as to the types of changes necessary.

A discussion of enzyme localization procedures almost inevitably begins with the alkaline phosphatase method of Gomori (1939) and Takamatsu (1939). This procedure marks the beginning of modern enzyme microscopic histochemistry; together with the very similar acid phosphatase method, it has been used more than any other histochemical enzyme method. The reason for this wide interest is that the data obtained have been interpreted as providing information on phosphate transformations, frequently with reference to the synthetic activity of the cells. Undoubtedly the availability and dependability of these procedures have also contributed to their popularity.

The alkaline phosphatase and acid phosphatase procedures, based on the ultimate formation of an insoluble sulfide, are two of the most important in the histochemistry of enzymes. Both procedures have been the subject of intense controversy and both have been examined recently with great care—the alkaline phosphatase procedure by Danielli (1958), and the acid phosphatase procedure by Holt (1959).

The problems involved with regard to alkaline phosphatase, or phosphomonoesterase I, as it is more properly called, hinge largely on the question of diffusion of the precipitate and of the enzyme. In this procedure the enzyme splits off the phosphate from a suitable substrate. The liberated phosphate then combines with calcium ions present in the solution, precipitating insoluble calcium phosphate. This precipitate is converted to cobalt phosphate, which is finally converted to black cobalt sulfide. The precipitate will form only after the phosphate exceeds a given concentration, and when an adequate number of crystallization nuclei or precipitation centers exist in the tissue. A delay in precipitation will permit the diffusion of the calcium phosphate from the site of production. The diffusion of the enzyme will also result in the false localization of the enzyme activity. The fact that in the histochemical tests alkaline phosphatase activity is found associated primarily with the nuclei whereas in isolated cell parts it is generally not found associated with the nuclei (Novikoff, 1959) has caused considerable doubt to be cast on the procedure (Novikoff, 1955). Experiments have been performed that have both tended to prove and to discredit the method. Danielli (1958), in his most recent analysis, believes it to be both valid and quantitative. However, a considerable number of workers remain doubtful (see Novikoff, 1955).

In an effort to improve the technique and to test its validity, other procedures were developed to localize alkaline phosphatase activity. The most successful of these is the azo dye method of Manheimer and Seligman (1948). In this procedure the enzyme is presented calcium β-naphthyl phosphate in the presence of naphthyl diazonium naphthyl-ene-1,5-disulfonate. The enzyme removes the phosphate, and the β-naphthyl combines with the naphthyl diazonium naphthylene-1,5-disulfonate to form an insoluble azo dye. The major disadvantage of this procedure lies in the instability of the diazonium compounds used. This necessitates the running of the reaction at low temperatures. The final azo dye is also soluble in organic solvents and thus must be mounted in glycerin-gelatin. The results obtained with the azo dye method are often, but not always, the same as with the cobalt sulfide method. This does not mean the localization obtained is necessarily correct, since enzyme diffusion can still be the major source of error. It does mean, however, that the probability of the diffusion of calcium phosphate as the sole cause of error is not very great.

The general consensus of opinion would seem to be that sites of high alkaline phosphatase activity, particularly where the localization is viewed in terms of cell types rather than of cell parts, can be localized by these procedures.

When alkaline phosphatase procedures are applied to plant tissues, particularly the Gomori cobalt sulfide method, modifications must be made. The most serious of these is the substitution of other phosphate compounds for glycerophosphate, which is generally inactive in plant material (Ross and Ely, 1951; Zalokar, 1960). A particularly good substrate appears to be adenosine-3-phosphate. In the azo dye method calcium β-naphthyl phosphate appears to work well (Zalokar, 1960). The methods of tissue preparation which work well are freeze-substitution and freeze-drying. Different *p*H's may have to be used, and substrate concentrations may have to be changed.

Acid phosphatase (phosphomonoesterase II) cannot be localized by the same procedure as is alkaline phosphatase, because calcium phosphatase is soluble at acid *p*H's. Indeed, even at *p*H 7.5 the solubility of calcium phosphatase is reaching a point at which localization is no longer precise. To localize acid phosphatase, lead is used in place of calcium, hence lead phosphate is formed. This offers an advantage in that lead phosphate can be converted to lead sufide directly, without the formation of an intermediate compound. Yet the lead offers a disadvantage in that it partially inhibits the enzyme.

The lead sulfide procedure has been termed one of the most fickle procedures in the field of enzyme histochemistry (Holt, 1959). The use of the procedure for intracellular localization has been criticized on the same points as has the use of alkaline phosphatase. The earliest studies indicate nuclear localization (Glick and Fischer, 1946), but later ones, in which fresh (Avers and King, 1960; Dyar, 1950), freeze-substituted (Zalokar, 1960), and freeze-dried tissue (Jensen, 1956) were used, all indicate a particulate localization in the cytoplasm. This localization has been characterized as mitochondrial. However, the data obtained from animal tissue indicates that acid phosphatase is associated with lysosomes (see Holt, 1959). Lysosomes are particles similar in size and shape to mitochondria. The evidence from electron microscope studies indicates that various types of organelles roughly the size of mitochondria but not mitochondria are present in plant cells (Whaley, Mollen-hauer, and Kephart, 1959). Thus, caution must be used in assigning names to sites of enzymes in the cytoplasm solely on the bases of microscopic evidence. After a careful analysis of the Gomori acid phosphatase reaction, Holt (1959) concluded that the procedure was valid and that the enzyme was probably associated with the lysosomes. Whereas in animal tissue both acid and alkaline phosphatase will utilize glycero-phosphate, in plant tissue only acid phosphatase will utilize glycero-phosphate as a substrate; alkaline phosphatase will not.

When used on a tissue level, the lead sulfide procedure for acid phos-phatase has proved far less controversial and has received wide use. The procedure has been used effectively in the study of wheat grains and seedlings (Glick and Fischer, 1945, 1946), germinating corn (Kug-ler and Bennett, 1947), cucurbit fruit development (Wilson, 1949), embryo sac and endosperm development in coconuts and in tissues fol-lowing irradiation (Shah, 1960; Sharma and Roy, 1956).

Just as methods other than the Gomori technique exist for alkaline phosphatase, so do alternate methods exist for the localization of acid phosphatase. Probably the best of these (Gomori, 1956) is the post-coupling procedure of Rutenberg and Seligman (1955). In this method sodium 6-benzoyl-2-naphthyl phosphate is used as the substrate. The enzyme splits off the phosphate, and the remainder of the molecule precipitates. This is then made visible in a second step by coupling the

6-benzoyl-2-naphthyl to tetrazotized diorthoanisidine to form a red to blue color, depending on the amount of coupling. The coupling does not occur in the incubation solution containing the enzyme but in a second solution, hence the name postcoupling reaction. This reaction is reported to give good results with *Neurospora* (Zalokar, 1960).

Acid and alkaline phosphatases must be considered as general phosphatases with low specificities. When specific phosphatase procedures are attempted difficulties frequently arise when proof of the degree of specificity is sought. The use of specific inhibitors is of great help in determining the exactness of the procedure. Frequently, marked differences in pattern of localization are used as proof of specificity of a reaction, but this must be done with considerable caution because of the possible interaction of such factors as tissue preservation.

The specific phosphatase procedures in Procedures V and VI are for 5-nucleotidase and glucose-6-phosphatase, both of which have been used on plant tissues (Avers, 1961; Avers and Grimm, 1959). These procedures give considerably different patterns of localization than do either acid or alkaline phosphatase. Both are modifications of the Gomori method and hence will not be discussed in detail. Another specific phosphatase is phosphamidase (Meyer and Weinmann, 1955).

The enzyme phosphorylase can be localized by staining the starch that is formed after the cell has been given glucose-1-phosphate (Yin and Sun, 1947). If no starch is present in the tissue before applying the procedure the new starch can be stained with the periodic acid-Schiff's method and permanent mounts made. If starch is already present, as is usually the case, then iodine must be used because with iodine the new starch will stain reddish, and the old starch will stain blue (Dyar, 1950). The test is a good one and has the advantage of simplicity.

The method for leucine aminopeptidase (Burstone and Folk, 1956; Nachlas, Monis, Rosenblatt, and Seligman, 1960) is based on the same type of reaction as was discussed with respect to alkaline phosphatase. A complex naphthylamide is used as the substrate. After the enzyme has removed the amide, the naphthol compound combines with, and is precipitated by, tetrazotized diorthoanisidine, forming an azo dye.

A postcoupling technique is used in the sulfatase procedure of Rutenberg, Cohen, and Seligman (1952). Again, a complex naphthyl is used, namely, 6-bromo-2-naphthyl sulfate. The enzyme splits off the sulfate, precipitating the 6-bromo-2-naphthyl, which, in the next step, is coupled with Naphthanil Diazo Blue B. The procedure gives precise localization, probably as a combination of the insolubility and protein-binding capacities of the precipitated naphthyl compound. Since the specificity of this procedure may not be as great as first believed, caution should be used in interpreting the results (Avers, 1961).

The esterase procedure given is the indigogenic method of Holt (1958)—an exceptionally well-conceived procedure. The substrate in this method is an indigogenic compound, 5-bromo-4-chloroindoxyl acetate. The enzyme releases the substituted indoxyl, which is oxidized to an indigoid dye. With this method it is possible to obtain very precise localization. The method localizes general esterase activity.

The enzymes discussed above are all hydrolytic enzymes, and the procedures demonstrate the various approaches possible for these enzymes. An examination of the dates of publication of the various techniques clearly shows the current trend toward the use of complex organic dyes in place of inorganic salts as the means of localization. The points made at the beginning of this discussion, concerning precipitation, solubility, rate of reaction, and protein binding, hold true for all procedures. Two problems not yet considered are: (1) lipid solubility of the reaction product; and (2) crystal formation in the final product. These points are better illustrated with the oxidative enzymes.

The reaction for cytochrome oxidase activity, the nadi reaction (named from the first two letters of the chemicals used) is an old one, having first been used by Winkler in 1907. It was not recognized as an enzyme reaction until fairly recently (Gomori, 1952). In this reaction, cytochrome oxidase (in the presence of cytochrome c) oxidizes a mixture of α-naphthol and dimethylparaphenylenediamine to indophenol. The enzyme is a sensitive one, and only fresh tissue can be used in the procedure. Sodium azide is an effective inhibitor. The cytochrome c present in the tissue is usually adequate for the test. An excellent control can be obtained by washing the cytochrome c from the tissue. To localize the cytochrome oxidase it should then only be necessary to add cytochrome c.

The chief difficulties experienced in employing these techniques are these: (1) the indophenol dye formed is highly lipid soluble; and (2) the reaction will occur even when conditions are such that the enzyme is inactive. This second reaction, frequently termed the stable nadi reaction, is probably due to the presence of fat peroxides, which catalyze the nonenzymatic formation of indophenol blue from the nadi reagent. This difficulty can be overcome by the use of specific inhibitors to distinguish between the enzymatic and nonenzymatic reactions. It is also useful to add catalase and peroxidase to the reaction mixture to destroy the peroxides present. As Van Fleet (1952) points out, lignin will give a pronounced reaction with the nadi reagent; this should be considered in interpreting the results.

The solubility of the end product is a much more difficult problem to solve, and has been approached by using other reagents in the nadi reaction or by using completely different reagents. Both types of procedures are presented here (Procedures XI, XII, and XIII). The modified nadi method of Nachlas, Crawford, Goldstein, and Seligman (1958) is based on the same principles as the original nadi reaction. The solubility of the end product is, however, greatly reduced. The procedure of Burstone (1959, 1960) employs aryl amines, which, on oxidation, form indamine-azine-type dyes. These dyes are capable of chelating with a number of metals to form insoluble complexes. The results obtained by this method are excellent and it should find widespread use.

Both the modified nadi reaction and the amine method for cytochrome oxidase can be adapted for use in localizing peroxidase activity. These, however, are not the traditional peroxidase procedures. The usual peroxidase methods are based on the oxidation of benzidine or guaiacol in the presence of peroxidase and hydrogen peroxide. The question of the validity of peroxidase tests, as well as of the other methods available in the literature, is discussed in an excellent review by Van Fleet (1952). The problems which arise in the benzidine-type test are the solubility of the end product, the possibility of false nonenzymatic localization due to copper and iron salts, and the possible confusion of aldehydes with peroxidase. Although the latter problems can be handled by specific inhibitors and controls, the problem of diffusion is a serious one when intracellular localization is desired. On the basis of careful comparative studies, Van Fleet (1952) concluded that the benzidine-type tests were valid. The diffusion of the final precipitate and possibly of the enzyme diffusion is great enough such that localization is not possible beyond the tissue level. Thus the use of the new amine method for cytochrome oxidase as the starting point for a peroxidase procedure may solve this diffusion problem. The present methods have been used to good advantage, particularly by Van Fleet (1947, 1950, 1959) and Reeve (1949), in problems of tissue development and differentiation in plants.

The localization of dehydrogenase activity was first demonstrated by using tetrazolium compounds with plant tissues (Jensen, Sacks, and Baldawski, 1951). The tissue is given a substrate such as succinate in the presence of the tetrazolium compound. The enzyme presumably then passes the electrons to the tetrazolium compound, which is converted to the insoluble formazan. However, continued work with tetrazolium reactions (Farber, Sternberg, and Dunlap, 1955a,b) has clearly indicated that the tetrazolium compounds do not accept electrons directly from the dehydrogenase enzymes but from a flavoprotein intermediate termed a diaphorase. When many types of substrates were used it was found that two diaphorases existed: one associated with dehydrogenase enzymes involving diphosphopyridine nucleotide (DPN-diaphorase), and one associated with dehydrogenase enzymes linked to triphosphopyridine nucleotide (TPN-diaphorase). Novikoff (1959) prefers the terms DPNH-tetrazolium reductase and TPNH-tetrazolium reductase to the diaphorase terms. The presence of an intermediate compound between the dehydrogenase and the tetrazolium means that localization of specific dehydrogenases is possible only in special cases (Nachlas, Walker, and Seligman, 1958a,b). At present it would appear that the tetrazolium methods can localize three units: DPN linked dehydrogenases through DPN-diaphorase, TPN linked dehydrogenases through TPN-diaphorase, and succinic dehydrogenase. More specific localizations should be interpreted with caution.

The first tetrazolium salt used was triphenyltetrazolium chloride, but this was soon abandoned because of the tendency of the formazan to form crystals and to dissolve in lipids. A continuing search was made to find new tetrazoliums which would form very small crystals, not dissolve in lipids, and react rapidly. An additional requirement was that the tetrazolium compound not inhibit the enzyme, a requirement true for all cytochemical reagents. A long list of tetrazolium compounds is now available, the best being neotetrazolium (NT), blue tetrazolium (BT), iodophenyl-nitrophenyl-phenyl tetrazolium (INPT), and nitro blue tetrazolium (Nitro-BT). This last compound, introduced by Nachlas, Tsow, de Souza, Cheng, and Seligman (1957) holds promise, since it appears to form exceedingly fine crystals and appears to have very low lipid solubility. The stability of the formazan of Nitro-BT is so high the tissue may be dehydrated and mounted in balsam. The possibility also exists that the use of this compound will permit the localization procedure to be carried out first, after which the tissue can be freeze-dried, paraffin-embedded, and sectioned to reveal greater detail. This possibility does not exist with most tetrazoliums, because the formazan is removed from the tissue during the handling.

In the Procedures section the Seligman and Rutenberg (1951) method is given, as well as the Nitro-BT procedure for succinic dehydrogenase (Nachlas, Tsow, de Souza, Cheng, and Seligman, 1951), DPN-diaphorase (Nachlas, Walker, and Seligman, 1958a), and TPN-diaphorase (Nachlas, Walker, and Seligman, 1958b). Unlike animal tissues, plant material must be used completely alive; even frozen tissue is inactivated.

Plants also appear to have greater supplies of substrate present in the cell, with the result that staining without added substrate is frequently high.

Until careful studies of the use of the tetrazolium compounds with plant tissues are made (Roberts, 1950a,b), the results from their casual use on plant material must be interpreted with caution. Anyone considering work in this area of enzyme histochemistry should consult the work of Farber, Sternberg, and Dunlap (1956a,b); Nachlas, Young, and Seligman (1957); Scarpelli, Hess, and Pearse (1958); Hess, Scarpelli, and Pearse (1958); and Pearse, Scarpelli, and Hess (1960).

On the whole there have been far too few attempts to carefully and quantitatively analyze histochemical enzyme localization procedures with animal tissues, and hardly any with plant material. The careful work of Doyle, Omoto, and Doyle (1951) on alkaline phosphatase is an example of what can be accomplished. The use of the interference microscope (Casselman, 1959b) holds great promise for quantitative work with enzyme histochemical procedures. The synthesis of radioactive reagents and their use in quantitative studies of enzyme localization (Shugar *et al.*, 1957, 1958) offers a great range of possibilities. It can only be hoped that a great deal of more careful work will be done in applying histochemical procedures to plant tissues. The work may not be easy, but the rewards are certain to be worthwhile.

Two procedures that are not given in the Procedures section but which are worthy of discussion are the substrate film method (Daoust, 1959) and the labeled antibody technique (Marshall, 1954). In the first method an enzyme substrate, for example, RNA for the enzyme RNA'ase, is dissolved in gelatin and poured onto a slide and allowed to become solid. The tissue is sectioned and placed on a second slide. The two slides are then pressed together such that the tissue is pressed into the substrate film on the first slide. After an appropriate incubation time the slides are separated and the substrate slide stained. The areas of enzyme activity will be visible by an absence of color. At present the technique is good only at the tissue level, but the results are interesting, and wider use can be expected. This procedure allows the localization of enzymes which are difficult to handle by other procedures. These include RNA'ase and DNA'ase.

In the second technique a highly purified enzyme is injected into a rabbit, which makes an antibody to the enzyme. The antibody is purified from the rabbit's blood and is then labeled with a fluorescent group. The labeled antibody is then put in solution and dropped on sections of tissue from the same organism that supplied the original enzyme. The labeled antibody reacts with the enzyme for which it was made. When viewed under an ultraviolet fluorescence microscope, the fluorescence emitted renders the site visible. The unique feature of this test is that the enzyme itself is localized, not the enzyme activity. This procedure, developed by Marshall (1954), has been little used, possibly owing to the technical difficulties involved in preparing the purified enzymes and the antibodies. As these procedures become more standard, it can only be hoped that greater use will be made of this extremely interesting technique.

The results which have been obtained with the electron microscope have been so spectacular that it is not surprising that attempts have been made to reduce histochemical procedures to this scale. Some interesting attempts have been made to adapt old techniques for use with the electron microscope and to formulate new ones (Barrnett, 1959; Barrnett and Palade, 1958; Gersh, 1959; Lehrer and Ornstein, 1959), although opinion is not universal as to the possibility of complete success (Pearse and Scarpelli, 1959). The purely morphological data which the electron microscope has already provided poses a major problem to the histochemist, namely, the precise identification of the sites of activity, since so many of the cytoplasmic particles that appear similar under the light microscope appear so dissimilar under the electron microscope. This problem was discussed in Chapter 8. Only in special cases can this problem be solved solely by data obtained with the light microscope. The work of Holt (1959) on acid phosphatase and lysosomes is an example of a successful attempt to solve the problem through light microscopy. Clearly, however, when the differences in the nature of the site can only be seen with the aid of the electron microscope, the localization procedures must be adapted for observation with the electron microscope. The need seems particularly pressing with regard to plant cells, in which the diversity of the cell organelles appears so high (Whaley, Mollenhauer, and Kephart, 1959).

Procedures

1. Acid Phosphatase (Phosphomonoesterase II)—Lead Sulfide Procedure (GOMORI, 1952; JENSEN, 1956)

A. Use fresh, freeze-substituted, or freeze-dried tissue.

B. If paraffin is present do not remove it. Fix the paraffin sections to the slide by pressing them onto a slide spread with Haupt's adhesive (minus the phenol) with a rolling motion of the finger or with a piece of Teflon plastic.

C. Place the slides directly into a substrate solution made by dissolving 0.6 g of lead nitrate in 500 ml of 0.05 M acetate buffer at pH 4.5, to which is added 50 ml of 0.1 M sodium glycerophosphate. Before using adjust to pH 5.0. If a precipitate forms in preparing the solution, carefully remove it by filtration.

D. Incubate the section at 37°C for $\frac{1}{2}$–18 hours.

E. Rinse in distilled water.

F. Rinse in 2% acetic acid.

G. Rinse in distilled water.

H. Place in a dilute ammonium sulfide solution (1–2 ml to a Coplin jar of water) for 5 minutes.

I. Rinse in distilled water, place in 95% ethyl alcohol and then in absolute ethyl alcohol.

J. Deparaffinize with xylene, and mount. Crystal violet may be used as a counter stain by putting a few ml of a saturated clove oil solution of the dye in the xylene.

K. The control consists of (a) tissue incubated in medium minus substrate, (b) tissue incubated in medium to which 0.001 M NaF is added, (c) tissue placed in the ammonium sulfide solution without being placed in the substrate solution, and (d) heat-killed tissue (5 minutes in boiling water) carried through the entire procedure.

The sites of acid phosphatase will appear as black deposits.

II. Acid Phosphatase (Phosphomonoesterase II)—Post-Incubation Coupling Procedure (RUTENBERG AND SELIGMAN, 1955, ZALOKAR, 1960)

A. Use fresh, frozen, freeze-dried, or freeze-substituted tissue.

B. Remove any paraffin present, and bring to water.

C. Place sections in a substrate solution made by dissolving 25 mg of sodium 6-benzoyl-2-naphthyl phosphate in 80 ml of distilled water and adding 20 ml of 0.5 M acetate buffer at pH 5.0 and 2.0 g of NaCl.

D. Incubate the sections at 25°C for $\frac{1}{2}$–2 hours.

E. Wash sections three times (10 minutes each) in cold water.

F. Transfer to a freshly prepared solution of tetrazotized diorthoanisidine (1 mg/ml) in water made alkaline with sodium bicarbonate. Keep this solution at 4°C.

G. Agitate sections gently for 3–5 minutes.

H. Wash three times in cold 0.85% sodium chloride and water.

I. Mount in glycerin-gelatin.

J. Controls are the same as in lead sulfide procedure for acid phosphatase, except step C is replaced by putting the sections in the tetrazotized diorthoanisidine without first putting them in the substrate.

Sites high in acid phosphatase activity will appear blue (dicoupling of the dye); sites low in activity will appear purple and red (monocoupling). The preparations are not stable and should be stored in a refrigerator.

III. Alkaline Phosphatase (Phosphomonoesterase I)—Cobalt Sulfide Method (GOMORI, 1952; ROSS AND ELY, 1951)

A. Use fresh, alcohol fixed, freeze-substituted, or freeze-dried tissue.

B. Either remove the paraffin or leave it in the sections, as in the acid phosphatase procedure.

C. Place the slides in a substrate solution made by mixing 5 ml of a 2% solution of calcium chloride, 2 ml of a 2% solution of magnesium chloride, 10 ml of an 0.1 M solution of barbital buffer, and 33 ml of water. Add enough substrate to make an 0.01 M solution [either adenosine-3-phosphate (Zalokar, 1960) or one of the substrates listed by Ross and Ely (1951)]. Adjust the pH to 9.4 with 1 N sodium hydroxide.

D. Incubate the sections at 37°C for $\frac{1}{2}$–12 hours.

E. Wash in distilled water.

F. Place in a 2% solution of cobalt nitrate (other soluble cobalt salts can also be used) for 1 minute.

G. Wash in distilled water.

H. Place in a dilute solution of ammonium sulfide (1–2 ml to a Coplin jar of water) for 5 minutes.

I. Wash in distilled water.

J. Dehydrate, remove paraffin if present, and mount. The tissue may be stained with crystal violet if desired.

K. Use controls similar to those used in the acid phosphatase procedure.

The sites of enzyme activity will appear black. The standard animal substrate (sodium glycerophosphate) will not work with plant tissue.

IV. Alkaline Phosphatase (Phosphomonoesterase I)—Azo Dye Method (GOMORI, 1952; MANHEIMER AND SELIGMAN, 1948)

A. Use fresh, freeze-dried, or freeze-substituted tissue.

B. Remove paraffin, and bring to water.

C. Immerse the slides in a freshly prepared substrate solution composed of 50 mg of calcium β-naphthyl phosphate, 50 mg of α-naphthyl diazonium naphthalene-1,5-disulfonate, 1 ml of 1% magnesium sulfate, 15 ml of barbital buffer at pH 9.4, and 84 ml of water.

D. Incubate the sections at 10°C for 10–30 minutes.

E. Wash the slides in water, and mount in glycerin-gelatin.

F. Use the same controls as for acid phosphatase.

The sites of enzyme activity will appear purplish-red. The preparations are not stable. Gomori (1952) used calcium α-naphthyl in place of the β-form. Other diazonium compounds can be used in place of α-naphthyl diazonium naphthalene-1,5-disulfonate. Among these are Blue B, Red RC, Bordeaux G.P., Red G or Fast Blue RR (Gomori, 1952).

V. 5-Nucleotidase (LILLIE, 1954; AVERS, 1961)

A. Use fresh, freeze-substituted, or freeze-dried tissue.

B. Either remove the paraffin and bring the sections to water or leave the paraffin in the tissue.

C. Make the substrate medium by adding 110 mg of anhydrous $CaCl_2$ (final conc. 0.1 M), 24.3 mg of $MgSO_4$ (final conc. 0.001 M Mg^{++}), and 17.4 mg of muscle adenylic acid (0.005 M) to 10 ml of 0.1 M tris-maleate buffer at pH 7.8 or higher.

D. Incubate the tissue in this medium for 30 minutes at 37°C.

E. Wash in water, and place in a 2% solution of cobalt nitrate for 1 minute.

F. Wash in water, and place in a dilute solution of ammonium sulfide for 5 minutes.

G. Wash in distilled water, dehydrate, remove any paraffin present, and mount.

H. Use controls similar to acid phosphatase. The site of enzyme activity will appear black.

The procedure given here is Avers' (1961) modification of Lillie's (1954) method. Using this method Avers demonstrated a nonparticulate distribution of the enzyme in the cells of grass roots.

VI. Glucose-6-Phosphatase (AVERS AND GRIMM, 1959; CHIQUOINE, 1955; WACHSTEIN AND MEISEL, 1956)

A. Use fresh tissue (freeze-dried tissue will also probably be active).

B. Place the tissue in a substrate solution composed of 20 mg of potassium glucose-6-phosphate, 125 ml of a 0.2 M tris-maleate buffer at pH 6.7, 3 ml of a 2% lead nitrate solution, and 7 ml of distilled water.

C. Incubate for 15 minutes to 2 hours at 32°C.

D. Wash in distilled water.

E. Place in dilute ammonium sulfide solution for 5 minutes.

F. Wash in distilled water.

G. Mount in glycerin-gelatin or fix, dehydrate, and mount.

H. As controls use solution minus substrate, heat-treated tissue, and normal tissue in complete substrate solution plus inhibitors.

The site of glucose-6-phosphatase activity will appear black. Avers and Grimm (1959) found a nonparticulate distribution of the enzyme in grass root cells similar to that of 5-nucleotidase.

VII. Phosphorylase—Starch Method (DYAR, 1950; YIN AND SUN, 1947)

A. Use fresh material. Free-hand sections work well.

B. Place the sections in a 1% solution of glucose-1-phosphate in acetate buffer at pH 6.0.

C. Incubate the sections for ½–2 hours at room temperature.

D. Place the sections in IKI solution to stain newly formed starch. If the tissue already contains starch, the old grains will appear dark blue, and the newly formed grains will appear reddish. The newly formed starch is easily identified (Dyar, 1950).

E. For controls: (1) completely remove the glucose-1-phosphate from the incubating medium, (2) replace the glucose-1-phosphate with glucose, (3) use heat-treated tissue, and (4) to a complete medium add 0.02 M sodium fluoride, which inhibits phosphatase but not phosphorylase.

VIII. Leucine Aminopeptidase (NACHLAS, MONIS, ROSENBLATT, AND SELIGMAN, 1960)

A. Use fresh, frozen, or freeze-dried tissue.

B. Immerse the sections in a substrate solution made up of 1.0 ml of a 4 mg/ml stock solution of L-leucyl-4-methoxy-2-naphthylamide HCl, 5.0 ml of 0.1 M acetate buffer at pH 6.5, 3.5 ml of 0.85% sodium chloride, 0.5 ml of 0.02 M potassium cyanide, and 5.0 mg of tetrazotized diorthoanisidine (Fast Blue B powder).

C. Incubate at 37°C for 5 minutes to 2 hours.

D. Rinse twice in 0.85% sodium chloride.

E. Transfer to 0.1 M cupric sulfate.

F. Dehydrate, and mount in permount.

The sites of enzyme activity will be red to purple.

IX. Sulfatase (RUTENBERG, COHEN, AND SELIGMAN, 1952; AVERS, 1961)

A. Use fresh, formalin-fixed, freeze-dried, or freeze-substituted tissue.

B. Remove any paraffin present, and bring to water.

C. Place the tissue in a substrate solution made by first dissolving 25 mg of potassium-6-bromo-2-naphthyl sulfate in 80 ml of hot 0.85% saline solution and then adding 20 ml of 0.5 M acetate buffer at pH 6.1.

D. Incubate the tissue for 5–30 minutes at 37°C.

E. Wash the tissue twice in 2 changes of cold 0.85% saline solution, 10 minutes each time.

F. Transfer to a freshly prepared, cold (2–4°C) solution of Naphthanil Diazo Blue B (1 mg/ml) in 0.05 M phosphate buffer at pH 7.6.

G. Leave tissue in this solution for 3–5 minutes, and gently agitate.

H. Wash in 3 changes of cold 0.85% saline solution and in 3 changes of water for 10 minutes each.

I. Mount in water or glycerin-gelatin.

J. Run controls in which the substrate is deleted from the reaction mixture and in which heat killed-tissue is carried through the entire procedure.

The site of the enzyme activity will be colored red to dark blue, depending on the amount of activity; the higher the activity, the darker the color.

This method was used by Avers (1961) in her study of root meristem cells. She found 15–20 minutes incubation at 37°C sufficient for the roots of *Phleum pratense* and *Panicum virgatum*. The enzyme appears associated with a cytoplasmic particle in these cells.

X. *Esterases—Indigogenic Method* (HOLT, 1958)

A. Use fresh, formal-calcium-fixed, freeze-substituted, or freeze-dried tissue.

B. Remove any paraffin present, and bring to water.

C. Place the material in a substrate solution composed of 1.5 mg of 5-bromo-4-chloroindoxyl acetate in 0.1 ml of absolute ethyl alcohol, 2.0 ml of 0.1 M tris buffer at pH 8.5, 1.0 ml of a solution of equal parts 5×10^{-2} M potassium ferricyanide and 5×10^{-2} M potassium ferrocyanide, 0.1 ml of 1 M calcium chloride, 5.0 ml of 2 M sodium chloride, and distilled water to make 10 ml.

D. Incubate for 5 minutes to 1 hour at 37°C.

E. Transfer the material to 30% alcohol containing 0.1% acetic acid. Use glass or stainless steel instruments to move the tissue.

F. Mount in glycerin-gelatin; or dehydrate, and mount in balsam.

The sites of esterase activity will be bluish-green.

XI. *Cytochrome Oxidase—Nadi Reaction* (GOMORI, 1952)

A. Use only fresh tissue.

B. Use a reaction mixture consisting of 25 ml of 0.05 M phosphate buffer at pH 7.2–7.6, 1 ml of 1% alpha-naphthol solution in 40% alcohol, and 1 ml of a 1% solution of dimethylparaphenylenediamine hydrochloride.

C. Incubate the tissue in this mixture in a shallow dish for 5–15 minutes or until the reaction is clearly visible.

D. Rinse the sections, and mount in glycerin-gelatin.

E. As controls use heat-, cold-, or alcohol-treated tissue in a complete reaction mixture and fresh tissue in a complete reaction mixture plus 0.005 M sodium azide. Controls and careful interpretation of the results are necessary, since lipids can be positive in this reaction without the presence of cytochrome oxidase.

The site of the enzyme activity will be blue.

Avers and King (1960) found the following modification of the reagent to be effective with roots: equal amounts of 0.01 M α-naphthol in 1% saline solution, 0.01 M dimethylparaphenylenediamine hydrochloride in 1% saline solution, and 0.05 M acetate buffer (pH 5.8) or 0.066 M phosphate buffer (p H 7.3).

XII. Cytochrome Oxidase—Revised Nadi Reaction
(NACHLAS, CRAWFORD, GOLDSTEIN, AND SELIGMAN, 1958)

A. Use only fresh tissue.

B. Incubate the tissue for 10–30 minutes at room temperature in a reaction medium of 3.0 ml of 0.1 M phosphate buffer at pH 7.4, 4.0 ml of α-naphthol (1 mg/ml), 4.0 ml of 4-amino-1-N,N-dimethylnaphthylamine (2 mg/ml), 3.0 ml of cytochrome c (5 mg/ml), and 1.0 ml of catalase (30 μg/ml).

C. Rinse, and mount in glycerin-gelatin.

D. Use the controls given in Procedure XI, step E, and see those of next procedure.

This procedure can be used to demonstrate peroxidase activity by deleting the cytochrome c and catalase or peroxidase from the reaction medium and adding 0.5 ml of 3% H_2O_2.

XIII. Cytochrome Oxidase—Amine Reaction
(BURSTONE, 1960)

A. Use fresh material.

B. Place the tissue in a substrate solution made by dissolving 10–15 mg of p-aminodiphenylamine (Variamine Blue RT Base) and 10–15 mg of either p-methoxy-p'-aminodiphenylamine (Variamine Blue B Base) or m-methoxy-p-aminodiphenylamine (Variamine Blue FG Base) in 0.5 ml of absolute ethyl alcohol. Add 35 ml of distilled water and 15 ml of 0.2 M tris buffer at pH 7.4, and filter.

C. Incubate the tissue for 15 minutes to several hours at room temperature.

D. Transfer directly to a Coplin jar containing 100 ml of 10% cobaltous acetate in 10% formalin plus 5.0 ml of 0.2 M acetate buffer at pH 5.2 for 1 hour.

E. Wash in running water for 5–10 minutes.

F. Mount in glycerin-gelatin.

G. For controls, use the complete substrate plus 0.001 M KCN or 0.001 M Na₂S. For another control, place some tissue in water at 60°C for 30 minutes, and then carry through the entire procedure. For an excellent control, place the tissue in an isotonic salt solution for 30 minutes, and then incubate in substrate solutions with and without cytochrome c. Cytochrome c should be removed from the tissue in the salt solution; a positive cytochrome oxidase reaction should be found only if cytochrome c is present. Catalase or peroxidase (2.0 mg per Coplin jar) should be added to check on the possibility of peroxidase activity influencing the localization. The procedure may be modified to localize peroxidase (see below).

The site of cytochrome oxidase activity will appear blue.

XIV. Peroxidase—Amine Reaction (BURSTONE, 1960)

A. Use fresh tissue.

B. Place the tissue in the same substrate solution as used in the cytochrome oxidase-amine reaction but with 0.25 ml of 3% hydrogen peroxide added.

C. Incubate for 15 minutes to 1 hour.

D. Transfer directly to cobaltous acetate-formalin solution used in the cytochrome oxidase procedure.

E. Wash in water.

F. Mount in glycerin-gelatin.

XV. Peroxidase—Benzidine Reaction (ISAAC AND WINCH, 1947)

A. Use fresh tissue.

B. Place the material in an incubating solution composed of 0.1 M phosphate buffer at pH 4.5, 0.1 M H₂O₂, and approximately 0.01 M benzidine. The concentration of the benzidine is not critical. The addition of 5% ammonium chloride to the reaction mixture is recommended by Van Duijn (1955) to precipitate the reaction product and increase resolution.

C. Use sections incubated without H_2O_2 or sections incubated in azide as controls.

The localization of peroxidase activity will be indicated by a blue to brown color. For an excellent discussion of this procedure and of similar microscopic histochemical methods and their application to plant material, see Van Fleet (1952, 1959).

XVI. Dehydrogenase—Tetrazolium Reaction
(SELIGMAN AND RUTENBERG, 1951)

A. Use only fresh material.

B. Use a reaction mixture consisting of 0.05 M substrate (succinate, lactate, pyruvate, citrate, or isocitrate), 0.1% neotetrazolium, and 0.05 M phosphate buffer at pH 7.3. Boil and cool the solution before using.

C. Place the sections or pieces of tissue in small vials completely filled with the reaction mixture. Place stoppers on the vials to exclude air.

D. Incubate for 5–20 minutes at 37°C.

E. Remove from the reaction mixture, and observe directly.

F. As controls use (1) the reaction mixture minus the substrate and (2) the complete reaction mixture containing 0.001 M N-ethyl maleimide or 0.2 M malonate. Also use a control of heat-killed tissue.

The sites of enzyme activity will appear as blue-black deposits. The reaction can frequently be greatly enhanced by the addition of trace amounts of methylene blue (Farber and Louviere, 1956).

XVIa. Succinic Dehydrogenase (NACHLAS, TSOW, DE SOUZA, CHENG, AND SELIGMAN, 1957)

A. Use only fresh tissue.

B. Place the tissue in a solution composed of 10 ml of a stock solution of equal volumes 0.2 M phosphate buffer at pH 7.6 and 0.2 M sodium succinate, and 10 ml of an aqueous solution containing 10 mg of Nitro-BT.

C. Incubate the tissue in this solution for 5–30 minutes at 37°C.

D. Wash for 1 minute, and dehydrate in an alcohol series starting with 30% ethyl alcohol.

E. Place in xylene for 10–20 minutes, and mount in balsam.

F. As controls use (1) the mixture without the substrate, (2) mixtures in which α-ketoglutarate, fumarate, or malate substitute for succinate, and (3) mixtures that contain succinate plus the inhibitor p-phenylenediamine (10^{-3} M). Also use heat-inactivated tissue as a control.

The sites of succinic dehydrogenase activity will appear deep blue.

XVIb. DPN-diaphorase (NACHLAS, WALKER, AND SELIGMAN, 1958a)

A. Use only fresh tissue.

B. Place the tissue in a solution composed of 0.3 ml of a 5 mg/ml solution of DPN, 0.3 ml of a 5 mg/ml solution of Nitro-BT, one of the following: 0.6 ml of 0.5 M sodium lactate, 0.3 ml of 2.5 M sodium malate, or 0.6 ml of 0.5 M sodium glutamate, and water to make 3 ml.

C. Incubate the tissue for 5–30 minutes at room temperature.

D. Rinse, and dehydrate in an alcohol series.

E. Place in xylene, and mount in balsam.

F. As controls use heat-killed tissue and incubation medium minus the substrate.

The site of enzyme activity will appear deep blue.

XVIc. TPN-diaphorase (NACHLAS, WALKER, AND SELIGMAN, 1958b)

A. Use only fresh tissue.

B. Place the tissue in a solution composed of 0.3 ml of 0.005 M manganese chloride, 0.2 ml of 5 mg/ml TPN, 0.3 ml of 5 mg/ml Nitro-BT, 1.1 ml of 0.05 M barbitol buffer at pH 7.4, 0.6 ml of 0.1 M sodium DL-isocitrate, and 0.5 ml of sodium L-malate (the substrates may be used independently and may be substituted with 0.004 M sodium glucose-6-phosphate).

C. Incubate for 5–30 minutes at room temperature.

D. Rinse, and dehydrate in an alcohol series.

E. Place in xylene, and mount in balsam.

F. As controls use heat-killed tissue and normal tissue in incubation medium minus the substrate.

The site of enzyme activity will appear deep blue.

LITERATURE CITED

Avers, C. J., 1958. Histochemical localization of enzyme activity in the root epidermis of *Phleum pratense*. *Am. J. Botany*, **45**:609–612.

———, 1961. Histochemical localization of enzyme activities in root meristem cells. *Am. J. Botany*, **48**:137–142.

Avers, C. J. and R. B. Grimm, 1959. Intergeneric differences in the activity of glucose-6-phosphatase in grass root epidermis. *Exptl. Cell Research*, **16**: 692–695.

Avers, C. J. and E. E. King, 1960. Histochemical evidence of intracellular enzymatic heterogeneity of plant mitochondria. *Am. J. Botany*, **47**:220–225.

Barrnett, R. J., 1959. The demonstration with the electron microscope of the end-products of histochemical reactions in relation to the fine structure of cells. *Exptl. Cell Research Suppl.*, **7**:66–89.

Barrnett, R. J. and G. E. Palade, 1958. Applications of histochemistry to electron microscopy. *J. Histochem. and Cytochem.*, **6**:1–12.

Burstone, M. S., 1959. New histochemical techniques for the demonstration of tissue oxidase (cytochrome oxidase). *J. Histochem. and Cytochem.*, **7**:112–122.

———, 1960. Histochemical demonstration of cytochrome oxidase with new amine reagents. *J. Histochem. and Cytochem.*, **8**:63–70.

Burstone, M. S. and J. E. Folk, 1956. Histochemical demonstration of aminopeptidase. *J. Histochem. and Cytochem.*, **4**:217–226.

Casselman, W. G. B., 1959a. *Histochemical Technique*. Wiley, New York.

———, 1959b. Some applications of interference microscopy in enzyme cytochemistry with particular reference to alkaline phosphatase. *Exptl. Cell Research Suppl.*, **7**:28–39.

Chiquoine, A. D., 1955. Further studies on the histochemistry of glucose-6-phosphatase. *J. Histochem. and Cytochem.*, **3**:471–478.

Danielli, J. F., 1958. The calcium phosphate precipitation method for alkaline phosphatase. *Gen. Cytochem. Methods*, **1**:423–443.

Daoust, R., 1959. The substrate film method in enzyme histochemistry. *Exptl. Cell Research Suppl.*, **7**:40–49.

Doyle, W. L., J. H. Omoto, and M. E. Doyle, 1951. Estimation of phosphatase in histological preparations. *Exptl. Cell Research*, **2**:20–38.

Dyar, M. T., 1950. Some observations on starch synthesis in pea root tips. *Am. J. Botany*, **37**:786–792.

Farber, E. and C. D. Louviere, 1956. Histochemical localization of specific oxidative enzymes. IV. Soluble oxidative-reduction dyes as aids in the histochemical localization of oxidative enzymes with tetrazolium salts. *J. Histochem. Cytochem.*, **4**:347–356.

Farber, E., W. H. Sternberg, and C. E. Dunlap, 1956a. Histochemical localization of specific oxidative enzymes. I. Tetrazolium stains for diphosphopyridine nucleotide diaphorase and triphosphopyridine nucleotide diaphorase. *J. Histochem. and Cytochem.*, **4**:254–265.

———, 1956b. Histochemical localization of specific oxidative enzymes. III. Evaluation studies of tetrazolium staining methods for diphosphopyridine nucleotide diaphorase, triphosphopyridine nucleotide diaphorase, and the succindehydrogenase system. *J. Histochem. and Cytochem.*, **4**:284–294.

Feder, N. and R. L. Sidman, 1958. Methods and principles of fixation by freeze-substitution. *J. Biophys. Biochem. Cytol.*, **4**:593–602.

Gersh, I., 1959. Fixation and staining, pp. 21–66. In *The Cell*, Vol. I. J. Brachet and A. E. Mirsky (Editors). Academic, New York.

Glick, D. and E. E. Fischer, 1945. Studies in histochemistry. XVI. Methods for histochemical localization of adenosine-triphosphatase, thiamine-pyrophosphatase and glycerophosphatase in grains and sprouts. *Arch. Biochem.*, **8**:91–96.

———, 1946. Studies in histochemistry. XVII. Localization of phosphatases in the wheat grain and in the epicotyl and roots of the germinating grain. *Arch. Biochem.*, 11:65–79.

Gomori, G., 1939. Microtechnical demonstration of phosphatase in tissue section. *Proc. Soc. Exptl. Biol. Med.*, 42:23–26.

———, 1952. *Microscopic Histochemistry, Principles and Practice.* Univ. of Chicago Press, Chicago.

———, 1956. Histochemical methods for acid phosphatase. *J. Histochem. and Cytochem.*, 4:453–461.

Hess, R., D. G. Scarpelli, and A. G. E. Pearse, 1958. The cytochemical localization of oxidative enzymes. II. Pyridine nucleotide-linked dehydrogenases. *J. Biophys. Biochem. Cytol.*, 4:753–760.

Holt, S. J., 1956. The value of fundamental studies of staining reactions in enzyme histochemistry, with reference to indoxyl methods for esterases. *J. Histochem. and Cytochem.*, 4:541–554.

———, 1958. Indigogenic staining methods for esterases. *Gen. Cytochem. Methods*, 1:375–398.

———, 1959. Factors governing the validity of staining methods for enzymes, and their bearing upon the Gomori acid phosphatase technique. *Exptl. Cell Research Suppl.*, 7:1–27.

Holt, S. J. and D. G. O'Sullivan, 1958. Studies in enzyme cytochemistry. I. Principles of cytochemical staining methods. *Proc. Roy. Soc., London*, B, 148:465–480.

Isaac, W. E. and N. H. Winch, 1947. Guaiacol-hydrogen peroxide and benzidine-hydrogen peroxide colour reactions in beans (*Phaseolus vulgaris* L.). *J. Pomol. and Hort. Sci.*, 23:23–37.

Jensen, C. O., W. Sacks, and F. A. Baldawski, 1951. The reduction of triphenyltetrazolium chloride by dehydrogenases of corn embryos. *Science*, 113:65–66.

Jensen, W. A., 1955. The histochemical

localization of peroxidase in roots and its induction by indoleacetic acid. *Plant Physiol.*, 30:426–432.

———, 1956. The cytochemical localization of acid phosphatase in root tip cells. *Am. J. Botany*, 43:50–54.

Kugler, O. E. and E. H. Bennett, 1947. Histochemical localization of acid phosphatase in germinating maize kernels. *Stain Technol.*, 22:9–15.

Lehrer, G. M. and L. Ornstein, 1959. A diazo coupling method for the electron microscopic localization of cholinesterase. *J. Biophys. Biochem. Cytol.*, 3:399–412.

Lillie, R. D., 1954. *Histopathological Technic and Practical Histochemistry.* 2nd ed. Blakiston, New York.

McGregor, S. M. and H. E. Street, 1953. The carbohydrate nutrition of tomato roots. IV. The nature and distribution of acid phosphatase. *Ann. Botany*, 17:385–394.

Manheimer, L. H. and A. M. Seligman, 1948. Improvement in the method for the histochemical demonstration of alkaline phosphatase and its use in the study of normal and neoplastic tissues. *J. Nat. Cancer Inst.*, 9:181–199.

Marshall, J. M., Jr., 1954. Distribution of chymotrypsinogen, procarboxypeptidase, desoxyribonuclease in bovine pancreas. *Exptl. Cell Research*, 6:240–242.

Meyer, J. and J. P. Weinman, 1955. A modification of Gomori's method for demonstration of phosphamidase in tissue sections. *J. Histochem. and Cytochem.*, 3:134–140.

Nachlas, M. M., D. T. Crawford, T. P. Goldstein, and A. M. Seligman, 1958. The histochemical demonstration of cytochrome oxidase with a new reagent for the Nadi reaction. *J. Histochem. and Cytochem.*, 6:445–456.

Nachlas, M. M., B. Monis, D. Rosenblatt, and A. M. Seligman, 1960.

Improvement in the histochemical localization of leucine aminopeptidase with a new substrate, L-leucyl-4-methoxy-2-naphthylamide. *J. Biophys. Biochem. Cytol.*, 7:261–264.

Nachlas, M. M., K-C Tsow, E. de Souza, C. S. Cheng, and A. M. Seligman, 1957. Cytochemical demonstration of succinic dehydrogenase by the use of a new *p*-nitrophenyl substituted ditetrazole. *J. Histochem. and Cytochem.*, 5:420–436.

Nachlas, M. M., D. G. Walker, and A. M. Seligman, 1958a. A histochemical method for the demonstration of diphosphopyridine nucleotide diaphorase. *J. Biophys. Biochem. Cytol.*, 4:29–38.

———, 1958b. The histochemical localization of triphosphopyridine nucleotide diaphorase. *J. Biophys. Biochem. Cytol.*, 4:467–474.

Nachlas, M. M., A. C. Young, and A. M. Seligman, 1957. Problems of enzymatic localization by chemical reactions applied to tissue sections. *J. Histochem. and Cytochem.*, 5:565–583.

Novikoff, A. B., 1955. Histochemical and cytochemical staining methods. In *Analytical Cytology*. 1st ed., Mellors, R. C. (Editor). McGraw-Hill, Blakiston Division, New York. pp. 2/1-2/63.

———, 1959. The intracellular localization of chemical constituents, pp. 69–168. In *Analytical Cytology*. 2nd ed. R. C. Mellors (Editor). McGraw-Hill, Blakiston Division, New York.

Novikoff, A. B., D. H. Hausman, and E. Podler, 1958. The localization of adenosine triphosphatase in liver: *In situ* staining and cell fractionation studies. *J. Histochem. and Cytochem.*, 6:61–71.

Padykula, H. A. and E. Herman, 1955a. Factors affecting the activity of adenosine triphosphatase and other phosphatases as measured by histochemical techniques. *J. Histochem. and Cytochem.*, 3:161–169.

———, 1955b. The specificity of the histochemical method for adenosine triphosphatase. *J. Histochem. and Cytochem.*, 3:170–183.

Pearse, A. G. E., 1961. *Histochemistry, Theoretical and Applied*. 2nd ed. J. and A. Churchill, London.

Pearse, A. G. E. and D. G. Scarpelli, 1959. Intramitochondrial localization of oxidative enzyme systems. *Exptl. Cell Research Suppl.*, 7:50–64.

Pearse, A. G. E., D. G. Scarpelli, and R. Hess, 1960. A cytochemical study of the dehydrogenases of mitochondria and mitochondrial particulates by a monotetrazolium-cobalt chelation method. *J. Biophys. Biochem. Cytol.*, 7:243–250.

Reeve, R. M., 1949. Histological observations on seed coats of succulent peas. *Food Research*, 14:77–89.

Roberts, L. W., 1950a. Survey of factors responsible for reduction of 2,3,5-triphenyltetrazolium chloride in plant meristems. *Science*, 113:692–693.

———, 1950b. A survey of tissues that reduce 2,3,5-triphenyltetrazolium chloride in vascular plants. *Bull. Torrey Botan. Club*, 77:372–381.

Ross, M. H. and J. O. Ely, 1951. Alkaline phosphatase in fixed plant cells. *Exptl. Cell. Research*, 2:339–348.

Rutenberg, A. M., R. B. Cohen, and A. M. Seligman, 1952. Histochemical demonstration of aryl sulfatase. *Science*, 116:539–543.

Rutenberg, A. M. and A. M. Seligman, 1955. The histochemical demonstration of acid phosphatase by a postincubation coupling technique. *J. Histochem. and Cytochem.*, 3:455–470.

Scarpelli, D. G., R. Hess, and A. G. E. Pearse, 1958. The cytochemical localization of oxidative enzymes. I. Diphosphopyridine nucleotide diaphorase and triphosphopyridine nucleotide diaphorase. *J. Biophys. Biochem. Cytol.*, **4**:747–752.

Seligman, A. M. and A. M. Rutenberg, 1951. Histochemical demonstration of succinic dehydrogenase. *Science*, **113**: 317–320.

Sharma, A. K. and M. Roy, 1956. Irradiation—its effect on young metabolic nuclei and phosphatase activity in plants. *La cellule*, **57**:338–352.

Shah, V. C., 1960. Histochemical studies of the activities of alkaline and acid phosphatases of normal and irradiated root tips of *Tulbaghia violacea* harv. *The Nucleus*, **3**:161–164.

Shugar, D., A. Szenberg, and H. Sierakowska, 1957. Quantitative histochemistry by means of radioactive indicators—alkaline phosphatase. *Exptl. Cell Research*, **13**:424–426.

Shugar, D., H. Sierakowska, and A. Szenberg, 1958. Quantitative histochemistry with radioactive indicators —alkaline phosphatase. *Acta biochim. Pol.*, **5**:27–46.

Sorokin, H. P., 1955. Mitochondria and spherosomes in the living epidermal cell. *Am. J. Botany*, **42**:225–231.

———, 1956. Studies on living cells of pea seedlings. I. Survey of vacuolar precipitates, mitochondria, plastids, and spherosomes. *Am. J. Botany*, **43**: 787–794.

Sorokin, H. P. and S. Sorokin, 1956. Staining of mitochondria with neotetrazolium chloride. *Am. J. Botany*, **43**:183–190.

Taft, E. B. and J. F. Scott, 1958. Effect of fixation and paraffin embedding on the activity of alkaline and acid phosphomonoesterases. *Lab. Invest.*, **7**:505–515.

Takamatsu, H., 1939. Histologische und biochemische Studien über die Phosphatase. Histochemische Untersuchungsmethodick der Phosphatase und deren Verteilung in verschiedenen Organen und Geweben. *Trans. Soc. Pathol., Japan*, **29**:492–498.

Van Duijn, P., 1955. An improved histochemical benzidine-blue peroxidase method and a note on composition of the blue reaction product. *Rec. trav. chim. Pays-Bas*, **74**: 771–778.

Van Fleet, D. S., 1947. The distribution of peroxidase in differentiating tissues of vascular plants. *Biodynamica*, **6**:125–140.

———, 1950. A comparison of histochemical and anatomical characteristics of the hypodermis with the endodermis in vascular plants. *Am. J. Botany*, **37**:721–725.

———, 1952. Histochemical localization of enzymes in vascular plants. *Botan. Review*, **18**:354–398.

———, 1959. Analysis of the histochemical localization of peroxidase related to the differentiation of plant tissues. *Can. J. Botany*, **37**:449–458.

Wachstein, M., and E. Meisel, 1956. On the histochemical demonstration of glucose-6-phosphatase. *J. Histochem. and Cytochem.*, **4**:592.

Whaley, W. G., H. H. Mollenhauer and J. E. Kephart, 1959. The endoplasmic reticulum and the golgi structures in maize root cells. *J. Biophys. Biochem. Cytol.*, **5**:501–506.

Wilson, K. S., 1949. Histochemical localization of acid phosphatase during the development of cucurbit fruits. *Am. J. Botany*, **36**:806–807.

Yin, H. C. and C. N. Sun, 1947. Histochemical method for the detection of phosphorylase in plant tissue. *Science*, **105**:650.

Zalokar, M., 1960. Cytochemistry of centrifuged hyphae of *Neurospora*. *Exptl. Cell Research*, **19**:114–132.

CHAPTER 16

Autoradiography

One of the most important and promising techniques in histochemistry is autoradiography. This technique, or rather, family of techniques, is based on the incorporation of radioactive isotopes by biological materials. The sites of the incorporated isotope are detected by a photographic emulsion placed over the tissues. The radiation emitted by the isotope exposes the emulsion over the site. When the emulsion is developed the site of the radioactive isotope in the tissue is marked by a deposit of silver grains.

Autoradiographs can be made on several levels. For example, on the macro scale whole plants can be used, in which case the localization is usually in terms of organs. On the micro scale localization can be accomplished in terms of tissues, cells, and cell parts. In recent years the degree of resolution obtained in the autoradiography of cells has been truly impressive.

The importance of cell autoradiography lies in the versatility of the procedure. The radioactive isotopes of greatest interest to biologists are carbon (C^{14}) and tritium (H^3). These can be introduced into a tremendous number of precursors, which can be incorporated into various cellular constituents. This versatility, when coupled with the high resolution of the procedures, gives the botanist a powerful technique with which to attack a wide range of problems. Just how wide this range is can be seen in a brief survey of the types of problems already studied through autoradiography.

Autoradiographic techniques have been used extensively in the study of DNA synthesis and chromosome duplication. Among the isotopes that have been used in these studies are H^3, C^{14}, P^{32}, and S^{35}. Some of the earliest work in this field was done by Howard and Pelc (1951a,b), who studied the general composition and nature of the chromosomes of *Vicia faba*. The distribution of DNA synthesized during mitotic division was first investigated through autoradiographs of C^{14}-labeled thymidine incorporated in the roots of *Crepis capillaris* (Plaut and Mazia, 1956). This work was expanded by Taylor (1958a) and by Taylor, Woods, and Hughes (1957), who used H^3-labeled thymidine. Taylor (1958b) and Wimber (1961) used autoradiographs to study other aspects of chromosome duplication. Wimber (1960) calculated the duration of the nuclear cycle on the basis of the H^3-labeled thymidine incorporated by the nuclei in the root tips of *Tradescantia paludosa*.

The relation of DNA, RNA, and protein synthesis to cell division and cell development in plants has been investigated through autoradiographic techniques, frequently in combination with microspectrophotometric analysis of the cells. Das, Patau, and Skoog (1958) and Patau and Das (1961) used this combination of methods in their study of DNA synthesis in excised tobacco pith tissue. Woodard, Rasch, and Swift (1961), in a beautifully designed investigation, used a similar set of procedures to study the course of both nucleic acid and protein metabolism during the mitotic cycle in root tips of *Vicia faba*. The synthesis of nucleic acids and proteins was studied through the autoradiography of C^{14}-labeled precursors in onion root tips by Jensen (1957) and in *Tradescantia* root tips by Sisken (1959). The relation of DNA synthesis and metabolism with respect to cell development in roots was examined by Pelc (1959), Pelc and LaCour (1959), and Jensen, Kavaljian, and Martinot (1960). In the latter work autoradiography was combined with quantitative histochemical measurement of the amount of DNA present. Clowes (1958a) used S^{35} and C^{14}-leucine to follow protein synthesis in roots.

The course of microsporogenesis in *Tradescantia* (Moses and Taylor, 1955) and in *Lilium* (Taylor and McMaster, 1954) were studied by a combination of autoradiographic and microspectrophotometric techniques. Autoradiographs were also used to study various aspects of microsporogenesis and microgametogenesis in a variety of organisms (Takats, 1959; Taylor, 1953, 1958c, 1959). Bell (1960) used H^3-labeled thymidine to trace the distribution of DNA during oögenesis in ferns.

Autoradiographs have also been employed in determining the distribution of cell divisions in roots (Clowes, 1956, 1958b, 1959; Gifford, 1960b; Jensen, Kavaljian, and Martinot, 1960) and in shoots (Clowes, 1959; Gifford, 1960a,b; Partanen and Gifford, 1958).

The site of RNA synthesis in the cells of both vascular and nonvascular plants has been studied through the use of labeled precursors and autoradiographs. Woods and Taylor (1959) grew roots of *Vicia faba* for various lengths of time in H^3-labeled cytidine and used autoradiographs to follow the appearance of the label in the different parts of the cell. Zalokar (1959, 1960) attacked a similar problem in *Neuro-spora* by using the centrifugation procedures described in Chapter 8. Zalokar used H^3-labeled leucine and H^3-labeled uridine to follow both RNA and protein production. The synthesis of RNA and protein in *Acetabularia* has been studied by means of autoradiographs by Olszewska and Brachet (1961) and Olszewska, DeVitry, and Brachet (1961).

Although investigators concerned with nucleic acid and protein metabolism have made the greatest use of autoradiography, several other groups of workers have made extensive use of this technique. One such group comprises the botanists and plant physiologists concerned with the movement of substances through the plant (Biddulph, 1956; Biddulph, Biddulph, and Cory, 1958; Gage and Aronoff, 1960; Perkins, Nelson, and Gorham, 1959; Thaine and Walters, 1955). However, the substances being translocated are water soluble, and special procedures must be developed for handling the tissue and for making the autoradiographs. These procedures will be discussed later in this chapter.

Cell wall development has also been studied through the autoradiography of labeled precursors. The formation of the primary wall has been studied by Böhner (1958), by Setterfield and Bayley (1957, 1958, 1959), and by Wardrop (1956, 1959). Lignification of the secondary wall has been investigated by Freudenberg, Reznik, Fuchs, and Reichert (1955) and Reznik (1960).

A variety of other problems have been approached through autoradiography, among which are the action of maleic hydrazide (Callaghan and Grun, 1961), the effect of X-irradiation on DNA synthesis (Das and Alfert, 1961), the localization of the products of photosynthesis (Dugger and Moreland, 1953), the protein uptake of plant cells (Jensen and McLaren, 1960; McLaren, Jensen, and Jacobson, 1960), the effect of kinetin on roots (Olszewska, 1959), the presence of DNA in chloroplasts (Stocking and Gifford, 1959), and the localization of crown gall bacteria in stem tissue (Stonier, 1956).

For more complete reviews of the literature, and for an extensive discussion of the technique, see Chapman-Andresen (1959), Dugger (1957), Ficq (1959), Fitzgerald (1959), Levi (1957), Pelc (1958), Taylor (1956). A bibliography of autoradiography has also recently been published (Lima-de-Faria, 1959).

Physical Bases of Autoradiography

Before discussing the procedures of autoradiography let us briefly consider the physical bases of the method. The most widely used radioactive isotopes (H³, C¹⁴, S³⁵, and P³²) emit β particles upon disintegration. A β particle—a moving electron—ionizes the matter through which it passes. The higher the charge, and the lower the velocity, the greater will be the amount of ionization. The higher radioisotopes, such as those of uranium, emit alpha particles, which consist of two protons and two neutrons. Owing to their higher mass, α particles have a higher ionizing capacity than do β particles.

A photographic emulsion contains many silver bromide crystals, which are slightly imperfect (Fitzgerald, 1959). These imperfections, termed electron traps, accumulate electrons freed from the crystal lattice by an ionizing particle. This concentration of negative charges attracts free silver ions, which are also present in the crystal. These are neutralized by the electrons, with the formation of metallic silver. This silver then acts as a locus for the growth of nuclei of metallic silver and is termed the latent image.

After the latent image has been formed, the emulsion is treated with a developer which provides additional electrons that reduce the silver bromide grains containing latent images. Silver bromide grains lacking latent images are reduced so slowly that few are reduced by the time all of those containing latent images are developed. Finally, fixative solutions containing sodium thiosulfate (hypo) are used to dissolve the silver bromide crystals, removing them from the emulsion while leaving the silver grains in place.

The number of silver grains produced by the passage of a β particle through an emulsion is determined by the velocity of the particle, the thickness of the emulsion, and the size and number of the silver bromide crystals in the emulsion.

All the isotopes of principal interest to the histochemist are beta emitters. Beta particles have varying energies. The amount of ionization they cause and the distance they penetrate the emulsion is in inverse ratio to the amount of energy they have. The half lives and energies of five common beta-emitting isotopes are shown below.

Isotope	Half life	Energy (Mev)
H³	31 years	0.013
C¹⁴	5840 years	0.155
S³⁵	88 days	0.167
Ca⁴⁵	152 days	0.255
P³²	14.5 days	1.718

On the basis of this information one would expect the beta from tritium, H³, to have a very short path in the emulsion and, because of this, to

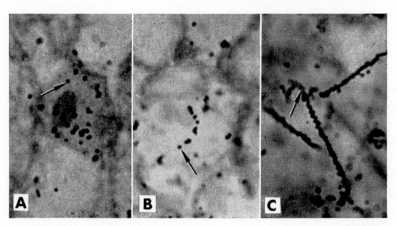

Figure 16-1. *Differences in tracks produced by (A) low-energy beta particle from H³, (B) medium-energy beta particle from C¹⁴, and (C) an alpha particle from U²³⁵. The emulsion is Ilford G-5. The arrows indicate the beginning of the track (1000×).*

yield few silver grains. The beta from carbon, C^{14}, would be expected to travel farther and to produce a larger number (a few to a dozen or so) of silver grains than tritium. The beta from phosphorus, P^{32}, on the contrary, has a very long path and produces few grains as a result of its rapid passage through the emulsion.

A few radioisotopes which emit alpha particles may be used in making autoradiographs. The increased mass of the alpha particle results in the formation of a dense, thick, relatively short track of silver grains. The difference in the types of tracks produced by a low energy beta from H^3, a medium energy beta from C^{14}, and an alpha from uranium can be seen in Fig. 16-1.

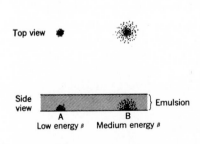

Figure 16-2
Effect of particle energy on resolution of site. Source A is a low energy beta emitter, source B is a medium energy emitter.

Factors Affecting Resolution

The energy of the particle emitted has a significant relation to the resolution which can be achieved by the autoradiograph. This can be shown by placing two point sources on a slide and covering them with an emulsion (Fig. 16-2). Source A is a low-energy beta emitter; source B is a medium-energy beta emitter. The halo of silver grains which forms over the source as a result of the emitted beta particles causes the source to lose distinctness. The higher the energy of the beta particle, the farther it will penetrate the emulsion and the larger will be the halo formed. The larger the halo, the more diffuse the source appears and the poorer the resolution which can be achieved.

How this difference in the energy of the particle influences the resolution of detail in biological material is shown in Fig. 16-3. This figure shows an alga (Fig. 16-3a), *Scenedesmus* (Chapman-Andresen, 1953) labeled with C^{14} (Fig. 16-3b) and with H^3 (Fig. 16-3c). Only the general shape of the alga is visible in the C^{14} autoradiograph. In the H^3 autoradiograph the exact form of the alga is visible, including the horns of the end cells, which are about 1 μ in diameter. With P^{32} the resolution would be much less than with C^{14}. Thus, other factors being equal, tritium yields high-resolution autoradiographs, C^{14}, medium-resolution autoradiographs, and P^{32}, poor-resolution autoradiographs.

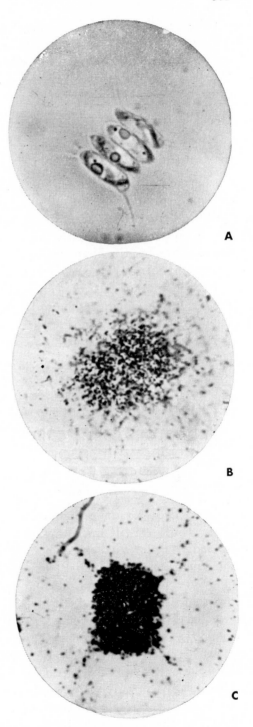

Figure 16-3. *Influence of the energy of beta particle on the resolution of detail in biological matter. A.* Scenedesmus, *unlabeled. B. Alga labeled with* C^{14}. *C. Alga labeled with* H^3 *(Kodak stripping film ARIO; 900×). [Courtesy of Dr. C. Chapman-Andresen.]*

Other factors, however, affect the resolution of autoradiographs, modifying these general conclusions in specific cases. Many of these factors are determined by the nature of the emulsion. The size, number, and uniformity of the crystals present in the emulsion are of great importance. The greater the number of crystals present, the greater the possibility of a beta particle ionizing a crystal close to the site of the emission, thus yielding a precise image of the site. The fewer the silver halide crystals, the coarser the image of the site. The size of the crystal also influences the sensitivity of the emulsion. The larger the crystals, the greater the possibility of a hit by a beta particle; hence the sensitivity of the emulsion, in terms of length of exposure required, is higher than in the fine-grained emulsions. However, the final size of the silver crystal may be so great as to obscure the site. Therefore, for highest resolution autoradiography, the finest grain size, 0.2–0.3 μ, is used, although at the expense of exposure time.

The thickness of both the emulsion and the tissue section is important in obtaining maximum resolution. The thicker the emulsion, the greater will be the halo and the more distinct the site. The thickness of the tissue section influences the amount of scatter of the particles, tending to decrease the resolution. The problem of self absorption by the tissue of the beta particles is also an important one, particularly with the low energy beta particles such as those emitted by H^3. Finally, the degree of contact between the tissue and the emulsion is a factor in determining resolution. The closer the contact between the tissue and emulsion, the higher will be the resolution.

Stripping-film Autoradiography

Now, let us examine these general considerations of resolution in terms of the actual procedures. The two most important autoradiographic procedures are the stripping-film and the liquid-emulsion methods. There are a host of other methods, covered in detail by Boyd (1955) and Fitzgerald (1959), but these are the two that are assuming increasing importance in histochemistry.

In the stripping-film method (Doniach and Pelc, 1950) the photographic emulsion is stripped from a glass plate and placed over the tissue on a slide. After a suitable exposure, ranging from a few hours to many days, the emulsion is developed by standard photographic procedures. The site of radioactivity is seen by the placement of the silver grains.

For maximum resolution with the stripping film method the emulsion should be thin. The silver halide crystals should be small, uniform in size, and large in number. The tissue section should be thin and in close contact with the emulsion. The Kodak autoradiographic film (AR.10), with an emulsion thickness of 5μ and a grain size of $0.2-0.3$ μ, offers resolution possibilities of 1μ or less for tritium (H^3), $1-2$ μ for C^{14} and S^{35}, and $2-3$ μ for P^{32} (Pelc, 1958). In normal practice the resolution obtained is less, usually $2-4$ μ with C^{14}, and more than 5μ with P^{32}.

Recently, Kodak developed a new autoradiographic emulsion (V 1042) for strip-film autoradiography which has an emulsion thickness of only $2-3$ μ. By the time the emulsion is on the slide over the tissue the thickness of the emulsion is much closer to 1.5 μ. This means increased resolution, particularly for C^{14}. With this emulsion, resolution for C^{14} is close to that of H^3.

There is one factor which affects the resolution and effectiveness of the stripping-film method—the presence of silver grains that have been exposed by agents other than the isotope in the tissue. These grains, called background, obscure the results of the autoradiograph when too numerous. The sources of background are many. Sliding pressure on the photographic plates as well as scratches and shocks will cause background. High temperatures, cosmic rays, static electricity, and stray light may also contribute. Various chemical agents, normally present in the tissue as reagents in stains used on the tissue before the autoradiographic procedure or as fumes from paints, woods, atmosphere, and so on, will also cause background. An important point to remember is that the background accumulates in the emulsion from the time it is made until it is used. Thus, great care should be used in handling and storing the plates. They should be placed in light-tight, water-tight, shielded containers and stored at $4°C$.

The stripping-film method has been used in numerous botanical investigations. The work of Howard and Pelc (1951a,b), Plaut and Mazia (1956), Taylor (1953; 1958a,b,c; 1959), Das, Patau, and Skoog (1958), Patau and Das (1961), and Woodard, Rasch, and Swift (1961) on nucleic acid metabolism and cell division and development in plants was accomplished through stripping-film autoradiographs. This method was also used in the study of mitotic distribution in root and stem tips by Clowes (1956, 1958b, 1959), Gifford (1960a,b), and Partanen and Gifford (1958). The cell wall investigations of Setterfield and Bayley (1957, 1958, 1959) were also based on this type of autoradiography.

The difference in energy of the beta particles of H^3 and C^{14} was used by Krause and Plaut (1960) and by Baserga (1961) as the basis for a stripping-film method in which the two isotopes can be distinguished. In this procedure the tissue is covered with two layers of emulsion separated by a thin plastic film. The H^3 beta particles expose silver particles only in the first layer of emulsion whereas the C^{14} beta particles expose silver grains in both. This procedure is an ingenious method for separating the site of compounds labeled with different isotopes in the same cell. The major difficulty with the procedure is the loss of resolution when C^{14} is used—a result of the distance separating the second layer of emulsion from the tissue.

Liquid-emulsion Autoradiography

In the liquid-emulsion procedure (Ficq, 1959) pieces of solid photographic emulsion are dissolved in water and poured over the tissue on a slide. The emulsion is allowed to dry and is exposed, again for a matter of days, to the ionizing radiation emitted from the radioactive element incorporated in the tissue. After development the site of the radioactive material is determined by the arrangement of the silver grains over the tissue.

With the liquid-emulsion procedure the problems involved in obtaining maximum resolution are different because the method of localizing the site is different. In this method the track of silver grains produced by the beta particle is used to indicate the site. In the stripping-film method the emulsion is made as thin as possible such that only a few grains are produced per beta particle, thus defining the site by producing an image of it in silver grains. In the liquid-emulsion method the emulsion is made 30–50 μ thick in order that the track will be visible under the microscope (Ficq, 1959). The site is then determined by following the track back to its source. The beginning of the track made by C^{14} and similar energy beta particles can be determined by the spacing of the silver grains: at the beginning of the track the grains are widely spaced because the energy of the particle is higher; the grains become closely spaced as the energy decreases (Fig. 16-1B). With alpha particles the track is so dense, and both ends are so similar, that spacing cannot be relied upon (Fig. 16-1C). However, it is usually very easy to determine which end of an alpha particle track is in focus with the tissue and which is not. Tritium (H^3) is a special case in the liquid-emulsion method because the energy of the beta particle is so small that the track is only one or two grains long (Fig. 16-1A). This means that for H^3 the results for the two methods are the same.

Because of this difference of track length and character, the liquid-emulsion procedure can be used to study the distribution of H^3- and C^{14}-labeled substances in the same cell (Fig. 16-4). This figure shows a nucleus that has been labeled with both H^3 and C^{14}. A side view of the site and the tracks (a) shows the difference between the two types. When viewed through a microscope the H^3 tracks and the beginnings of the

C^{14} tracks are in focus with the tissue (b). As the plane of focus is raised, the H^3 tracks are detected. The actual appearance of the tracks is shown in Fig. 16-5. The tissue shown was given H^3-labeled thymidine and C^{14}-labeled uridine. The resolution is as high as if the isotopes were used singly.

Many of the factors defining resolution in the liquid-emulsion procedure are the same as in the stripping film method. The size and number of the crystals are equally important and are essentially the same in the two types of procedures. The thickness of the section is also important, as is the closeness of contact between the emulsion and the tissue. The contact is particularly good in the liquid-emulsion method, since the emulsion actually flows into the cut cells and, to a limited degree, embeds the upper portion of the section.

Background in the form of tracks which can be confused with or added to the tracks resulting from the isotopes such

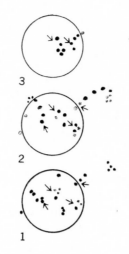

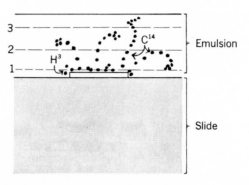

Figure 16-4
Diagram of an autoradiograph of a cell labeled with both C^{14} and H^3. The numbers of the broken lines in the lower figure correspond to the numbers of the three circles above. The circles represent levels of focus as viewed with the microscope.

as C^{14} is very low in this method. There is essentially no accumulated background because only tracks produced after the emulsion has dried on the slide appear at all. There are frequently, however, a varying number of scattered silver grains that may confuse the picture when too numerous. These may appear if the emulsion is old, if the emulsion has been subjected to high temperatures, or if the light in the darkroom is too bright. Chemicals present in the tissue, or fumes present in the air will cause silver to deposit. These silver grains are usually not important if the beta particles give distinct tracks, as do those emitted by C^{14}, but may become important if H^3 is used, since the tracks produced by H^3 are quite short.

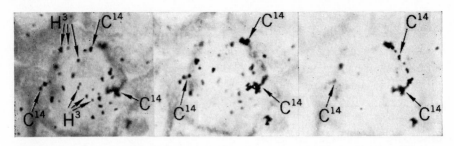

Figure 16-5. *Tissue containing C14-labeled uridine and H3-labeled thymidine. The three photographs correspond to the three levels indicated in Fig. 16-4.*

The resolution which can be obtained using the liquid-emulsion procedure is essentially the same as that obtained in the stripping-film method —1 μ or less for tritium; 1–2 μ for C^{14} under optimum conditions but 2–4 μ under most conditions. Phosphorus can be used only under special conditions in which many tracks originate from the same site (see Levinthal and Thomas, 1957).

Both Kodak and Ilford make emulsions suitable for use in the liquid-emulsion methods. The Kodak emulsion most commonly used is Kodak NTB nuclear track liquid emulsion. The standard Ilford emulsion is G-5 in gel form. Ilford, however, has recently developed a series of emulsions with varying sensitivity and grain size. The grain size of G-5 is approximately 0.27 μ, whereas for the new K-5 it is 0.20 μ, and for L-5, 0.15 μ. The K-5 is the most sensitive and is recommended for general use. Ilford emulsions are available from Ilford, Ltd., Ilford, England.

The liquid-emulsion procedure, although not as widely used as the stripping-film method, has been employed in a considerable number of investigations involving plant tissue. Zalokar (1959, 1960) used it in his studies on protein and nucleic acid synthesis in *Neurospora*. The synthesis of protein and nucleic acids in *Acetabularia* (Olszewska and Brachet, 1961; Olszewska, DeVitry, and Brachet, 1961) and root tips (Jensen, 1957; Jensen, Kavaljian, and Martinot, 1960) was approached by this technique. A slightly different liquid-emulsion procedure was used by Wimber (1959, 1960, 1961) in his studies on chromosome reduplication in *Tradescantia paludosa*.

An adaptation of the liquid-emulsion procedure which will probably assume considerable importance in the future consists in the use of this method on the level of the electron microscope (Pelc, Coombes, and Budd, 1961; Przybylski, 1961). This is a logical development of the procedure, and should find wide application in research with plant tissue.

Comparison of Methods

Although the basic difference between stripping-film and liquid-emulsion autoradiography has been made by an emphasis on the types of image obtained in the final preparation, it must be pointed out that this difference holds only for the two methods given here. Tracks can also be obtained with thick stripping film. Similarly, if the emulsion is diluted and the slides drained, a thin emulsion will be obtained that will give essentially the same results as are obtained with the stripping film. There are many ways of making autoradiographs; the ones given here are presented because they appear to be the most versatile and the easiest to master.

Both the stripping-film and the liquid-emulsion procedure offer certain advantages and disadvantages. On the whole these tend to balance one another, and the choice of technique becomes a personal rather than a scientific matter. The question of background in the stripping film is balanced by the instability of the liquid emulsion. The slight difference in sensitivity in favor of the liquid-emulsion method is balanced by the need to interpret tracks. Resolution is essentially the same for both methods, particularly if tritium is used. Some workers find the stripping-film method easier than the liquid-emulsion procedure, yet others find the reverse to be true.

Autoradiography of Soluble Materials

The problem of dealing with highly soluble substances is one frequently met in the autoradiography of plant tissues. Studies in the absorption (Branton, 1961) and translocation (Biddulph, 1956; Gage and Aronoff, 1960; Perkins, Nelson, and Gorham, 1959) of substances by plants usually require methods which permit the precise localization of soluble materials.

There are actually two phases to this problem. One is the retention of the material in the tissue during fixation and dehydration. This part of the problem will be treated shortly in the general discussion of tissue preparation for autoradiography. It is sufficient at present to say that freeze-drying usually offers a satisfactory solution to this phase of the problem. The second phase of the problem involves preventing movement of the soluble materials when making the autoradiographs. In both methods the tissue is subject to a period in an aqueous solution. In the liquid-emulsion method this occurs during the application of the emulsion, and continues until the emulsion hardens. In the stripping-film method, this occurs during the application of the film. Various procedures have been devised to eliminate this contact with an aqueous phase. Two of the most useful of these are given in the Procedures section.

In the first of these procedures, the section is first deparaffinized and the tissue is then covered by a thin nylon film. This film is sealed to the slide, and the emulsion is applied in the same manner as in the stripping-film method, the film preventing contact of the tissue with water. After the exposure period, the emulsion is stripped from the slide and developed. The developed emulsion is finally mounted on a separate slide. The nylon film is removed from the slide, and the tissue is stained. The tissue may actually be treated in a number of ways; for example, it may be extracted with a solvent and a second autoradiograph made.

This procedure has two major drawbacks: (1) the autoradiograph and the tissue are separated, and (2) it is a reasonably difficult procedure to master. The results of the Andresens at the Carlsberg Laboratory are impressive (Andresen, Chapman-Andresen, Holter, and Robinson, 1953; Chapman-Andresen and Holter, 1955) and demonstrate some of the potentials of the procedure.

In the second procedure, devised by Branton (1961), the tissue section, with the paraffin present, is pressed onto the emulsion. After the exposure period, the sections are coated with cellulose acetate, the paraffin is removed, and the emulsion is developed. The results from this procedure are quite remarkable (Fig. 16-6). By using freeze-dried tissue, highly soluble substances can be easily localized by this method. For other similar methods see Gage and Aronoff (1960), Perkins, Nelson, and Gorham (1959) and Thaine and Walters (1955).

Quantitative Autoradiography

There is, finally, the question of quantitative autoradiography. A good deal of careful work has been done on this question but many problems remain unsolved in quantitative histochemistry (Levi, 1957). In autoradiographs obtained by the liquid-emulsion method, some counting is usually necessary. The difference in the number of tracks from two sites is not always immediately recognized, and counts must be made. An example is the distribution of C^{14}-labeled adenine in the cell; counts are necessary to distinguish between the relative activity of the cytoplasm, nucleus, and nucleolus (Jensen, 1957). In fact, with the liquid-emulsion technique, one frequently ends up with a graph rather than with a picture. The data in most cases, however, are quantitative in a relative rather than in an absolute sense, although precise quan-

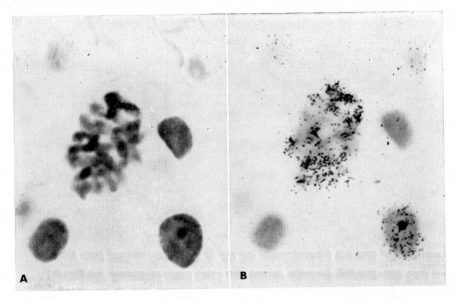

Figure 16-6. *Tissue labeled with H³-labeled thymidine; autoradiographs made by the dry-tissue, press-on method. A. Focus on the nuclei and chromosomes. B. Focus on the silver grains. Preparation stained with Delafield haematoxylin (1000×).* [*Courtesy Dr. D. Branton.*]

titative studies can be made with the liquid-emulsion technique if enough care is used (Levi, 1957).

The use of stripping-film autoradiographs in quantitative studies involves counting individual silver grains. This may be done manually (Andresen, Chapman-Andresen, and Holter, 1952) or by various machines (Dudley and Pelc, 1953; Gulberg, 1957; Mazia, Plaut, and Ellis, 1955; Rogers, 1961). Although direct counting is laborious, it is probably easier and better for most laboratories not completely devoted to autoradiography. Numerous studies (Levi, 1957; Pelc, 1957) have shown that the number of grains is proportional to the exposure. Thus, comparative studies can be made with little difficulty. Few studies, however, have been carried to the point of relating the number of grains to the actual amount of radioactivity present. A model for this type of work is the paper of Andresen, Chapman-Andresen, Holter, and Robinson (1953) on quantitative autoradiographic studies of the amoeba.

The use of autoradiographs for quantitative studies on both an absolute and relative basis will undoubtedly become increasingly common. There is, in fact, a great need for quantitative studies, since the interpretation of autoradiographs is not always as simple as it may first appear.

The use of autoradiography in conjunction with other procedures should become more frequent, particularly as the application of autoradiography is so great.

Amount of Activity Required

With any method of autoradiography there exists the problem of determining the amount of radioisotope to use and the length of exposure necessary. These two factors are directly related: the higher the amount of activity present, the shorter the exposure; the lower the amount of activity present, the longer the exposure. There is no simple answer to the question of how much activity to use. The amount taken up by the tissue and the distribution of the isotope in the tissue are important factors. Various attempts have been made to evolve formulas which will provide the answer as to the amount of activity to use given a desired grain density and a desired exposure time (Fitzgerald, 1959). These have not proved completely satisfactory and are not in general use.

In the case of stripping film, the problem is to accumulate enough silver grains such that the distribution of the active material is clear. The number of grains resulting from the isotope must be substantially higher than the background, and the background should always be as low as possible. The conditions and factors involved in different experiments vary so greatly, however, that a rigid set of standards is difficult, if not impossible to establish.

When using C^{14} and similar isotopes with the liquid-emulsion method, the major problem is to produce enough tracks to demonstrate the location of the isotope but not so many that their interpretation becomes impossible. The liquid-emulsion method can localize smaller amounts of radioactive material than can the stripping-film method and usually requires shorter exposure times. These factors must all be taken into account when determining the concentration of the isotope and the exposure time. For H^3 the problem is similar to that of the stripping-film method.

In actual practice, with both methods, the most common approach consists in trying 3 or 4 different concentrations and several exposure times on the same tissue and then determining from the results the proper concentration and exposure. In general, $1-50 \mu$ C/ml of tritium and $0.1-2 \mu$ C/ml of C^{14} is found to be a useful range in work with many plant parts. The amount of activity and exposure is generally lower for liquid-emulsion than for stripping-film autoradiographs. Exposure times for liquid-emulsion autoradiographs are frequently 1–4 days whereas for stripping-film autoradiographs exposures normally run 1–30 days or longer.

In general, it would seem best to use the lowest amount of radio-activity possible. The effect that radiation of the isotope has on the experiment appears to be most critical in investigations of nucleic acid metabolism (Plaut, 1959). Some evidence indicates that H^3-labeled thymidine is incorporated at a different rate than C^{14}-labeled thymidine (Krause and Plaut, 1960). At higher concentration H^3-labeled thymidine appears to cause some chromosomal aberrations (Plaut, 1959), yet the general conclusion from the data thus far collected (Natarajan, 1961; Taylor, 1958b, 1959; Wimber, 1959; Wimber, Quastler, Stein, and Wimber, 1960) appears to be that, at lower concentrations of H^3-labeled thymidine, no significant effect on chromosome duplication is found. However, the possibility of experimental difficulty from this source must be considered, although for most experiments it appears small.

Preparation and Staining of the Tissue

The preparation of the tissue for autoradiography must be considered with some care. The method used in handling the tissue will depend largely on the purpose of the experiment and on the type of data required. The extent to which the method of preparation will change the results obtained can be seen in Fig. 16-7. The pea roots shown in this figure were given Fe^{59}. One set was fixed with the standard fixative, 4% neutral formalin, and was dehydrated through an alcohol series and paraffin infiltrated. The second set was freeze-dried. Autoradiographs were made by a modified stripping-film method. The photograph on the left shows the chemically fixed material; the one on the right shows the freeze-dried material. Clearly the method of preparation has had a marked effect on the localization obtained, and it would seem fair to say that the freeze-dried tissue probably represents the correct picture.

For the localization of highly soluble materials, freeze-drying is the only completely acceptable method. This conclusion was reached by Biddulph (1956), by Biddulph, Biddulph, and Cory (1958), and by Gage and Aronoff (1960) in their work on translocation in plants. Similar conclusions were drawn by McIlrath (1950), in his attempts to localize soluble P^{32}, and Branton (1961), in his studies of iron distribution. Freeze-dried tissue should also be useful in the study of other botanical problems, such as ion absorption and movement. The work of Branton (1961) is an example of this type of approach to this classical problem.

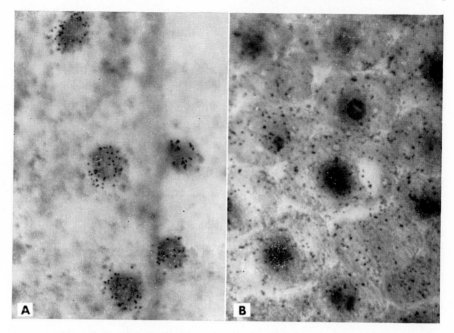

Figure 16-7. *Effect of procedure on the results obtained from autoradiography. A. Cells of barley root grown in Fe^{59}, fixed in neutral formalin, and autoradiograph made using the stripping-film procedure. B. Cells of barley root grown in Fe^{59}, freeze-dried, and autoradiograph made by the dry-tissue, press-on method.* [*Courtesy Dr. D. Branton.*]

Freeze-substitution can be used to great advantage in preparing tissue for autoradiography when the substance to be localized is not removed by lipid solvents. Zalokar (1960) used freeze-substituted material in his studies on nucleic acid investigations in *Neurospora*. A variety of anthers were freeze-substituted by Takats (1959), in his study of DNA transfer during microsporogenesis. Freeze-substituted material appears useful in investigations involving a relatively wide variety of cell constituents.

Most autoradiographs, however, particularly those dealing with DNA, have been made using chemically fixed tissue, the fixative of choice being a 1:3 mixture of acetic acid and alcohol. This fixative has been used, for example, on ferns (Bell, 1960), on tobacco pith tissue growing in culture (Das, Patau, and Skoog, 1958), on *Tradescantia* anthers (Moses and Taylor, 1955), on *Acetabularia* (Olszewska and Brachet, 1961), and on root tips of *Vicia faba* (Natarajan, 1961). A few other fixatives have also been employed. For example, Gifford (1960) fixed stem tips in formalin-propionic acid-alcohol, and Setterfield and Bayley

(1957, 1958, 1959), in their cell wall studies, used 70% ethyl alcohol. Fixatives containing chromium, permanganate, or osmium cannot be used.

Sections or squash preparations may be used for autoradiographs. Slides of either preparation must be treated with an adhesive which not only holds the tissue to the slide but holds the emulsions as well. This is necessary for all types of autoradiographs. The gelatin-chrome alum adhesive given in Chapter 9 (p. 199) is highly recommended. Egg albumin can also be used, but Haupt's adhesive cannot.

When mounting sections on the slides a minimum of water should be used to prevent possible distortion. Water can be avoided altogether if sections are pressed on the slides with a piece of Teflon plastic. For squashes, the methods described in Chapter 4 are applicable.

There are three ways to observe the tissue in an autoradiograph, namely: (1) by leaving the tissue unstained and observing it with phase contrast, (2) by staining the tissue before the autoradiograph is made, and (3) by staining the tissue after the autoradiograph has been made.

The first method is the simplest if a phase contrast microscope is available. This method was used by Setterfield and Bayley (1957, 1958, 1959) in their studies on the cell wall, by Woods and Taylor (1959) in following the incorporation of RNA precursors, and by Howard and Pelc (1951a) in their work with chromosomal incorporation of S^{35}. Excellent results can be obtained by this method, and it is possible to combine phase microscopy with dark field illumination to make the silver grains appear as bright spots against the tissue (Branton, 1961).

The second method, that of staining the tissue before the autoradiograph has been made, has proved most successful with Feulgen stained nuclei and chromosomes. Savage and Plaut (1958) have demonstrated in a careful study that no labeled thymidine is lost in the hydrolysis of DNA in the Feulgen reaction if the standard conditions are employed. Feulgen-stained squashes were used by Taylor (1958a,b,c), by Das, Patau, and Skoog (1958), and by Wimber (1959, 1961), whereas Feulgen-stained sections were used by Woodard, Rasch, and Swift (1961). The dye usually fades somewhat during developing, particularly in the liquid-emulsion method. Most stains cannot be used before the autoradiographs are made, either because the color fades during developing or because the dye affects the emulsion.

The third method which involves staining the tissue after the autoradiograph is made is the most difficult but the most frequently used. Here the problem is to stain the tissue without staining the emulsion so deeply that the tissue cannot be seen. Obviously the problem is greater in liquid-emulsion autoradiographs, in which the emulsion is fairly thick. Unna's pyronin-methyl green stain, described in Chapter 11, is a suitable combination. With this stain 70% alcohol is used to clear the emulsion and to differentiate the tissue. Unna's stain has been used with autoradiographs of *Acetabularia* (Olszewska and Brachet, 1961) and root tips (Jensen, 1957; Olszewska, 1959). Azure B is another nucleic acid stain which can be used with autoradiographs, although it is recommended for use only with liquid-emulsion autoradiographs because the acid pH at which the dye is most effective tends to dissolve the emulsion. This is not a problem with the thick liquid-emulsion autoradiographs, but it can be a problem with stripping-film autoradiographs. Azure B was used with autoradiographs of onion root tips by Jensen, Kavaljian, and Martinot (1960). Erlich's acid haematoxylin is a good stain for both types of autoradiographs (Fitzgerald, 1959). No cell wall stain has been found which yields satisfactory results with autoradiographs.

The Future of Autoradiography

Of all the techniques discussed in this book, autoradiography has perhaps the greatest application. A minimum of equipment is necessary to obtain excellent autoradiographs, and the standard procedures are not difficult. Thus, in the future there should be an increase in the use of autoradiography in botanical research, with a marked trend toward quantitative studies.

Procedures

1. Liquid-Emulsion Method (FICQ, 1959)

A. Use freeze-dried, freeze-substituted, or chemically fixed tissue. The chemical fixative recommended is acetic acid-alcohol (1:3); avoid the use of fixatives containing chromium, permanganate, and osmium.

B. Section at less than 5 μ if the tissue contains H^3, and at 5–10 μ if the tissue contains C^{14}. Tissue may also be Feulgen-stained and squashed.

C. Mount the sections on slides that have been coated with gelatin-chrome alum adhesive (Chapter 9, page 199).

D. Remove the paraffin with xylene or toluene. Rinse in absolute alcohol, and air-dry.

E. Fill a large beaker (1000 ml) with water at 50°C. Prepare two small beakers (25 ml). In one, place an amount of distilled water equal to approximately $\frac{1}{3}$ the amount of emulsion to be used; over the top of the other, place two layers of fine cheesecloth, and secure with a rubber band (Fig. 16-8). Carry all three beakers, a glass rod, and one or two Kleenex tissues (or similar tissue) into the darkroom.

F. Keep the emulsion (K_5 or G_5-Ilford in gel form) at approximately 4°C. The life of this emulsion is not more than 2–3 months. Allow the emulsion to come to room temperature. In the darkroom (use a Wratten safelight lamp series 1 to illuminate the darkroom), open the container and use the glass rod to push the pieces of emulsion into the small beaker of water. Then, holding the bottom of the small beaker in the warm water of the larger beaker, stir the emulsion and water with the glass rod until the emulsion is completely dissolved. The emulsion should have the consistency of rich cream.

G. Next, pour the emulsion through the cheesecloth covering the second small beaker. This is done to remove air bubbles stirred into the emulsion. Remove the cheesecloth from the beaker now containing the emulsion, and wipe the glass rod with a Kleenex.

H. Hold slide horizontally, and pour the emulsion on the center of the slide. An amount roughly the size of a dime (20 mm. diameter) will give the proper thickness in the finished slide. Carefully and quickly

Figure 16-8. *Liquid emulsion procedure.*

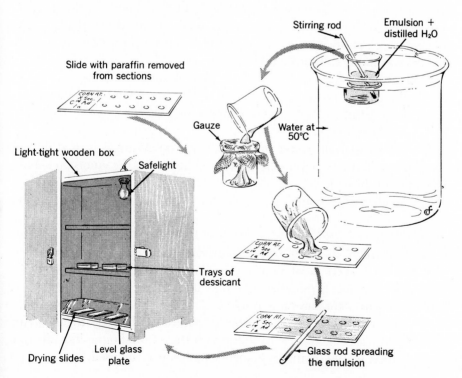

spread the emulsion with the glass rod, taking care to avoid rubbing the tissue.

I. Lay the slide on a glass plate in a box roughly $2 \times 2 \times 2$ ft fitted with a light-tight door and with trays containing calcium chloride. Care must be taken to prevent the emulsion from getting between the slide and the glass plate, or it will be difficult to remove the slide from the plate. Only when the emulsion has dried (3–5 hours) will it reach full sensitivity.

J. Leave the slides with the dried emulsion on the glass plate, or store them in light-tight, brown plastic boxes.

K. After the proper exposure time—determined by the amount of activity present but usually 2–4 days—develop the emulsion in a solution composed of 1.125 gm of amidol (diaminophenol), 4.5 gm of anhydrous sodium sulfite, 2 ml of 10% solution of KBr, and 250 ml of water. Develop in the dark at 14°C or less for 20 minutes.

L. An optional stop bath of 1% acetic acid may be used.

M. Fix in sodium thiosulfate (hypo) at $\frac{1}{3}$ saturation for 30–45 minutes or until the emulsion is clear. Use the hypo solution at 14°C.

N. Wash in running water or in many changes of water for at least 1 hour. It is very important to maintain a low temperature (absolutely not more than 14°C) during the washing period, since the thick emulsion slows diffusion of the chemicals used in the developing; if the temperature is allowed to raise, bubbling will occur in the emulsion over the tissue, ruining the autoradiograph.

O. Place the slides in 70% ethyl alcohol for 30 minutes. This expands the gelatin in the emulsion and aids in the staining of the tissue.

P. Stain with methyl green-pyronin or with Azure B for 5–30 minutes, depending on the tissue.

Q. Differentiate in water or 70% alcohol. If Azure B is used do not use TBA as in the usual method. With either stain, the emulsion should lose most of the dye.

R. Air-dry, and mount the cover slips with any permanent medium.

II. Stripping-film Method (DONIACH AND PELC, 1950)

A. Use freeze-dried or freeze-substituted material. If chemical fixatives are used, acetic acid-alcohol (1:3) is recommended; fixatives containing heavy metals should be avoided. FAA is a reasonably good chemical fixative for autoradiography.

B. Section at 5–10 μ for C^{14}-labeled material and at less than 5 μ for H^3-labeled material, and fix to slides with the autoradiographic adhesive described on p. 199. Feulgen-stained squashes may be used.

C. Deparaffinize, and hydrate to water. Keep in water until covered with emulsion.

D. Use Kodak autoradiographic stripping film, either AR 10 or V 1042. This film consists of a glass plate, a layer of gelatin, and a layer of emulsion (Fig. 16-9). The emulsion is 4 μ thick and has a grain size of 0.2 μ. Store the film in a refrigerator in heavy metal or lead container.

E. In a darkroom illuminated by a very dim red light, use a razor blade to cut out an area of emulsion about $1\frac{1}{2}$ in. square. Avoid using the film near the edge of the plate. Slip the razor blade under a corner of the square, and pull upward slowly. This may be difficult if the humidity is high, but can be corrected by placing the plate in a desiccator for 10 minutes. Handle the film with extreme care during this process, since stretching will cause the formation of latent images.

F. Invert the stripped film, and float the film emulsion-side down on distilled water at 21–24°C. To insure that the water is dust-free, filter it through a hard grade of filter paper. Allow the film to remain on the water a few minutes.

G. Slip a slide, tissue upward, into the water below the floating film, and lift the film out on top of the section.

H. Dry by placing in front of an electric hair drier without heat. Wrap several layers of lens paper over the nozzle of the drier to prevent dust from blowing on the moist film. Care must also be taken to prevent sparks from the drier from exposing the emulsion. This can be accomplished by placing the

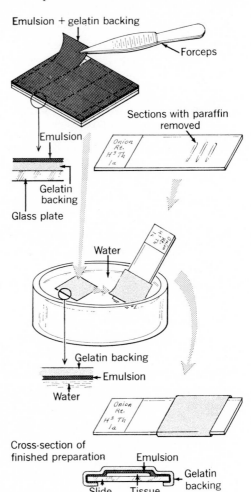

Figure 16-9
Preparation of stripping-film autoradiographs.

drier, except for the nozzle, in a bag of black, closely woven cloth.

I. Expose at 4°C in a brown plastic slide box wrapped in black paper. Desiccant may be placed in the box, or the box may be stored in a desiccator placed in a refrigerator.

J. For developing, use Kodak D-19B or D-19 developer, diluted 1:2 with distilled water. Filter through fine filter paper before using.

K. Develop for 5 minutes at 18°C.

L. Place directly in Kodak acid fixer at 18°C until clear.

M. Wash in running tap water for 30 minutes at about 18°C.

N. Dry at room temperature under dust-free conditions, or stain directly from washing bath.

O. Any number of stains can be used, such as haematoxylin or Unna's stain.

P. After the final dehydration, mount in balsam or in a similar permanent mounting medium.

III. Restripping Method (ANDRESEN, CHAPMAN-ANDRESEN, AND HOLTER, 1952)

A. Cut, mount, and deparaffinize as described for the stripping-film method. Place a mark of India ink on the slide to aid in the subsequent orientation of the restripped emulsion. A radioactive isotope may be placed in the ink, but usually enough remains on the emulsion such that this is unnecessary.

B. Place a nylon film over the tissue (Fig. 16-10). To make these films dissolve Dupont nylon (type FM6901) in warm amyl alcohol. Allow drops of this solution to fall on a dust-free water surface. The film should be thin enough such that light reflected from its surface forms interference patterns. Lift the film from the surface of the water with a circular wire frame, and allow it to dry in a desiccator. Cover the tissue with the film by placing the wire frame with the film on the slide such that the nylon film covers the section. Dip a fine glass rod with a smooth tip into a solution of nylon in amyl alcohol (the same solution as used to make the film), and press on the film in a circle around the sections. Before completing the circle, gently blow the nylon film against the sections. This will prevent the inclusion of air bubbles and will insure contact between the nylon film and the section. The nylon film will break away from the holder when the circle is complete. Apply additional nylon solution around the edge to make it water tight.

C. Place the stripping film over the slide and nylon film, as in the previous method, and handle the slide in the same fashion until developing.

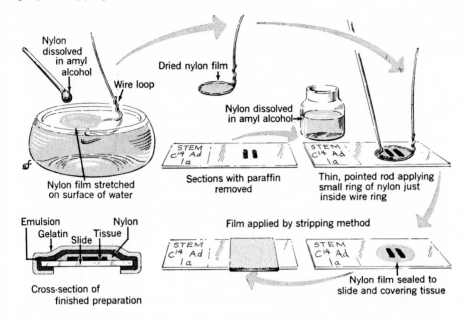

Figure 16-10. *Preparation of slides for the restripping procedure.*

D. After exposure restrip the film from the sections by cutting the emulsion at the edge of the slide and gently pulling it away from the section (Fig. 16-11). When the film is partly freed from the slide, grip it with a plastic clamp (Fig. 16-11), and separate it completely from the slide.

E. Transfer the clamp and film to the D19B developer, and develop for 5 minutes at 18°C.

F. Place in acid fixing bath for 10 minutes at 18°C.

G. Wash in distilled water for 15 minutes. Running water is not necessary, but use at least two changes.

H. After washing, free the film from the clamp and mount it emulsion-side up on a slide with a small brush.

I. After the emulsion is dry cover it with a cover slip; use balsam or some other mounting medium.

J. Carefully remove the nylon film from the tissue, and stain the tissue in any way that is desired. The tissue may also be extracted and another autoradiograph made. Since the tissue has not been in contact with the developer or hypo, it is in the same condition when the nylon film is removed as it was at the beginning of the autoradiographic procedure and can therefore be used in enzyme localization studies.

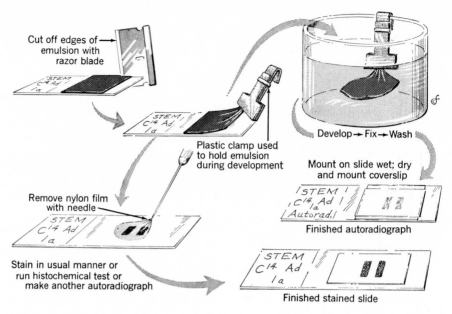

Figure 16-11. *Developing restripping autoradiographs*

IV. Dry Tissue Procedure (BRANTON, 1961)

A. Prepare the tissue, and section as for the other autoradiographic methods. Cut the ribbon into short pieces.

B. In the darkroom float the stripping film emulsion-side up on distilled water at 25 °C (Fig. 16-12). This is contrary to the other two stripping-film methods.

C. Wrap the film around a slide coated with adhesive. Use the method given in Procedure II, steps E–G (except that the emulsion side of the film is up), drain, and air-dry.

D. Carefully place paraffin sections on the surface of the emulsion, and cover with a thin sheet of Teflon plastic sheeting. (The sections may be arranged on the Teflon in the light and pressed firmly enough to it such that they will partially adhere to it; then, in the dark room the Teflon can simply be turned over, and the sections will be in place.)

E. Place the slide, tissue, and Teflon sheet in a hand press of the type used to emboss seals in paper, but with a flat surface in place of the seal. Press on the slide such that the tissue comes in close contact with the emulsion. Remove the slide from the press, and carefully take off the Teflon sheet. The tissue is pressed on the emulsion in this manner to improve the resolution. It is important that the pressure be applied straight down and that the slide not be moved when the pressure is applied. If the slide is stationary, and if the pressure is applied in this way, the background will be no higher than in ordinary stripping-film methods. A sliding or lateral movement during the period in which the pressure is applied will result in increased background.

F. Expose for the required time.

G. Coat the slides and tissue by dipping them for 30 seconds in a solution containing 0.5 g of cellulose acetate dissolved in 100 ml of 2-butanone plus 10 ml of acetone. Move the slides rapidly to a staining dish, and allow them to drain and dry in a vertical position. The staining dish should be kept covered to assure slow evaporation of the cellulose acetate solvents. Rapid evaporation may result in tissue movement, which is to be avoided.

H. After several hours remove the paraffin by placing the slides in xylene. Bring the slide to water by passing it through a graded alcohol series (98%, 95%, 70%, H₂O).

Figure 16-12. *Dry-tissue, press-on autoradiographic procedure.*

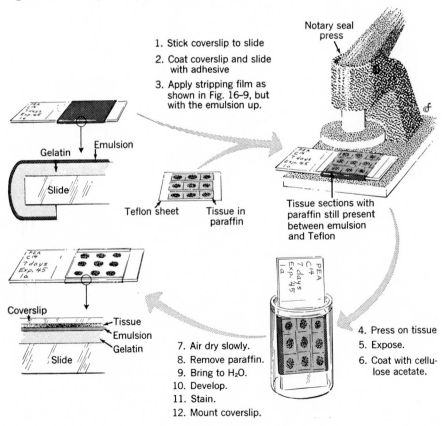

1. Stick coverslip to slide
2. Coat coverslip and slide with adhesive
3. Apply stripping film as shown in Fig. 16–9, but with the emulsion up.

Emulsion
Gelatin
Slide

Teflon sheet   Tissue in paraffin

Notary seal press

Tissue sections with paraffin still present between emulsion and Teflon

Coverslip
Tissue
Emulsion
Gelatin
Slide

4. Press on tissue
5. Expose.
6. Coat with cellulose acetate.

7. Air dry slowly.
8. Remove paraffin.
9. Bring to H₂O.
10. Develop.
11. Stain.
12. Mount coverslip.

I. Develop, and clear as in the usual stripping-film procedure, and stain without allowing the slides to dry at any time.

J. Pass the slides through a graded alcohol series to xylene, and mount the cover slips with permanent mounting medium. In this procedure the tissue is above the emulsion rather than below, as in the other methods.

LITERATURE CITED

Andresen, N., C. Chapman-Andresen, and H. Holter, 1952. Autoradiographic studies on the amoeba *Chaos chaos* with 14C. *Compt. rend. trav. lab. Carlsberg, Sèr. chim.*, **28**:189–220.

Andresen, N., C. Chapman-Andresen, H. Holter, and C. V. Robinson, 1953. Quantitative autoradiographic studies on the amoeba *Chaos chaos* with ^{14}C. *Compt. rend. trav. lab. Carlsberg, Sèr. chim.*, **28**:499–527.

Baserga, B., 1961. Two-emulsion autoradiography for the simultaneous demonstration of precursors of deoxyribonucleic and ribonucleic acid. *J. Histochem. and Cytochem.*, **9**:586.

Bell, P. R., 1960. Interaction of nucleus and cytoplasm during oögenesis in *Pteridium aquilinum* (L.) *Kuhn. Proc. Royal Soc.*, B, **153**:421–432.

Biddulph, S., 1956. Visual indications of S^{35} and P^{32} translocation in the phloem. *Am. J. Botany*, **43**:143.

Biddulph, S., O. Biddulph, and R. Cory, 1958. Visual indications of upward movement of foliar-applied P^{32} and C^{14} in the phloem of the bean stem. *Am. J. Botany*, **45**:648.

Böhner, H., 1958. Untersuchungen Über das Wachstum und den Feinbau der Zellwände in der Avena-Koleoptile. *Planta*, **50**:461–497.

Boyd, G. A., 1955. Autoradiography in biology and medicine. Academic, New York.

Branton, D., 1961. Transport and cellular localization of iron in pea plants. PhD thesis, Univ. of California, Berkeley.

Callaghan, J. J. and P. Grun, 1961. Incorporation of C^{14}-labeled maleic hydrazide into the root-tip cells of *Allium cernuum, Vicia faba,* and *Tradescantia paludosa. J. Biophys. Biochem. Cytol.*, **10**:567–575.

Chapman-Andresen, C., 1953. Autoradiographs of algae and ciliates exposed to tritiated water. *Exptl. Cell Research*, **4**:239–242.

———, 1959. Autoradiographic techniques as applied to unicellular organisms. *Pubbl. Staz. Zool. Napoli, suppl.*, **31**:100–114.

Chapman-Andresen, C. and H. Holter, 1955. Studies on the ingestion of ^{14}C glucose by pinocytosis in the amoeba *Chaos chaos. Exptl. Cell Research, suppl.*, **3**:52–63.

Clowes, F. A. L., 1956. Localization of nucleic acid synthesis in root meristems. *J. Exptl. Botany*, **21**:307–312.

———, 1958a. Protein synthesis in root meristems. *J. Exptl. Botany*, **9**:229–238.

———, 1958b. Development of quiescent centres in root meristems. *New Phytol.*, **57**:85–88.

———, 1959. Adenine incorporation and cell division in shoot apices. *New Phytol.*, **58**:16–19.

Das, N. K. and M. Alfert, 1961. Accelerated DNA synthesis in onion root meristem during X-irradiation. *Nat. Acad. Sci.*, 47:1–6.

Das, N. K., K. Patau, and F. Skoog, 1958. Autoradiographic and microspectrophotometric studies on DNA synthesis in excised tobacco pith tissue. *Chromosoma*, 9:606–617.

Doniach, J. and S. R. Pelc, 1950. Autoradiographic technique. *Brit. J. Radiol.*, 23:184–192.

Dudley, R. A. and S. R. Pelc, 1953. Automatic grain counter for assessing quantitatively high-resolution autoradiographs. *Nature*, 172:992–993.

Dugger, W. M., Jr., 1957. Autoradiography with plant tissue. *Botan. Review*, 23:351–388.

Dugger, W. M., Jr. and D. E. Moreland, 1953. An autoradiographic technique for detailed studies with plant tissues. *Plant Physiol.*, 28:143–145.

Ficq, A., 1959. Autoradiography, pp. 67–90. In *The Cell*, vol. I. Brachet, J. and A. E. Mirsky (Editors). Academic, New York.

Fitzgerald, P. J., 1959. Autoradiography in cytology, pp. 381–430. In *Analytical Cytology*, 2nd ed. R. C. Mellors (Editor). McGraw-Hill, Blakiston Division, New York.

Freudenberg, K., H. Reznik, W. Fuchs, and M. Reichert, 1955. Untersuchung über die Entstehung des Lignins und des Holzes. *Naturwiss*, 42:29–35.

Gage, R. S. and S. Aronoff, 1960. Radioautography of tritiated photosynthate arising from HTO. *Plant Physiol.*, 35:65.

Gifford, E. M., Jr., 1960a. Incorporation of H^3-thymidine into nuclei of shoot apical meristems. *Science*, 131:360.

———, Jr., 1960b. Incorporation of H^3-thymidine into shoot and root apices of *Ceratopteus thalictroides*. *Am. J. Botany*, 47:834–837.

Gullberg, J. E., 1957. A new change-over optical system and a direct recording microscope for quantitative autoradiography. *Exptl. Cell Research, suppl.*, 4:220–230.

Howard, A., and S. R. Pelc, 1951a. Nuclear incorporation of P^{32} as demonstrated by autoradiographs. *Exptl. Cell Research*, 2:178–187.

———, 1951b. Synthesis of deoxyribose nucleic acid and nuclear incorporation of S^{35} as shown by autoradiographs. In *Ciba Foundation Conference on Isotopes in Biochemistry*. G. W. Wolstenholme (Editor). Blakiston Co., Philadelphia.

Jensen, W. A., 1957. The incorporation of C^{14}-adenine and C^{14}-phenylalanine by developing root tip cell. *Proc. Nat. Acad. Sci.* (US), 43:1038–1046.

Jensen, W. A., L. G. Kavaljian, and S. Martinot, 1960. The incorporation of ^{3}H-thymidine by developing root tip cells. *Exptl. Cell Research*, 20:361–367.

Jensen, W. A. and A. D. McLaren, 1960. Uptake of proteins by plant cells—the possible occurrence of pinocytosis in plants. *Exptl. Cell Research*, 19:414–417.

Krause, M. and W. Plaut, 1960. An effect of tritiated thymidine on the incorporation of thymidine into chromosomal deoxyribonucleic acid. *Nature*, 188:511–512.

Levi, H., 1957. A discussion of recent advances towards quantitative autoradiography. *Exptl. Cell Research, suppl.*, 4:207–220.

Levinthal, C. and C. A. Thomas, 1957. Molecular autoradiography: the β-ray counting from single virus particles and DNA molecules in nuclear emulsions. *Biochim. et Biophys. Acta.*, 23:453–465.

Lima-de-Faria, A., 1959. Bibliography on autoradiography. *Hereditas*, 45:632–648.

Mazia, D., W. S. Plaut, and G. W. Ellis, 1955. A method for the quantitative assessment of autoradiographs. *Exptl. Cell Research*, 9:305–312.

McIlrath, W. J., 1950. The adaptability of several histological techniques to the preparation of P³² radioautographs from plant tissues. *Proc. Iowa Acad. Sci.*, 57:135–140.

McLaren, A. D., W. A. Jensen, and L. Jacobson, 1960. Absorption of enzymes and other proteins by barley roots. *Plant Physiol.*, 35:549–556.

Moses, M. J. and J. H. Taylor, 1955. Desoxypentose nucleic synthesis during microsporogenesis in *Tradescantia*. *Exptl. Cell Research*, 9:474–488.

Natarajan, A. T., 1961. Chromosome breakage and mitotic inhibition induced by tritiated thymidine in root meristems of *Vicia faba*. *Exptl. Cell Research*, 22:275–281.

Olszewska, M., 1959. Etude autoradiographique de l'influence de la kinétine sur l'incorporation d'adénine dans les cellules du méristème radiculaire *d'Allium cepa*. *Exptl. Cell Research*, 16:193–201.

Olszewska, M. J. and J. Brachet, 1961. Incorporation de la dl-méthionine ³⁵S dans les fragments nuclées et enuclées *d'Acetabularia mediterranea*. *Exptl. Cell. Research*, 22:370–380.

Olszewska, M., F. DeVitry, and J. Brachet, 1961. Influence d'irradiations UV localisées sur l'incorporation de l'adenine-8-¹⁴C, de l'uridine-³H et de la DL-methionine-³⁵S dans l'algue *Acetabularia mediterranea*. *Exptl. Cell Research*, 24:58–63.

Partanen, C. R. and E. M. Gifford, Jr., 1958. Application of autoradiographic techniques to studies of shoot apices. *Nature*, 182:1747–1748.

Patau, K., and N. K. Das, 1961. The relation of DNA synthesis and mitosis in tobacco pith tissue cultured *in vitro*. *Chromosoma*, 11:553–572.

Pelc, S. R., 1957. Quantitative aspects of autoradiography. *Exptl. Cell Research*, suppl., 4:231–237.

———, 1958. Autoradiography as a cytochemical method with special reference to C¹⁴ and S³⁵. *Gen. Cytochem. Methods*, 1:279–317.

———, 1959. Metabolic activity of DNA as shown by autoradiographs. *Lab. Invest.*, 8:225–233.

Pelc, S. R., J. D. Coombes, and G. C. Budd, 1961. On the adaption of autoradiographic techniques for use with the electron microscope. *Exptl. Cell Research*, 24:192–195.

Pelc, S. R. and L. F. LaCour, 1959. H³-thymidine in newly differentiated nuclei of roots of *Vicia faba*. *Experientia*, 15:131–133.

Perkins, N. J., C. D. Nelson, and P. R. Gorham, 1959. A tissue-autoradiographic study of the translocation of C¹⁴-labelled sugars in the stems of young soybean plants. *Can. J. Botany*, 37:871–877.

Plaut, W., 1959. The effect of tritium on the interpretation of autoradiographic studies on chromosomes. *Lab. Invest.*, 8:286.

Plaut, W. and D. Mazia, 1956. The distribution of newly synthesized DNA in mitotic division. *J. Biophys. Biochem. Cytol.*, 2:573–588.

Przybylski, R. J., 1961. Electron microscope autoradiography. *Exptl. Cell Research*, 24:181–184.

Reznik, H., 1960. Beiträge zu Physiologie der Verholzung. *Planta*, 54:333–364.

Rogers, A. W., 1961. A simple photometric device for the quantitation of silver grains in autoradiographs of tissue sections. *Exptl. Cell Research*, 24:228–239.

Savage, R. E. and W. Plaut, 1958. The effect of HCl hydrolysis on the retention of thymidine in DNA. *J. Biophys. Biochem. Cytol.*, 4:701–706.

Sisken, J. E., 1959. The synthesis of nucleic acids and proteins in the nuclei of *Tradescantia* root tips. *Exptl. Cell Research*, 16:602–615.

Setterfield, G. and S. T. Bayley, 1957. Studies on the mechanism of deposition and extension of primary cell wall. *Can. Jour. Botany*, 35: 435–444.

———, 1958. Deposition of wall material in thickened primary walls of elongating plant cells. *Exptl. Cell Research*, 14:622–625.

———, 1959. Deposition of cell walls in oat coleoptiles. *Can. J. Botany*, 37: 861–870.

Stocking, C. R. and E. M. Gifford, Jr., 1959. Incorporation of thymidine into chloroplasts of *Spirogyra*. *Biochem. and Biophys. Research Comm.*, 1:159–164.

Stonier, T., 1956. Radioautographic evidence for the intercellular location of crown gall bacteria. *Am. J. Botany*, 43:647–655.

Takats, S. T., 1959. Chromatin extrusion and DNA transfer during microsporogenesis. *Chromosoma*, 10:430–453.

Taylor, J. H., 1953. Autoradiographic detection of incorporation of P^{32} into chromosomes during meiosis and mitosis. *Exptl. Cell. Research*, 4:169–179.

———. 1956. Autoradiography at the cellular level, pp. 545–576. In *Physical Techniques in Biological Research*, Vol. III. Oster, G. and A. W. Pollister (Editors). Academic, New York.

———, 1958a. The mode of chromosome duplication in *Crepis capillaris*. *Exptl. Cell Research*, 15:350–357.

———, 1958b. Sister chromatid exchanges in tritium labeled chromosomes. *Genetics*, 43:515–529.

———, 1958c. Incorporation of phosphorus-32 into nucleic acids and proteins during microgametogenesis of *Tulbaghia*. *Am. J. Botany*, 45:123–130.

———, 1959. Autoradiographic studies of nucleic acids and proteins meiosis in *Lilium longiflorum*. *Am. J. Botany*, 46:477–484.

Taylor, J. H. and R. D. McMaster, 1954. Autoradiographic and microphotometric studies of deoxyribose nucleic acid during microgametogenesis in *Lilium longiflorum*. *Chromosoma*, 6:489–521.

Taylor, J. H., P. S. Woods, and W. L. Hughes, 1957. The organization and duplication of chromosomes as revealed by autoradiographic studies using tritium-labeled thymidine. *Proc. Natl. Acad. Sci.* (US), 43:122–128.

Thaine, R. and M. C. Walters, 1955. Experiments on the application of autoradiographic techniques to the study of problems in plant physiology. *Australian Jour. Biol. Sci.*, 8: 354–368.

Wardrop, A. B., 1956. The nature of surface growth in plant cells. *Australian Jour. Botany*, 4:193–198.

———, 1959. Cell-wall formation in root hairs. *Nature*, 184:996–997.

Wimber, D. E., 1959. Chromosome breakage produced by tritium-labeled thymidine in *Tradescantia paludosa*. *Proc. Natl. Acad. Sci.* (US), 45:839–846.

———, 1960. Duration of the nuclear cycle in *Tradescantia paludosa* root tips as measured with H^3-thymidine. *Am. J. Botany*, 47:828–834.

———, 1961. A synchronous replication of deoxyribonucleic acid in root tip chromosomes of *Tradescantia paludosa*. *Exptl. Cell Research*, 23:402–407.

Wimber, D. E., H. Quastler, O. L. Stein, and D. R. Wimber, 1960. Analysis of tritium incorporation into individual cells by autoradiography of squash preparations. *J. Biophys. Biochem. Cytol.*, 8:327–331.

Woodard, J., E. Rasch, and H. Swift, 1961. Nucleic acid and protein metabolism during the mitotic cycle in *Vicia faba. J. Biophys. Biochem. Cytol.*, 9:445–462.

Woods, P. S. and J. H. Taylor, 1959.

Studies of ribonucleic acid metabolism with tritium-labeled cytidine. *Lab. Invest.*, 8:309–318.

Zalokar, M., 1959. Nuclear origin of ribonucleic acid. *Nature*, 183:1330.

———, 1960. Sites of protein and ribonucleic acid synthesis in the cell. *Exptl. Cell Research*, 19:559–576.

APPENDIX **A**

Histochemical Reagents

Compiled below is a list of chemical supply houses from which the reagents mentioned in the text can be obtained. Following this is a list of the more specialized reagents (synonyms are given for some). The initials placed after the chemical formulas indicate the supply houses from which they can be obtained. This is not meant to be a thorough list of sources, nor are any recommendations of sources to be implied. The investigator is urged to contact the various companies and to keep abreast of their constantly changing and expanding lists of reagents.

SOURCES

(**BL**) Bios Laboratories, Inc., 17 West Sixtieth St., New York 23, N.Y.

(**CCBR**) California Corporation for Biochemical Research, 3625 Medford St., Los Angeles 63, Calif.

(**CTC**) Chem Trac Corp., 130 Alewife Brook Parkway, Cambridge 40, Mass. (Specialize in radioactive compounds)

(**DL**) Dajac Laboratories, The Borden Chemical Co., 5000 Langdon St., Philadelphia 24, Penn., P.O. Box 9522 (Specialize in reagents for microscopic histochemistry)

(**DPI**) Distillation Products Industries, Eastman Organic Chemicals Department, Rochester 3, N.Y.

(**EG**) Edward Gurr, Ltd., 42 Upper Richmond Rd. West, London, S.W. 14, England (Specialize in histological dyes)

(**ELS**) ESBE Laboratory Supplies (Division of Starkman Biological Laboratory), 459 Bloor St. West, Toronto, Ontario, Canada

(**Har**) Harleco, Hartman-Leddon Co., Philadelphia 43, Penn.

(**MRL**) Mann Research Laboratories, Inc., 136 Liberty St., New York 6, N.Y.

(**MCB**) Matheson, Coleman, and Bell, 2909 Highland Ave., Norwood (Cincinnati 12), Ohio

(**NENC**) New England Nuclear Corp., 575 Albany St., Boston 18, Mass. (Specialize in radioactive compounds)

(**NI**) Nichem, Inc., P.O. Box 5737, Bethesda 14, Md. (Specialize in radioactive compounds)

(**NCC**) Nuclear-Chicago Corp., 333 East Howard Ave., Des Plaines, Ill. (Specialize in radioactive compounds)

(**NBC**) Nutritional Biochemical Corp., 21010 Miles Ave., Cleveland 28, Ohio

(**RSC**) Research Specialties Co., 2005 Hopkins St., Berkeley 7, Calif. (Specialize in radioactive compounds)

(**SL**) Schwarz Laboratories, Inc., 230 Washington St., Mount Vernon, N.Y. (Carry both radioactive and nonradioactive biochemical reagents)

(**SCC**) Sigma Chemical Co., 3500 DeKalb St., St. Louis 18, Mo.

(**SYCC**) Sylvania Chemical Co., Orange, N.J. (Supplies fluorescent antibody reagents)

(**TL**) Tracerlab, 1610 Trapelo Road, Waltham 59, Mass. and 2030 Wright Ave., Richmond, Calif. (Specialize in radioactive compounds)

(**WL**) Winthrop Laboratories, Special Chemicals Department, 1450 Broadway, New York 18, N.Y.

(**WBC**) Worthington Biochemical Corporation, Freehold, N.J. (Specialize in enzymes)

REAGENTS

4-amino-1-N,N-dimethylnaphthylamine [See Nachlas, Crawford, Goldstein and Seligman (1958), Chapter 15]

p-amino-diphenylamine (Variamine Blue RT Base) (**SCC**)

2-amino-2-methyl-1-propanol (**CCBR**) (**DPI**) (**MCB**) (**SCC**)

2-amino-2-methyl-1,3-propanediol (**CCBR**) (**DPI**) (**MCB**) (**SCC**)

1-amino-8-naphthol-3:6-disulfonic acid (H acid, 8-amino-1-naphthol-3: 6-disulfonic acid monosodium salt) (**DPI**) (**MCB**)

1-amino-8-naphthol-4-sulfonic acid (S acid, 8-amino-1-naphthol-5-sulfonic acid) (**CCBR**) (**DPI**) (**MCB**)

Anthrone (**CCBR**) (**DPI**) (**MCB**)

4-benzoylamino-2,5-dimethoxyaniline (Fast Blue RR) (**BL**)

6-benzoyl-2-naphthyl phosphate (**CCBR**)

3:4-benzpyrene (Benzo(a)pyrene) (**CCBR**) (**DPI**) (**SCC**)

5-bromo-4-chloroindoxyl acetate (**SCC**)

6-bromo-2-naphthyl sulfate, K (**CCBR**)

Caffeine (**CCBR**) (**DPI**) (**MCB**)

Carbazole (**DPI**) (**MCB**)

Chloramine-T (**DPI**) (**MCB**)

Chloranilic acid (2,5-dichloro-3,6-dihydroxyquinone) (**DPI**) (**MCB**)

1-(4-chloromercuriphenylazo)-naphthol-2 (Mercury Orange) (**DL**)

Deoxycytidine (**CCBR**) (**SCC**)

Diazo blue B (Tetrazotized diorthoanisidine, tetrazotized o-dianisidine, naphthanil Diazo Blue B) (**CCBR**) (**DL**) (**ELS**) (**SCC**)

Diazo red RC (Diazotized p-chloro-o-anisidine, diazotized-2-amino-4-chloroanisole, naphthanil Diazo Red RC) (**CCBR**) (**DL**) (**ELS**)

2,4-dichloro-α-naphthol (2,4-dichloro-1-naphthol) (**DPI**)

2,6-dichlorophenol indophenol (**MCB**) (**SCC**)

2,6-dichloro-quinone chlorimide (**CCBR**) (**DL**) (**DPI**) (**MCB**)

2,2'-dihydroxy-6,6-dinaphthyldisulfide (**DL**) (**SCC**) (**SL**)

1,6-dihydroxynaphthalene (1,6-naphthalenediol) (**DPI**)

p-dimethylamino benzaldehyde (**DPI**) (**MCB**)

N,N-dimethyl-1-naphthylamine (**DPI**)

N,N-dimethyl-p-phenylenediamine·HCl (p-amino-dimethyl-aniline· HCl) (**DL**) (**DPI**) (**MCB**) (**SCC**)

2,4-dinitro fluorobenzene (1-fluoro-2,4-dinitrobenzene) (**CCBR**) (**DL**) (**DPI**) (**MCB**) (**SCC**)

2,4-dinitrophenyl hydrazine (**DPI**) (**MCB**) (**SCC**)

1,5-diphenyl carbohydrazide (**DPI**) (**MCB**)

Dithizone (**DL**) (**DPI**) (**MCB**)

Haematoxylin (Hematoxylin) (**DL**) (**DPI**) (**ELS**) (**MCB**)

Hydroxylamine hydrochloride (**DPI**) (**MCB**)

3-hydroxy-2-naphthaldehyde (2-hydroxy-3-naphthaldehyde) (**CCBR**) (**DL**) (**SCC**)

8-hydroxyquinoline (8-quinolinol) (**DPI**) (**MCB**)

2-hydroxy-3-naphthoic acid hydrazide (3-hydroxy-2-naphthoic acid hydrazide) (**CCBR**) (**DL**) (**MCB**) (**SCC**)

Iodoacetate (Iodoacetic acid) (**DL**) (**DPI**) (**MCB**)

2-(*p*-iodophenyl)-3-*p*-nitrophenyl-5-phenyl-tetrazolium chloride (**CCBR**) (**DL**) (**SCC**)

m-methoxy-*p*-aminodiphenylamine (Variamine Blue FG Base) (**SCC**)

p-methoxy-*p*-aminodiphenylamine (Variamine Blue B Base) (**SCC**)

5-methyl deoxycytidine (**SCC**)

α-naphthyl diazonium naphthalene 1,5-disulfonate (**CCBR**) (**DL**)

N-(1-naphthyl)-ethylene-diamine dihydrochloride (1-naphthyl-ethylenediamine dihydrochloride) (**DPI**) (**MCB**) (**SCC**)

B-naphthyl phosphate (**CCBR**)

Neotetrazolium chloride (**CCBR**) (**DL**) (**SCC**)

Nitro BT (2,2'-di-*p*-nitrophenyl-5,5'-diphenyl-3,3'-(3,3'-dimethoxy-4, 4'-biphenylene)-ditetrazolium chloride) (**DL**)

p-nitrophenyl phosphate (Sigma 104) (**CCBR**) (**DL**) (**SCC**)

Orcinol (**CCBR**) (**DL**) (**DPI**) (**MCB**) (**SCC**)

p-phenylenediamine (**DPI**) (**MCB**)

Phloroglucinol (**DPI**) (**MCB**)

Pyridine (**DPI**) (**MCB**)

Quinalizarin (**DPI**) (**MCB**)

3-quinolhydrazine (3-hydrozinoquinoline) (**DPI**)

Thioglycollic acid (**DPI**) (**SCC**)

Titian Yellow (Titan yellow) (**DPI**) (**ELS**)

2,3,5-triphenyltetrazolium chloride (2,3,5-triphenyl-2H-tetrazolium chloride) (**CCBR**) (**DL**) (**DPI**) (**SCC**)

tris (hydroxymethyl)amino-methane (**CCBR**) (**DL**) (**DPI**) (**SCC**)

Buffers

The buffers given below are some of the most commonly employed in histochemistry. The concentration of the buffer solution can be changed easily by recalculating the stock solution.

I. Citrate-Phosphate Buffer, *p*H 2.2–8.0

Stock solutions consist of (a) 0.5 *M* sodium phosphate, dibasic (71.01 g dissolved and diluted to make 1 liter) and (b) 0.5 *M* citric acid (105.6 g dissolved and diluted to make 1 liter). Mix as indicated below, and dilute to 200 ml.

*p*H	(a)	(b)	*p*H	(a)	(b)
2.2	1.60 ml	39.20 ml	5.2	42.88 ml	18.56 ml
2.4	4.96	37.52	5.4	44.60	17.70
2.6	8.72	35.64	5.6	46.40	16.80
2.8	12.68	33.66	5.8	48.36	15.82
3.0	16.44	31.78	6.0	50.52	14.74
3.2	19.76	30.12	6.2	52.88	13.56
3.4	22.80	28.60	6.4	55.40	12.30
3.6	25.96	27.12	6.6	58.20	10.90

*p*H	(a)	(b)	*p*H	(a)	(b)
3.8	28.40 ml	25.80 ml	6.8	61.80 ml	9.10 ml
4.0	30.84	24.58	7.0	65.88	7.06
4.2	33.12	23.44	7.2	69.56	5.22
4.4	35.28	22.36	7.4	72.68	3.66
4.6	37.40	21.30	7.6	74.92	2.54
4.8	39.44	20.28	7.8	76.60	1.70
5.0	41.20	19.40	8.0	77.80	1.10

II. Citrate Buffer, *p*H 3.4–5.5

Stock solutions consist of (a) 0.2 *M* citric acid (4.2 g dissolved in 100 ml of water) and (b) 0.2 *M* sodium citrate (5.9 g dissolved in 100 ml of water). Mix as indicated below.

*p*H	(a)	(b)	*p*H	(a)	(b)
3.4	80 ml	20 ml	4.5	55 ml	45 ml
3.6	76	24	4.8	46	54
3.8	70	30	5.0	40	60
4.0	65	35	5.3	35	65
4.2	61	39	5.5	30	70

III. Phosphate Buffer, *p*H 5.6–8.0

Stock solutions consist of (a) *M*/15 sodium phosphate dibasic (9.47 g dissolved and diluted to make 1 liter) and (b) *M*/15 potassium phosphate, monobasic (9.08 g dissolved and diluted to make 1 liter). Mix as indicated below.

*p*H	(a)	(b)
5.6	10.0 ml	190.0 ml
5.8	16.5	183.5
6.0	25.0	175.0
6.2	36.0	164.0
6.4	53.5	146.5
6.6	74.5	125.5
6.8	99.0	101.0
7.0	122.0	78.0
7.2	143.0	57.0
7.4	161.0	39.0
7.6	172.5	27.5
7.8	182.5	17.5
8.0	189.0	11.0

IV. Acetate Buffer, pH 3.8–5.6

Stock solutions consist of (a) 0.2 *M* acetic acid (1.2 ml in 100 ml of water) and (b) 0.2 *M* sodium acetate (2.7 g in 100 ml of water). Mix as indicated below.

pH	(a)	(b)	pH	(a)	(b)
3.8	87 ml	13 ml	4.8	40 ml	60 ml
4.0	80	20	5.0	30	70
4.2	73	27	5.2	21	79
4.4	62	38	5.4	14.5	85.5
4.6	51	49	5.6	11	89

V. Tris-Maleate Buffer, pH 5.8–8.2

Dissolve 29 g of maleic acid and 30.3 g of tris (hydroxymethyl)aminomethane in 500 ml of water. Add 2 g of charcoal, shake, let stand for 10 minutes, and filter. Mix 40 ml of this stock solution with the amount of *N* NaOH indicated below, and dilute to make 100 ml. The final concentration of the buffer is 0.2 *M*.

pH	*N* NaOH	pH	*N* NaOH	pH	*N* NaOH
5.8	9.0 ml	6.6	16.5 ml	7.6	22.5 ml
6.0	10.5	6.8	18.0	7.8	24.2
6.2	13.0	7.0	19.0	8.0	26.0
6.4	15.0	7.2	20.0	8.2	29.0

AUTHOR INDEX

SUBJECT INDEX

References to the directions for performing procedures are in **boldface** *type.*

401